Energy efficiency in buildings

CIBSE Guide

ENERGY EFFICIENCY
DEPARTMENT OF THE ENVIRONMENT,
TRANSPORT AND THE REGIONS

Preface

Building services engineers have responsibility for the comfort and health of building occupants, which means most of us for most of our lives. In seeking to achieve this, buildings consume about half of the UK's energy supply.

As concern for global issues relating to the environment increases, the role of the building services engineer becomes ever more important in the design and operation of buildings and their use of energy. Therefore, it is essential to understand the opportunities which exist for improving the effectiveness with which energy is used in buildings.

This new CIBSE Guide, the first to deal specifically with energy issues, is intended to highlight the opportunities for saving energy in buildings while maintaining the comfort and health of their occupants. We hope that the guidance it contains will be read and applied widely.

G W Brundrett
CIBSE President, March 1998

Note from the publisher

This publication is primarily intended to provide guidance to those responsible for the design, installation, commissioning, operation and maintenance of building services. It is not intended to be exhaustive or definitive and it will be necessary for users of the guidance given to exercise their own professional judgement when deciding whether to abide by or depart from it.

Foreword

This is the first time that the CIBSE has endeavoured to bring together in one volume a range of information related entirely to energy efficiency in buildings. Energy plays a part in all aspects of building services and this is reflected in most of the Institution's publications.

It is perhaps surprising that, until now, there has been no CIBSE Guide which deals exclusively with the many facets of energy efficiency in buildings. This publication seeks to fill that gap and at the same time confirm the Institution's dedication to energy conservation and the preservation of the environment.

This volume in the series of CIBSE Guides is essentially a reference book, which also identifies other documents dealing with the various topics in more detail. It is not intended that it should be read from beginning to end in one go, but rather that the reader can consult a section that is of particular interest in respect of the project in hand.

Those involved in the production of this Guide have recognised that the content cannot cover every aspect of what is, after all, a very extensive and sometimes controversial subject. There will, however, be opportunities in the future to up-date the content in order to deal with further subjects and areas of concern, as well as covering new developments.

The Institution offers its grateful thanks to all those who have contributed to this volume and, in particular, to the Department of the Environment, Transport and the Regions and BRECSU/BRE, without whose collaboration and perseverance this Guide would not have seen the light of day.

D D Lawrence
Chairman, CIBSE Energy Publications Joint Steering Committee, March 1998

Acknowledgement

The Chartered Institution of Building Services Engineers gratefully acknowledges the support and funding provided for the development of this CIBSE Guide by the Department of the Environment, Transport and the Regions. This support was provided as part of the Department's Energy Efficiency Best Practice programme managed on behalf of the Department by the Building Research Energy Conservation Support Unit (BRECSU) at the Building Research Establishment (BRE). The BRECSU project managers were Colin Lillicrap, Chris Hall and Tony Johnson and many other BRE staff contributed to the guide.

ENERGY EFFICIENCY

BRECSU Advisory Panel

C Lillicrap (BRECSU/BRE) (Chairman)
K J Butcher (CIBSE Editorial Manager)
A Field (DETR)
C M R Hall (BRECSU/BRE)
A J Johnson (BRECSU/BRE)
P G Jones (Building Energy Solutions) (Lead Editor/Author)
D D Lawrence (Laing Technology Group Ltd (retired), representing CIBSE)
P J Mayo (John Lewis Partnership plc, representing CIBSE)

BRECSU editorial team

P G Jones (Building Energy Solutions) (Lead Editor/Author)
D Cheshire (Building Energy Solutions) (Assistant Editor/Author)
J Webber (BRECSU/BRE) (Assistant Editor)

Technical advisors

R C Aldworth (consultant)
W T Bordass (William Bordass Associates)
D Butler (BRE)
H Falkner (ETSU/AEA Technology plc)

J W Field (Target Energy Services Ltd)
D L Loe (BRECSU/BRE)
J Palmer (John Palmer Associates)
G P Smith (Birling Systems Design Ltd)

Principal authors and contributors

B S Austin (Arup Research and Development)
A B Birtles (formerly of BRECSU)
P Concannon (Oscar Faber Group Ltd)
M Cook (BRECSU/BRE)
R A De Ritter (NIFES Consulting Group)
B S Greenstreet (London Stock Exchange)
C M R Hall (BRECSU/BRE)
D Hart (Hart Consultants)
S J Irving (Oscar Faber Group Ltd)
P J Jackman (BSRIA)
P G Jones (Building Energy Solutions)
D M Lush (consultant to Ove Arup and Partners)
C J Parsloe (BSRIA)
M Patel (Department for Education and Employment)
G E F Read (NIFES Consulting Group)
G P Smith (Birling Systems Design Ltd)
R G Venning (Arup Research and Development)
P A Warburton (Arup Associates)

Acknowledgements

J Agomobar (BBC)
C Ashford (BRECSU/BRE)
P Bell (WIMTECH)
W R Berry (consultant)
G D Braham (Derrick Braham Associates)
G W Brundrett (consultant)
N Burns (BRECSU/BRE)
J A Clarke (University of Strathclyde)
R Cohen (Halcrow Gilbert Associates)
M J Corcoran (University of Strathclyde)
J Crawshaw (British Institute for Facilities Management)
P Crilly (Cogen Systems)
V H C Crisp (BRE)
P Dolley (ETSU/AEA Technology plc)
M Duggan (HVCA)
C Fenton (Halcrow Gilbert Associates)
M Finbow (NBA Tectonics Ltd)
E Gibson (Energy Council)
A E T Glenny (Philips Lighting Ltd)
P Godwin (formerly of BRECSU)
D Green (Combined Heat and Power Association)
P F Grigg (BRE)
J Happy (BRECSU/BRE)
P Harris (Cheriton Technology Management Ltd)
N Hayes (BRECSU/BRE)
N P Howard (Davis Langdon & Everest)
B C Hutt (W S Atkins Consultants Ltd)
P Ibbotson (J Sainsbury plc)
A Jackson (Electricity Association)
D Jaunzens (BRE)
I Jones (NORWEB)
W P Jones (consultant)
M Kolokotroni (BRE)
M Lai (CIMA)
D D Lawrence (Laing Technology Group Ltd (retired))
J Leonard (British Council for Offices)
P Le Manquais (Thorn Lighting Ltd)
G J Levermore (UMIST)

P J Littlefair (BRE)
I F MacLean (Thorn Lighting Ltd)
J Pearson (British Gas)
E Perera (BRE)
C Pout (BRE)
A Richardson (British Gas)
A I Slater (BRE)
D F Smith (Otis Plc)
N Strachan (formerly of ETSU)
C Strickland (British Council for Offices)
C Sutherland (Sutherland Associates Ltd)
D Warriner (BRE)
A C Watson (Building Design Partnership)
R Weston (Combined Power System Ltd)
J Wilczek (ETSU/AEA Technology plc)
R P A Willan (Willan Group Ltd)
J Williams (IEE)
A Wilson (consultant)
R Wiltshire (BRECSU/BRE)
D W Wood (Gibb Ltd)
A J Wright (EA Technology Ltd)

Co-ordinating editors

K J Butcher (CIBSE)
B W Copping (CIBSE)

Copy editors

K J Butcher (CIBSE)
M Finbow (NBA Tectonics Ltd)

CIBSE Publishing Manager

R E Yarham

Contents

Principles of energy efficiency

> An energy efficient building provides the required internal environment and services with minimum energy use in a cost effective and environmentally sensitive manner.

The following principles have been developed from the CIBSE policy statement on energy, see Appendix A1.1, and provide a framework for engineers to put the policy into practice. Where possible, building services engineers should make every effort to follow the principles shown below.

Principle	Measures for implementation of principle	Relevant section(s) of Guide	
		Part A: Designing the building	Part B: Operating and upgrading the building
Integrated building design	Design the most energy efficient buildings and services possible. Provide holistic designs which are responsive to the external climate whilst still meeting the needs of the occupants.	2 to 5	—
The energy efficient brief	Ensure the client's brief includes energy efficient criteria for all buildings, new or refurbished. Review the project in relation to these criteria as the design progresses.	2	—
The integrated design team	Work with other members of the design team in order to optimise building energy performance.	2	—
Reduce demand	Keep energy demand to a minimum through careful design of built form and services using ambient energy and passive solutions. Make every effort to avoid the need for air conditioning, where possible.	2 to 12	—
Design for operation	Design for commissionability, maintainability and manageability by keeping solutions simple and eliminating potential failure pathways.	2 to 12	—
Optimise plant	Select the most efficient plant and ensure that plant and equipment are not oversized.	6 to 11	19
Use effective controls	Introduce energy efficient controls which operate systems efficiently, safely and economically, whilst still allowing individual occupants to alter their own comfort levels, but avoiding systems defaulting to 'on'.	5 to 10	19
Ensure complete handover	Ensure that building services are properly commissioned and handed over to managers, operators and occupants.	13	—
Improve operation	Encourage energy efficient operation of buildings through management, policy, maintenance, monitoring and control.	—	14 to 21
Understanding the building	Provide managers, engineers, operators and occupants with suitable documentation to ensure they understand the design intention and how the buildings are meant to function.	13	14
Monitoring and feedback	Develop a strong element of feedback to improve understanding from previous good and bad experience related to these principles. Introduce appropriate metering to improve information and to detect faults rapidly.	12	20, 21
Build-in energy efficiency	Always consider introducing energy efficient technologies throughout the design and upgrade processes but avoid unnecessary complications. Seek opportunities for improving existing buildings during operation, maintenance, alteration and refurbishment.	4 to 11	18, 19
Environmental impact	Minimise adverse effects on the external environment. Minimise emissions and select environmentally friendly materials and fuels.	4 to 11	17, 19

1 Introduction

1.1 Objectives and scope

This Guide shows how to improve energy performance, reduce running costs and minimise the environmental impact of buildings by:

— designing energy efficient new buildings and refurbishment of existing buildings

— operating buildings energy efficiently

— demonstrating the value of energy efficiency to clients and developers

— enabling engineers to overcome barriers to energy efficiency in discussions with clients and other members of the design and construction team.

An energy efficient building provides the required internal environment and services with minimum energy use in a cost effective and environmentally sensitive manner. There is, therefore, no conflict between energy efficiency and comfort. Hence, energy efficiency can be combined with other aspects of sound engineering practice, as set out in the other CIBSE Guides.

This document is primarily targeted at building services engineers. With its holistic approach, parts of it will also be useful to other members of the design team including architects and surveyors. It should also be useful to other building professionals such as energy managers, facilities managers, developers, clients, property agents and occupiers. Sections of particular relevance to each reader are shown in 1.3.

This document covers opportunities for achieving energy efficiency and complements existing guidance by CIBSE and others. It refers readers to more detailed guidance including the Department of the Environment, Transport and the Region's (DETR) Energy Efficiency Best Practice programme. It does not cover process energy or detailed design methods. Although it concentrates on non-domestic buildings, much of the information is also relevant to the domestic sector.

The document promotes a holistic approach to design by recognising that there is a strong interaction between the building envelope, heating and cooling systems, lighting, etc. The overall design intent should always be considered before implementing individual measures.

1.2 Reasons for the Guide

Buildings consume nearly half the energy used in the UK. All building professionals have a responsibility to reduce this through good practice. Tangible benefits from energy efficiency range from the individual to the national level are:

— improved building design and operation

— better working environments

— life-cycle cost savings

— added market value of buildings

— environmental: mainly through reduced emissions of carbon dioxide (CO_2) and reduced consumption of finite fossil fuels.

1.2.1 National energy use

The energy bill for most existing commercial and public buildings could be reduced by at least 20%[1] using measures regarded as cost effective by most common investment criteria.

New buildings and major refurbishment represent even greater potential. New low-energy buildings consume 50% less energy than similar existing buildings and 20% less than typical new buildings.

In 1995 the total energy consumption of the UK was 6367 PJ (1.76×10^9 MW h) of which 2878 PJ was used in buildings[2]. The total cost of energy in buildings was around £23 billion per annum. Figures 1.1 to 1.3 illustrate national energy use by sector, building type and fuel used in non-domestic buildings.

Typical energy breakdowns for various types of building are shown in Applications Manual AM5[3] and in the DETR Energy Efficiency Best Practice programme's *Energy Consumption Guides*. Electricity consumption is rising in

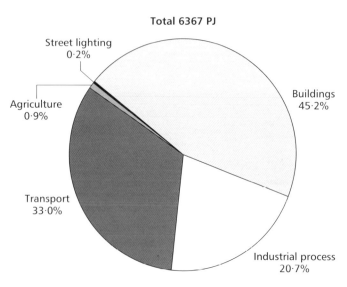

Figure 1.1 Total UK delivered energy use by sector in 1994 (source: Pout BRE 1997. Reproduced by permission of BRE)

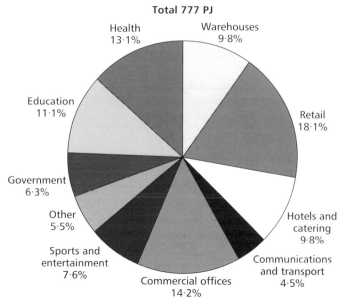

Figure 1.3 Service sector energy use by building type in 1994 (source: Pout BRE 1997. Reproduced by permission of BRE)

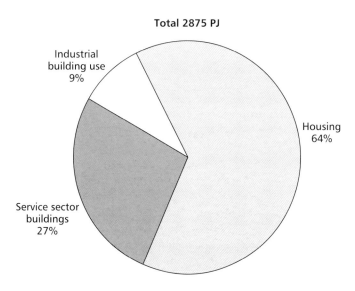

Figure 1.2 Total UK delivered energy use by buildings in 1994 (source: Pout BRE 1997. Reproduced by permission of BRE)

most existing buildings, often due to increased equipment, particularly related to information technology, and sometimes air conditioning to remove internal heat gains. The current trend in new-build toward more passive solutions, improved design integration and more efficient engineering systems may mitigate this rising trend.

1.2.2   Environmental issues

Burning fossil fuels contributes to atmospheric pollution, resulting in a wide range of damage both to the environment and public health, see CIBSE policy statement on global warming, Appendix A1.4. Increased atmospheric concentration of CO_2 caused by burning fossil fuels is increasing global temperature. Improving energy efficiency will help reduce global warming. Burning fossil fuels also results in emissions of SO_x and NO_x, both of which contribute to acid rain.

The efficiency of electricity production in most thermal power stations is typically between 30% and 50%. The

consumption of electricity can therefore lead to 2 to 3 times the CO_2 emissions per delivered unit of energy than the consumption of fossil fuels.

The UK government is committed to returning the emission of CO_2 to 1990 levels by the year 2000, and to a further 20% reduction by 2010. UK CO_2 emissions from energy use in non-domestic buildings are shown in Figure 1.4. These could be reduced by roughly 20% through the introduction of cost-effective energy efficiency measures.

Where possible, building professionals should use more sustainable materials when designing and upgrading buildings. In particular, the embodied energy used in manufacturing and delivering construction materials, including that related to local sourcing and recycling of building services components, should always be considered at the design stage. Wider environmental issues related to buildings and building services are covered in the BSRIA *Environmental Code of Practice*[4].

1.2.3   Legislation and codes of practice

There is an increasing level of legislation addressing energy and environmental issues.

The 1994 *Building Regulations*[5] for England and Wales include more stringent thermal performance measures for new and refurbished buildings, and new measures covering energy efficient heating and lighting controls. A further revision of the *Regulations* is under development to address the energy efficiency of air conditioning and mechanical ventilation in both new and refurbished buildings.

The Statutory Instrument, *Control of Fuel and Electricity*[6], specifies a maximum heating level of 19°C in all non-domestic buildings. The law has not been rigorously enforced because, in some circumstances, it reduces the comfort of occupants.

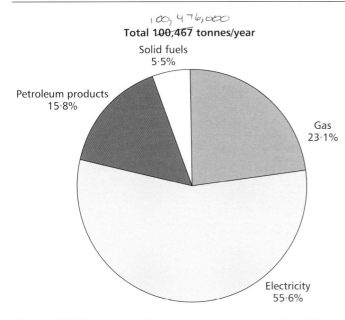

100,476,000
Total 100,467 tonnes/year

Solid fuels
5·5%

Petroleum products
15·8%

Gas
23·1%

Electricity
55·6%

Figure 1.4 UK CO$_2$ emissions from energy use in non-domestic buildings by fuel in 1994 (source: Pout BRE 1997. Reproduced by permission of BRE)

Although not statutory, *BS 8207: Code of practice for energy efficiency in buildings*[7] makes recommendations for achieving energy efficient performance in buildings. It considers both design and operation and provides a framework which can be applied to new designs or to refurbishment. It also highlights the timing of critical design decisions in relation to the RIBA *Plan of Work*[8].

ISO 14001: Environmental management systems[9] (which supersedes *BS 7750*) also encourages energy efficiency, as it requires monitoring of any significant environmental impact and a commitment to its reduction.

The *Building Research Establishment Environmental Assessment Method (BREEAM)*[10] is a non-statutory means of judging buildings against environmental targets and standards.

1.2.4 The role of building professionals

Building professionals should make energy efficiency a key part of their professional activities. They should always encourage clients to include energy efficiency in the brief at all stages in a building's life whether designing, operating or upgrading. Clients and financiers should be made aware of the investment case for energy efficiency. Building professionals should help clients to develop a brief which sets out both user and client requirements and constraints, balancing these against capital costs, running costs and environmental objectives.

Building professionals will benefit by:

— providing an added-value service to their clients by improving their buildings

— reducing plant capital cost, particularly where mechanical cooling has been avoided or minimised

— enhancing the standing of all building professionals by improving occupants' use and perception of buildings

Table 1.1 Sections of the Guide relevant to readers from various professions

Reader	Part	Section
Building services designers	Designing the building	1 – 13
Building owners/operators	Operating and upgrading the building	14 – 21
Energy managers/consultants	Operating and upgrading the building	14, 18 – 21
Architects/surveyors	Designing the building	1 – 13
Developers/financiers	Designing the building	1 – 5, 14

— increasing building marketability by promoting buildings as assets in which to invest

— obtaining repeat work through satisfied customers.

Recent work has indicated that buildings that are designed and managed in an energy efficient way can be more comfortable and their staff more productive, making investment in good energy efficient design and management even more cost effective to a client organisation[11].

1.3 How to use the Guide

1.3.1 Structure

This Guide starts by setting out an overall framework for energy efficiency within which the building professional has the freedom to design, operate or upgrade a building. The 'principles of energy efficiency' stated at the front of this Guide are broadly based on the CIBSE policy statement on energy, see Appendix A1.1, and aim to help professionals put the policy into practice.

The main body of this Guide is divided into two parts as shown in Figure 1.5.

— *Part A: Designing the building:* consists of sections 2 to 13 and deals with new buildings and major refurbishment.

— *Part B: Operating and upgrading the building:* consists of sections 14 to 21 and covers the management and maintenance of buildings, highlighting measures that can be retrofitted in existing buildings. The reader is referred back to Part A where there is a large element of design.

A diagram at the top of the first page of each section indicates the relationship of that section to the rest of the Guide.

The first section in each part provides a strategic overview of the process being covered. The last two sections in each part help check that the main options have been considered and that the final outcome meets expectations. The sections of this Guide particularly relevant to readers from various professions are shown in Table 1.1. Appendix A1 consists of relevant CIBSE policy statements and Appendix A2 gives some standard conversion factors and properties of fuels.

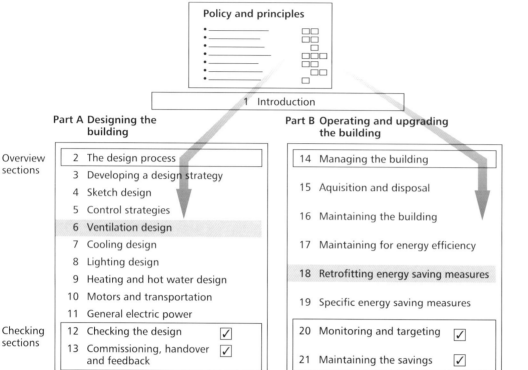

Figure 1.5 Structure of the Guide

1.3.2   Investing in energy efficiency

Although environmental reasons are strong, in practice cost savings usually drive energy efficiency. This Guide therefore concentrates on cost effective measures. Savings in operating costs will flow directly into the building user's profit. Well-managed organisations tend to re-invest some of the savings in further energy efficiency measures, setting up a snowball effect. Additional investment may also be justified for environmental reasons.

Energy efficiency measures should generally be considered in their order of economic payback, complexity and ease of application. Measures fall into three broad types: no-cost/low-cost requiring no investment appraisal, medium cost requiring only a simple payback calculation, and high capital cost measures requiring detailed design and a full investment appraisal.

Investment in energy efficiency should be treated on the same basis as any other financial decision and should have no more onerous conditions placed upon it than any other investment. A variety of financial appraisal methods can be used to assess the viability of energy saving measures (see 18.3). Assessments should always take into account the wider benefits such as improvements in comfort and the environment. This can be achieved using a life-cycle approach.

Energy efficient buildings need cost no more to build than conventional buildings. The integration of the fabric and services design can present opportunities to reduce capital cost. For example, the cost of external shading can be offset by minimising or avoiding air conditioning plant.

References

1   *Introduction to energy efficiency in buildings* Booklets EEB 1–13 (London: Department of the Environment, Transport and the Regions) (1994)

2   *Digest of UK energy statistics* (London: Stationery Office)

3   *Energy audits and surveys* CIBSE Applications Manual AM5 (London: Chartered Institution of Building Services Engineers) (1991)

4   Halliday S P *Environmental code of practice for buildings and their services* (Bracknell: Building Services Research and Information Association) (1994)

5   *The Building Regulations Part L: Conservation of Fuel and Power* (London: Stationery Office) (1995)

6   *Control of Fuel and Electricity (Amended) Order 1980* Statutory Instrument 1980/1013 (London: Stationery Office) (1980)

7   *BS 8207: Code of practice for energy efficiency in buildings* (London: British Standards Institution) (1985)

8   *Plan of work for design team operation: RIBA Handbook* (London: Royal Institute of British Architects) (1973)

9   *BS EN ISO 14001: Environmental management systems* (London: British Standards Institution) (1996)

10   *BREEAM/New Offices An environmental assessment for new office designs* Version 1/93 (Garston: Building Research Establishment) (1993)

11   Bordass W T, Bromley A K R and Leaman A J *Comfort, control and energy efficiency in offices* BRE Information Paper IP3/95 (Garston: Building Research Establishment) (1995)

Bibliography

Arnold D *The role of the building services engineer* (CIBSE Presidential Address) (London: Chartered Institution of Building Services Engineers) (1994)

Our common future Sustainable development report (New York: United Nations)

Proposal for a Council Directive introducing a tax on carbon dioxide and energy COM 92 226 (Brussels: Commission of European Communities) (June 1992)

Berkovitch I Taxing carbon *IEE Review* (January 1993)

Energy efficiency in buildings House of Commons Environment Committee Fourth report Session 1992-93 (London: Stationery Office) (1993)

Environmental issues in construction RP 445 (London: Construction Industry Research and Information Association) (1992)

Energy on the boardroom agenda — Making a corporate commitment (Garston: Building Research Energy Conservation Support Unit/Department of the Environment, Transport and the Regions) (1992)

Organisational aspects of energy management GIR 12 (Garston: Building Research Energy Conservation Support Unit/Department of the Environment, Transport and the Regions) (1993)

Reviewing energy management GIR 13 (Garston: Building Research Energy Conservation Support Unit/Department of the Environment, Transport and the Regions) (1993)

Part A   Designing the building

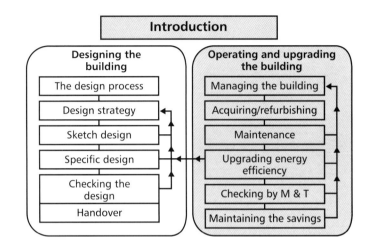

2   The design process

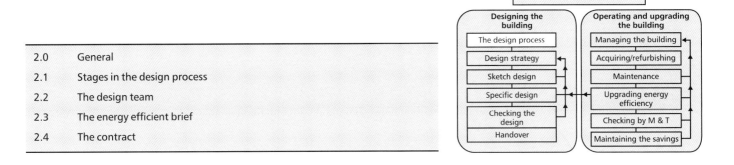

This section shows how and when energy efficiency can be included in the design process, in line with the principles given at the front of this Guide. Designers should seek a balance between overall cost and good design practice, while meeting the occupier's business needs. Energy efficiency plays a central part in any good design and is exceptional in being cost-effective over the life cycle of the building.

2.0   General

The process of energy efficient design should always include:

— identifying user requirements

— designing to meet these requirements with minimal energy use

— establishing an integrated design team with a brief and contract that promotes energy efficiency

— setting energy targets at an early stage and designing within them

— designing for manageability, maintainability, operability and flexibility

— checking that the final design meets the targets.

Success depends on understanding the interactions between people, building fabric and services, as shown in Figure 2.1[1]. This integrated design approach requires the successful collaboration of client, project manager, architect, engineer and quantity surveyor at the early conceptual stage of the project[2,3,4].

The most significant influence in energy efficiency is often the way the building is used by the management and occupants. Hence, the principles of energy efficiency at the front of this guide place great emphasis on management issues. Activity, hours of occupancy, control settings etc. all vary enormously and represent the greatest unknown at the design stage. Designers need to take account of this variability and promote better building management through improved design. A good management regime, which is responsive to the needs of the occupants and fully in control of the building, can have a major effect on energy consumption.

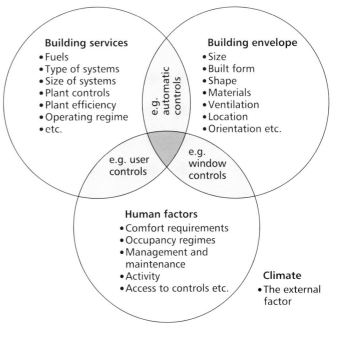

Figure 2.1 Key factors that influence energy consumption

The integration of building envelope, services and 'human factors' should be covered in the brief and is a key part of the sketch design stage. The early design concept needs to be tested against the client's criteria, which normally include cost, quality of the internal environment and compliance with energy and environmental targets, e.g. by using *BREEAM*[5]. If it does not meet the criteria, the design team should review the design concept or the client's requirements. This iterative process is essential in reaching an effective energy efficient design.

Generally, owner-occupiers will be more interested in low running costs than will speculative developers. However,

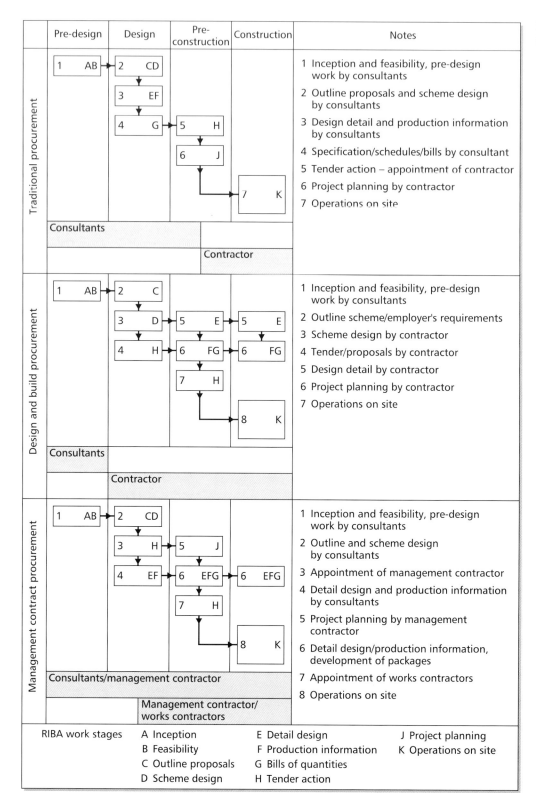

Figure 2.2 Common methods of building procurement

	Pre-design	Design	Pre-construction	Construction	Notes
Traditional procurement	1 AB	2 CD / 3 EF / 4 G	5 H / 6 J	7 K	1 Inception and feasibility, pre-design work by consultants 2 Outline proposals and scheme design by consultants 3 Design detail and production information by consultants 4 Specification/schedules/bills by consultant 5 Tender action – appointment of contractor 6 Project planning by contractor 7 Operations on site

Consultants | Contractor

	Pre-design	Design	Pre-construction	Construction	Notes
Design and build procurement	1 AB	2 C / 3 D / 4 H	5 E / 6 FG / 7 H	5 E / 6 FG / 8 K	1 Inception and feasibility, pre-design work by consultants 2 Outline scheme/employer's requirements 3 Scheme design by contractor 4 Tender/proposals by contractor 5 Design detail by contractor 6 Project planning by contractor 7 Operations on site

Consultants | Contractor

	Pre-design	Design	Pre-construction	Construction	Notes
Management contract procurement	1 AB	2 CD / 3 H / 4 EF	5 J / 6 EFG / 7 H	6 EFG / 8 K	1 Inception and feasibility, pre-design work by consultants 2 Outline and scheme design by consultants 3 Appointment of management contractor 4 Detail design and production information by consultants 5 Project planning by management contractor 6 Detail design/production information, development of packages 7 Appointment of works contractors 8 Operations on site

Consultants/management contractor | Management contractor/works contractors

RIBA work stages			
A Inception	E Detail design	J Project planning
B Feasibility	F Production information	K Operations on site
C Outline proposals	G Bills of quantities	
D Scheme design	H Tender action	

developers should recognise that buildings that are energy efficient and therefore have low running costs can attract a premium in the market place and are increasingly likely to do so in the future.

2.1   Stages in the design process

Standard plans of work[6] usually need to be modified to meet the requirements of the building users and the contract being undertaken. In particular, provision should be made to review energy issues throughout the plan to ensure that the energy concepts are not gradually diluted or dropped. The plan should also formalise the responsibility for energy and ensure that energy issues are well communicated during the design process[7,8]. A speculative development that will be fitted out by the occupant will need a different approach to energy efficiency than a bespoke building for an owner-occupier. Examples of these different approaches are shown in Figure 2.2.

The plan of work should identify specific points at which the design team will report on how the design meets the client's brief. Table 2.1 illustrates this in relation to RIBA *Plan of Work*[6] stages.

Table 2.1 Reporting on energy efficient design

Work stages	Details to be reported by the design team	Energy efficiency considerations
(A) Inception	Prepare general outline of requirements Plan future action	Establishment of energy and environmental objectives, criteria and targets Establish an appropriate team
(B) Feasibility	Appraisal and recommendations of how project will proceed Show it is feasible, functionally, technically and financially	Ensure good communication within the design team with a goodplan of work Develop a clear design strategy that integrates fabric, services and human factors
(C) Outline proposals	The brief as far as has been developed Explanation of major design decisions and definition of user requirements Firm estimate with outline cost plan	Site considerations Building form and arrangement on site Outline servicing and energy strategy, e.g. naturally ventilated, mechanically ventilated, air-conditioned, daylighting etc. Selection of fuel/energy types
(D) Scheme design	Statement of the fully developed brief Explanation of scheme outline specification Cost plan Future timetable	Design of fenestration taking into account the ramifications on heating, cooling fans and pumps, and lighting energy Selection of building thermal characteristics; levels of insulation and thermal response Decisions on main plant arrangements and control strategies, and main vertical and horizontal routes for services Decisions made on lighting and daylighting systems, and their control
(E/F) Detail design/production information	Preparation of the production drawings, specifications, schedules etc	Detailed plant/system design Detailed design of system controls Provisions for monitoring system condition and energy use Commissioning requirements and acceptance procedures Building/system management requirements and documentation

There will be a significant level of overlap between the individual activities taking place throughout the design process. This is illustrated in Figure 2.3, taken from *BS 8207*[9] which highlights the timing of critical design decisions that influence the energy performance. *BS 8207* also makes recommendations for achieving energy efficient performance in buildings and hence provides a framework that can be applied to new designs or refurbishment. It should be noted that the environmental objectives of reducing carbon dioxide emissions and environmental pollution are particularly important for design decisions 1, 4, 6, 10 and 16 in Figure 2.3.

2.2 The design team

The multi-disciplinary design team should be appointed at inception, prior to the conceptual stage of the design, and comprise typically an architect, building services engineer, quantity surveyor, structural engineer and client representatives. Each member should consider the energy implications of each design decision; the design team should also obtain feedback from the client during the design process.

The design team should:

— make the client aware of the implications that decisions have on life cycle costs

— provide an energy efficient design that takes account of energy management and maintenance needs

— provide projections of energy performance and running costs

— propose further options for energy efficiency, highlighting the potential benefits

— produce good documentation which makes the design intent clear.

Ideally, all team members should be involved for the entire duration of the project[2]. The client's requirements must be clearly identified and any changes addressed by the team as the project develops, any implications being reviewed with the client, as necessary.

2.3 The energy efficient brief

The energy efficient brief should be no more complex than is appropriate for the type and size of building[2,10]. It should incorporate:

— the client's intentions, requirements and investment criteria

— energy targets

— environmental targets e.g. *BREEAM* credits

— life cycle costs

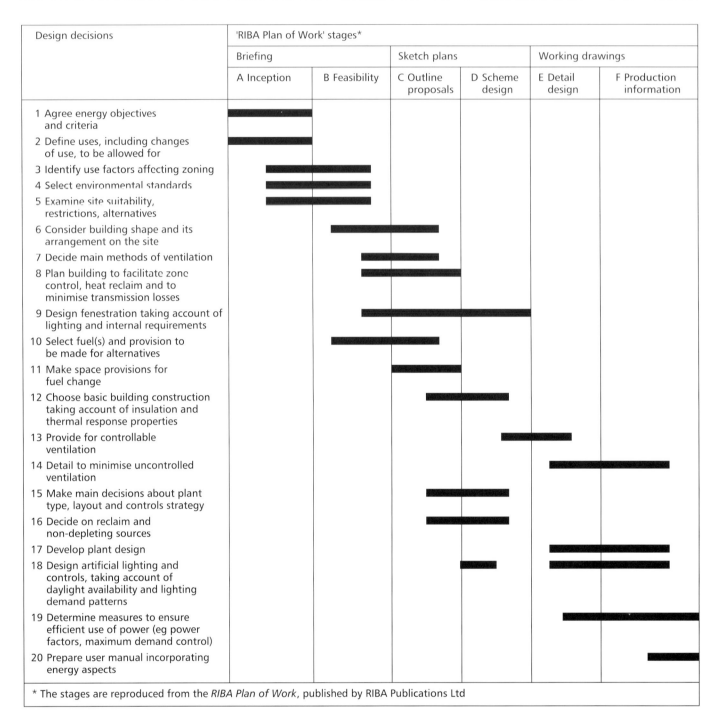

Figure 2.3 Timing of design decisions (reproduced from *BS 8207: Code of practice for energy efficient buildings* by permission of the British Standards Institution and the Royal Institute of British Architects. This extract from *BS 8207: 1995* is reproduced with the permission of BSI under licence no. PD\1998 0963. Complete editions of the standard can be obtained by post from BSI Customer Services, 389 Chiswick High Road, London W4 4AL.)

— the intentions to include energy efficient equipment

— a requirement to undertake integrated design.

Where possible, a range of options should be considered before deciding on the overall design concept. It is possible to meet a particular brief through a number of design solutions and it is important at the briefing stage to establish the aims and objectives of the design to ensure that they are reflected in these solutions.

The energy implications of the internal environment and loads specified in the brief should be explained to the client by the building services engineer. Unrealistic criteria can result in plant being oversized with energy and cost penalties. For example, excessive lighting levels will increase both capital and running costs. Equally, specifying very narrow bands of temperature or humidity is likely to increase energy consumption. This is particularly true if air conditioning is required as this can increase building energy consumption by up to 50%[11]. Humidification and dehumidification should only be specified where absolutely essential.

Internal and external design conditions should be selected in accordance with CIBSE Guide A1: *Environmental criteria for design*[12]. However, designers should agree an acceptable range for the internal environmental standards, as these can have a significant effect on plant sizing and energy consumption. For example, maximum summer indoor temperatures might be selected that typically are not exceeded for 97.5% of the time. Flexible options should also be considered, such as to allow bands of temperature, humidity or ventilation to float across seasons.

Higher air change rates usually mean increased energy consumption, particularly with mechanical ventilation, although heat recovery and 'free' cooling may redress the balance. Areas where smoking is allowed require around four times the ventilation rate per person, so restricting these areas reduces energy consumption and improves the quality of the internal environment.

The level of occupant control can have a very significant impact on the way systems are used and hence on future energy consumption. Occupants' response to their environment is influenced by:

— the quality of the environment

— the perceived level of individual control

— the quality of the management of services and response to complaints

— the desire to be close to a window.

Results from building user surveys[13] show a 'virtuous circle' of characteristics, with responsive and effective management of buildings leading to staff satisfaction, better energy efficiency and improved productivity. Where occupants' tolerance of the internal environment is low, the building is unlikely to function efficiently. This is more likely to be the case in air conditioned buildings as they tend to exclude the external environment.

In essence, this means that buildings that make good use of natural light and ventilation, in which occupants have the opportunity to make local adjustments, often provide more acceptable environments and hence greater energy efficiency.

2.4   The contract

The building design contract should promote energy efficiency by ensuring that all building professionals work together creatively to achieve an integrated and energy efficient design. Energy efficient buildings often require greater professional skill and design input. The team must, therefore, have enough time at an early stage to formulate an integrated sketch design.

To realise energy efficient designs, each stage of a contract needs to be carefully assessed to ensure that the design intent is followed through to actual performance, and the predicted returns realised. Although this can result in an enhanced fee component on a contract, it ensures that the client's brief is addressed.

Fee structures based entirely on the capital cost of the building services may not encourage energy efficiency, which often requires more design input and a lower plant capital cost. Lump sum fees based on the estimated time spent are therefore becoming more common, allowing greater scope for energy efficient design.

References

1   Jones P G, Cheshire D and Lillicrap C Energy efficient buildings: what is integrated design? *CIBSE National Conference 1997* (London: Chartered Institution of Building Services Engineers) (1997)

2   *Briefing the design team for energy efficiency in new buildings* GPG 74 (London: Department of the Environment, Transport and the Regions) (1994)

3   Halliday S P *Environmental code of practice for buildings and their services* (London: Building Services Research and Information Association) (1994)

4   *The benefits of including energy efficiency early in the design stage — Anglia Polytechnic University* GPCS 334 (London: Department of the Environment, Transport and the Regions) (1997)

5   *BREEAM/New Offices — An environmental assessment for new office designs* Version 1/93 (Garston: Building Research Establishment) (1993)

6   *Plan of Work for design team operation: RIBA Handbook* (London: Royal Institute of British Architects) (1973)

7   Parsloe C J *The allocation of design responsibilities for building engineering services — a code of conduct to avoid conflict* TN 8/94 (Bracknell: Building Services Research and Information Association) (1994)

8   Wild L J *Design information flow* TN 17/92 (Bracknell: Building Services Research and Information Association) (1992)

9   *BS 8207: Code of practice for energy efficient buildings* (London: British Standards Institution) (1985)

10   *A performance specification for the energy efficient office of the future* GIR 30 (London: Department of the Environment, Transport and the Regions) (1995)

11   *Energy efficiency in offices — a technical guide for owners and single tenants* ECON 19 (London: Department of Environment, Transport and the Regions) (1997)

12   *Environmental criteria for design* CIBSE Guide A1 (London: Chartered Institution of Building Services Engineers) (1986)

13   Bordass W T, Bromley A K R and Leaman A J *Comfort, control and energy efficiency in offices* IP3/95 (BRE) (1995)

Bibliography

Environmental criteria for design CIBSE Guide A1 (London: Chartered Institution of Building Services Engineers) (1986)

Best practice in the specification for offices (Reading: British Council for Offices) (1997)

Goulding J R, Lewis J O and Steemers T C *Energy in Architecture: The European passive solar handbook* EUR 13446 (1992)

Owning and operating costs CIBSE Guide B18 (London: Chartered Institution of Building Services Engineers) (1986)

Perera E and Parkings L Build tight — ventilate right *Building Services Journal* (June 1992)

Hancock C, Oreszczyn T and Iwaszkiewicz C Energy conscious design; the role of design advice *CIBSE National Conference 1994* (London: Chartered Institution of Building Services Engineers) (1994)

Al-khafaji M Effective energy management: the designer's role *CIBSE National Conference 1994* (London: Chartered Institution of Building Services Engineers) (1994)

Halliday S and Smerdon T Feedback as part of the building design process *CIBSE National Conference 1995* (London: Chartered Institution of Building Services Engineers) (1995)

The benefits of including energy efficiency early in the design stage — Anglia Polytechnic University GPCS 334   (London: Department of the Environment, Transport and the Regions) (1997)

Energy efficiency in offices — A guide for the design team GPG 34   (London: Department of the Environment, Transport and the Regions) (1993)

de Saules T *Handover information for building services* TN15/95 (London: Building Services Research and Information Association) (1995)

3 Developing a design strategy

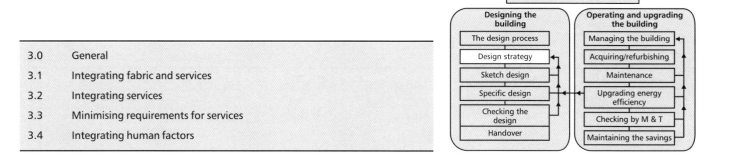

A coherent sketch design is at the heart of an energy efficient building[1-4]. This section outlines how to develop an integrated design strategy in line with the principles at the front of this Guide. Section 4 contains more detail on site considerations, built form, ventilation, daylighting and fuel selection.

3.0 General

Building design is an iterative process, often requiring design teams to re-think fundamental aspects of the design. Figure 3.1 indicates how an energy efficient design can be achieved through an integrated approach.

An overall design philosophy should be established to underpin the whole design process. Some key issues that have a strong influence on the energy efficient design philosophy are shown in Table 3.1.

3.1 Integrating fabric and services

The first step in developing an integrated design is to establish the function of the building envelope as the primary climatic modifier, supported by the services to trim conditions. Good fabric design can minimise the need for services. Where appropriate, designs should avoid simply excluding the environment, but should respond to factors like weather and occupancy and make good use of natural light, ventilation, solar gains and shading, when they are beneficial.

For example, decisions taken on the provision of daylight will directly influence the window design, the amount of glazing and the type of glass. They will also affect the building's susceptibility to solar gain and influence:

— the need for solar control and/or air conditioning

— the size, capacity and space required to accommodate central plant

— the air and water distribution systems.

Several iterations may be needed to reach an effective design as it is tested against the performance criteria of:

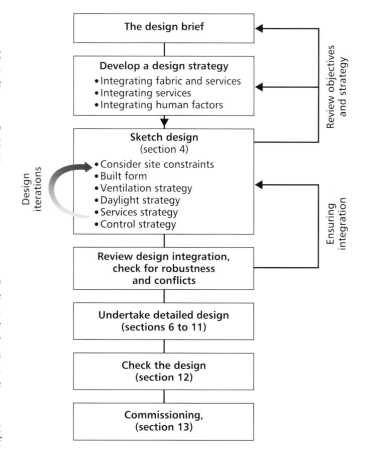

Figure 3.1 Integrated design

— cost

— quality of the internal environment

— space requirements

— energy use

Table 3.1 Issues that influence the energy efficient design philosophy

Building envelope	Building services	Human factors
Climate excluding or climate responsive?	Heavily serviced, mixed mode or passive solutions?	Balance between central automation and local occupant controls?
Use building fabric for thermal storage?	Use natural daylight/ventilation?	Responsive to occupancy/activity or fixed systems?
Thermally heavyweight or lightweight?	Complex or simple systems/controls?	Do occupants require loose comfort bands or tight regimes?
Deep or shallow plan?	Use flexible comfort criteria?	
Highly glazed or little glazing?	Use heat recovery and free cooling?	Easy or difficult to manage?
Openable or fixed windows?	Use combined heat and power?	Easy or difficult to maintain?
		Allow for future flexibility?

Select issues on the x and y axes to see how they may interact

Services issues	Deep plan/ shallow plan	Orientation	Percentage glazing	Lightwells and atria	Airtightness	Thermal response
Cooling	Deep plan may need greater cooling and mechanical ventilation	Consider locating cooled zones on north façade to reduce potential cooling loads	Minimise solar gains	Minimise solar gains	Take care that facilities for summer cooling are airtight in winter	Store heat in thermal mass and effect on response times
Heating	Deeper plan reduces heat loss area	Position less heated buffer zones on north façade to reduce heat loss	Solar gains contribute to heating	Minimise heat loss via atria i.e. avoiding heating	Minimise air infiltration to reduce heat loss	Store heat in thermal mass and effect on response times
Electric lighting and daylight	Use shallow plan for maximum daylight penetration or lightwells/atria	Calculate sun angles and use north light or shading to limit solar gains	Increased glazing will increase daylight but may also increase solar gains and need for shading	Use atria to increase natural daylight		
Natural ventilation	Use shallow plan to allow natural ventilation	Draw air from north façade to give cooler air	Ventilation depends on number of openable windows	Use atria to encourage natural air circulation	Seal building envelope and allow only controlled ventilation	Utilise effect of thermal mass on response of building to external conditions
Mechanical ventilation and air conditioning	Consider shallow plan with mixed-mode to allow natural ventilation at certain times	Orientated to avoid solar gains	Reduce percentage glazing to minimise effect of solar gains on air conditioning	Consider atria with mixed mode to allow natural ventilation and daylight at certain times	Ensure building envelope is sealed	Utilise effect of thermal mass on response time of air conditioning
	Deep plan/ shallow plan	**Orientation**	**Percentage glazing**	**Lightwells and atria**	**Airtightness**	**Thermal response**

Fabric issues

Figure 3.2 Interaction between fabric and services

— robustness

— ease of operation.

Avoiding dependence on mechanical plant, e.g. air conditioning, can reduce capital and running costs. Where air conditioning is unavoidable, the principles of integrated design can still help to reduce the size and complexity of the system, and hence its capital and running costs.

Figure 3.2 indicates some of the issues that need to be considered when integrating fabric and services. For example, a low percentage glazed area may result in higher lighting loads than expected. However, a large glazed area may not be helpful if the blinds have to be used to limit glare.

3.2   Integrating services

The next step is to ensure that the services operate in harmony without detrimental interaction or conflict. For example, the levels, control and efficiency of lighting have a significant effect on the need for cooling. It may also be appropriate to reconsider the building form so that more use can be made of daylight if this minimises energy demands for lighting and cooling.

Many energy problems can be traced to a conflict between building services. An energy efficient design strategy should avoid such conflicts. Some of the key interactions are shown in Figure 3.3.

Heating	Avoid simultaneous heating and cooling	Select issues on the X and Y axes to see how they may interact			
Electric lighting	Reduce incidental gains from lights to minimise cooling	Include contribution of lighting towards heating			
Daylight/ glazing	Minimise solar gains to reduce cooling loads	Minimise heat loss and maximise useful heat gain through glazing	Use suitable switching and daylight linking controls to minimise use of electric lighting		
Natural ventilation	Consider mixed-mode to use natural ventilation and avoid mechanical cooling where possible	Account for effect of open windows		Balance solar gains from glazing with increased natural ventilation. Avoid conflicts between window opening and blinds	
Mechanical ventilation and air conditioning	Use free cooling and 'coolth' recovery	Use heat recovery	Reduce electric lighting to reduce loads on air conditioning	Solar gains from glazing may increase loads on air conditioning, Heat loss may require simultaneous perimeter heating	Use natural ventilation instead of air conditioning where possible, or consider mixed-mode
	Cooling	Heating	Electric lighting	Daylight/ glazing	Natural ventilatiion

Figure 3.3 Interaction between building services

Simultaneous heating and cooling can be a major problem. Although this can be minimised by good controls, sometimes the problem originates from the basic design. For example, perimeter heating with core air conditioning may result in wasted energy if controls are adjusted by the occupants to compensate for local discomfort.

Zoning services is an important factor in achieving an energy efficient integrated design. Services should be matched to the actual requirements of each area. Areas with different requirements should not be heated, cooled, or lit to the same standards. Zones should be established in relation to the building, its occupancy and use, and the means of supplying the services. Generally, it helps to establish the same zones for different services to minimise conflict. For example, where a heating zone overlaps a cooling zone there is potential for simultaneous heating and cooling.

Excessive casual gains from lighting due to poor control can lead to significant cooling loads. This is particularly true in summer, when daylight levels may be sufficient for lights to be turned off. Good lighting control, including suitable manual override, can help to avoid this problem.

Mechanical cooling systems often operate when the external air could be used for cooling. Air conditioning systems may operate solely to negate the heat added to the air by the fans. The change to 'free' cooling and/or natural ventilation during winter can save significant energy, when humidification is not required.

Heat recovery provides a means of integrating services. For example, integrating lighting and air conditioning systems by extracting air through luminaires enables a proportion of the energy consumed by the lamps to be recovered to supplement heating in winter. The summer cooling load is also reduced by preventing a proportion of the lighting heat load from entering the room. The light output of fluorescent lamps also increases due to the lower operating temperature, although overcooling must be avoided.

Many conflicts between services are control issues (see section 5). However, the underlying reasons for conflict should be identified and eliminated to prevent carrying a flawed design forward. It is not good policy to hope that the control system will resolve these conflicts.

3.3 Minimising requirements for services

Over-specification of services should be avoided in order to minimise capital and running costs[5]. Continually reviewing the need for services, the true demands likely to be made on them, and avoiding unnecessary complexity will improve energy efficiency and will often result in a better building.

Building services engineers have a responsibility to challenge the assumptions underpinning the design in order to avoid over provision of services. An over-serviced building does not necessarily mean a 'high quality' building[6,7]. For example:

— Are the design margins excessive? (See section 4.)

— Are the design parameters unnecessarily restrictive? (For example, attempting to control relative humidity to 50 ± 5% all year round in an office.)

— Is the plant over sophisticated, necessitating more complex controls and increasing the likelihood that systems will be difficult to understand and control?

— Have natural sources such as daylight and cooler outdoor air been used to the full?

— Is the overall design intrinsically energy efficient, or is it likely to result in high running costs?

At an early stage, it should be possible to modify the design to reduce the capacity, size and complexity of the services. This can reduce the capital cost of the services without having to remove features from the design. For example, reducing the need for air conditioning by adopting a mixed mode approach could prevent the loss of a well-specified building management system (BMS) through budget cuts, thus retaining good control.

In general, a 'simple' approach is the best way of promoting good installation, operation and maintenance[6,7]. Simple services promote a good understanding of how the building and plant are intended to work. This generally improves building management and hence energy efficiency.

3.3.1 Optimising internal heat gains

Internal gains arising from occupants, equipment, lighting and solar radiation, etc. will normally offset a significant part of the fabric and ventilation heat losses. This can reduce heating plant capacity and running costs provided that the controls can respond to changes in internal gains, preventing overheating.

In summer, these heat gains can increase the need for mechanical cooling. To allow passive control of summertime temperatures, the level of heat gains within the space should be kept to a minimum[8–10].

To minimise energy consumption, it is important to establish a balance between the benefits of the gains in winter and the disadvantages in summer [11,12]. Office case studies[6] suggest that too many buildings use over elaborate methods to remove or avoid heat that could have been designed out. Common problems included:

— excessive window area with inappropriate or non-functioning solar control systems: reasonable window sizes (say 30% of main facade area) with simple, useable blinds and control devices are often preferable (see section 4).

— inefficient lighting: some 'passive' offices had installed lighting loads of 25 W/m², while good practice is 10–12 W/m² to achieve 400 lux (see section 8).

— poor lighting control: often caused by a lack of appreciation of the associated human factors, e.g. occupants objecting to frequent automatic switching.

— unnecessary internal heat gains: gains can be either from inefficient office equipment; excessive operation or poor location.

— over-design: can occur through over estimation of heat gains, particularly office equipment (see section 11). Recently there has been a trend to more realistic equipment gain levels (typically 10–15 W/m² in many offices) and to treat higher gains as 'specials'.

3.3.2 Optimising natural ventilation

Establishing a ventilation strategy can help to minimise the need for services[8] (see section 4). Natural ventilation can be optimised by the following measures:

— Question the need for full air conditioning: a passive or mixed mode approach may reduce capital cost.

— Further reduce the need for mechanical ventilation in mixed mode designs; e.g. improved zoning can lead to the separation of areas of high heat gain and result in smaller plant.

— Enhance window design to prevent poor usability. Too often there are not enough types of opening, insufficient user choice, and operational difficulties because window control gear is unsuitable or out of reach

— Use stack-assisted ventilation, often via roof lights in atria, to help ventilate deep plan buildings. Air outlets should be at least 3 m above the windows of the uppermost floor to prevent upper floors becoming much warmer than lower floors. In addition, people sitting near ventilation stacks or atria are not always as tolerant of high summertime temperatures as those sitting near external windows.

— Consider storing heat in the fabric during the day and removing it at night. Case studies[6] have indicated that windows for night ventilation need to be more useable, weather-tight and secure. Fan-powered systems often consume too much additional electricity and yet provide inefficient cooling[13].

3.3.3 Optimising daylighting

Daylighting should be an integral part of an overall lighting strategy (see section 4). Natural lighting may be optimised by:

— ensuring that electric lights remain off when there is sufficient daylight

— ensuring that daylight does not produce glare as this can lead to a blinds-down/lights-on situation, particularly where there are display screens

— ensuring that daylight is useable through good distribution using splayed reveals, light shelves, prisms etc.

— avoiding dark internal surfaces which absorb useful daylight

— introducing light into deep plan rooms by means of light wells or atria in order to minimise the use of electric lights

— ensuring that lighting controls take account of daylight availability, workstation layout and user needs; careful integration of manual and automatic control often provides the most effective solution.

It is essential to achieve a balance between useful daylight and unwanted solar gains. Increased daylight may result in less use of electric lighting and hence reduced cooling loads. However, increased solar gains during the summer could outweigh the benefits.

3.3.4 Thermal storage

Using the building itself as a passive thermal store can sometimes improve energy efficiency. In particular, night cooling of the building fabric is possible by passing cool night air across internal surfaces or through ventilation ducts in the structure (see section 4). It may be possible at the sketch design stage to further optimise the thermal response of the building to allow better use of the fabric as a storage medium. This requires a balance between:

— thermal capacity

— thermal response

— insulation levels

— complexity of controls.

All these should be matched to the occupancy patterns and method of heating and cooling being employed.

Active thermal storage devices have often been used effectively to smooth out peak demands, reducing the peak capacity of plant[14]. This can also help to keep plant operating at improved load factors and better efficiencies. Thermal storage can result in reductions in plant capital costs due to lower capacities, although the costs of the storage and the more complex controls can outweigh the savings. Reduced efficiency can arise from losses where there are less favourable operating regimes. For example, in the case of ice storage where chiller COPs tend to be reduced and pumping increased.

3.3.5 Heat recovery

Heat recovery systems can form a fully integrated part of a design, resulting in lower running costs and possibly reduced plant capacities. These systems most commonly recover heat from ventilation systems, using devices such as heat wheels or run-around coils to recover energy from exhaust air, then use it to pre-heat or pre-cool supply air. There must be sufficient energy being rejected at times when it can be used to justify the added complications and running costs of installing heat recovery devices (see 6.3.5 and 19.3.4).

3.3.6 'Free' cooling

Generally, 'free' cooling uses the cooling capacity of ambient air to directly cool the space. External air at say 10°C can be used to meet a cooling load and hence reduce the energy consumed by mechanical refrigeration plant (see 6.3.4).

Because the maximum cooling requirement usually coincides with maximum outside temperature, free cooling is unlikely to reduce the peak cooling load or size of chiller. However, it can reduce the running hours of the chiller and associated equipment, particularly when internal gains occur all year. These savings usually occur at lower cooling demand and hence at lower chiller efficiencies. Enthalpy controls are generally used in air recirculation systems to increase automatically the amount of fresh air when the ambient conditions can provide a useful cooling and/or dehumidification effect.

Free cooling can also be achieved using a mixed mode (changeover) approach. Fan energy consumption can be reduced by shutting-off the air conditioning system in winter, provided that adequate ventilation is maintained by natural means. Free cooling can also be obtained direct from cooling towers (see section 7).

3.3.7 Minimising distribution losses

Minimising the distribution lengths of ducts and pipework by siting pumps and fans as near to the loads as possible reduces transport losses. Distribution lengths are influenced by:

— the shape of the building

— the number and location of plant rooms

— the provision of space for distribution (riser shafts and ceiling voids).

This emphasises the need for an integrated design to ensure that plant room requirements are properly considered at the earliest design stage. It may be possible to reduce transport losses by decentralising plant, although this should be balanced against possible reduced plant efficiencies and increased maintenance costs. Usually, it is more energy efficient to transport hot water to a heater battery than warm air to a terminal unit.

Significant energy savings can also be achieved by reducing unnecessary pressure drops in the system by the careful sizing, routing and detailing of ductwork and pipework. In particular, pinch points or index runs require much higher pressure drops than much of the rest of the system.

3.4 Integrating human factors

Ensuring that management and occupants' requirements are met is a central part of energy efficient design.

Buildings and services that are responsive to the needs of the occupant are generally more successful in achieving comfort, acceptability and efficiency. Occupants usually prefer some means of altering their own environment while management will require good overall control of systems. Comfort levels do not always need to be within a tight specification to achieve an acceptable environment. Controls are the main interface between the occupants and the building services; these are discussed further in section 5.

A building will only provide comfortable conditions and low running costs for the user if it can be readily managed and easily maintained, and if it responds speedily to the changing needs of occupants[15]. These attributes must be planned for at the design stage since rectifying problems near completion, or when the building is occupied, seldom works and is always expensive.

3.4.1 Manageability

Many buildings do not realise their full potential for energy efficiency, often due to over complex design, effectively making them difficult to manage and sometimes unmanageable[15]. Newer buildings tend to be more complex in order to service an increasing range of activities, facilities and user needs. Avoiding unnecessary complexity and agreeing management requirements can improve energy efficiency but demands a strategic approach at an early stage. The energy efficient management of buildings is covered in more detail in section 14.

Potential conflicts need to be kept to a minimum and interactions between systems anticipated, rather than left to chance. Systems should default to 'off' or 'standby', not allowed to by-pass or be left on continuously. They should also operate robustly, rapidly and predictably, giving intelligible responses, especially during intense use. Good ergonomic design, rapid feedback and clear diagnostics are essential features in the design, not optional extras.

It is important to take account of the different points of view of designers, managers, users and corporate decision-makers. This approach helps to reduce misunderstandings between members of the design team, between the design team and client and within the client group. Effective strategy combines vision, clarity, attention to detail and requires regular review.

3.4.2 Maintainability

Ease of maintenance will influence future energy efficiency and should be addressed at the design stage. The requirements of space, position, access, repair and replacement of services should be considered so that equipment can be commissioned, monitored and maintained. Designers should include adequate access and monitoring facilities. It should be easy to check or change features such as set-points, control authority, filter elements, and chiller efficiencies, and also for alarms and faults to be registered quickly and easily.

The specification should also make clear the need for, and extent of, properly planned operating and maintenance procedures so that the design targets for the minimum use of energy are achieved. Energy efficiency will only be achieved in practice if the building is operated as the designer intended. Maintaining buildings for energy efficiency is covered in section 16 and in various BSRIA publications[16,17].

3.4.3 Flexibility

Inflexible designs can become prematurely redundant, whereas designing for flexibility can influence future energy efficiency. Flexibility is often best achieved by considering future adaptation of the building and its services and planning contingency strategies, rather than trying to create all-purpose spaces and systems. For example, one might allow space in plant rooms for upgrades, space for cooling coils in the air handling units and provision for additional cooling capacity in spaces where occupancy and equipment densities may increase.

References

1   *A performance specification for the energy efficient office of the future* GIR 30 (London: Department of the Environment, Transport and the Regions) (1995)

2   *Avoiding or minimising the use of air-conditioning — A research report from the EnREI Programme* GIR 31 (London: Department of the Environment, Transport and the Regions) (1995)

3   Baker N V *Energy and environment in non-domestic buildings. A technical design guide* (Cambridge: Cambridge Architectural Research/Building Research Energy Conservation Support Unit) (1994)

4   *Daylighting in buildings* Thermie Maxibrochure (Building Research Energy Conservation Support Unit/OPET) (1994)

5   *Best practice in the specification for offices* (Reading: British Council for Offices) (1997)

6   Bordass W T and Leaman A J Future buildings and their services — Strategic considerations for designers and their clients *CIBSE National Conference 1995* (London: Chartered Institution of Building Services Engineers) (1995)

7   Bordass W T, Bromley A K R and Leaman A J *Comfort, control and energy efficiency in offices* IP3/95 (Garston: Building Research Establishment) (1995)

8   *Natural ventilation in non-domestic buildings* CIBSE Applications Manual AM10 (London: Chartered Institution of Building Services Engineers) (1997)

9   *CIBSE Code for interior lighting* (London: Chartered Institution of Building Services Engineers) (1994)

10   *Internal heat gains* CIBSE Guide A7 (London: Chartered Institution of Building Services Engineers) (1986)

11   *Calculation of energy demands and targets for the design of new building and services* CIBSE Energy Code Part 2(a) Heated and naturally ventilated buildings (London: Chartered Institution of Building Services Engineers) (1981)

12   Baker N V and Steemers K *The LT Method 2.0. An energy design tool for non-domestic buildings* (Cambridge Architectural Research/Building Research Energy Conservation Support Unit) (1994)

13   Barnard N *Dynamic energy storage in the building fabric* TN 9/94 (Bracknell: Building Services Research and Information Association) (1994)

14   *Ice storage systems* CIBSE Technical Memoranda TM18 (London: Chartered Institution of Building Services Engineers) (1994)

15   Bordass W T and Leaman A Design for manageability *Proceedings of Buildings In The Age Of Paradox* (York: Institute of Architectural Studies, University of York) (1995)

16   *Building services maintenance* BSRIA Reading Guide RG6/95 (Bracknell: Building Services Research and Information Association) (1995)

17   Parsloe C *Design for maintainability* AG 11/92 (Bracknell: Building Services Research and Information Association) (1993)

Bibliography

Fundamentals ASHRAE Handbook (Atlanta, GA: American Society of Heating, Refrigeration and Air Conditioning Engineers) (1997)

HVAC Applications ASHRAE Handbook (Atlanta, GA: American Society of Heating, Refrigeration and Air Conditioning Engineers) (1995)

Window design CIBSE Applications Manual AM2 (London: Chartered Institution of Building Services Engineers) (1987)

BS 8206: 1985: Lighting for buildings: Part 2: Code of practice for daylighting (London: British Standards Institution) (1985)

BS 8207: 1985: Energy efficiency in buildings (London: British Standards Institution) (1985)

Halliday S and Smerdon T Feedback as part of the building design process *CIBSE National Conference 1995* (London: Chartered Institution of Building Services Engineers) (1995)

Brown A and Steemers K Integrating shading and daylighting for energy efficiency and comfort *CIBSE National Conference 1995* (London: Chartered Institution of Building Services Engineers) (1995)

Bordass W T, Bromley K and Leaman A Are you in control? *Building Services Journal* (April 1993)

Energy efficiency in offices — a technical guide for owners and single tenants ECON 19 (London: Department of Environment, Transport and the Regions) (1997)

Jaunzens D and Bordass W T Building design for mixed mode systems *CIBSE National Conference 1995* (London: Chartered Institution of Building Services Engineers) (1995)

Air-to-air heat recovery CIBSE Research Report RR2 (London: Chartered Institution of Building Services Engineers) (1995)

Thermal storage: Environmental benefits CIBSE Research Report RR6 (London: Chartered Institution of Building Services Engineers) (1998)

Engineering design calculations and the use of margins CIBSE Research Report RR4 (London: Chartered Institution of Building Services Engineers) (1998)

4 Sketch design

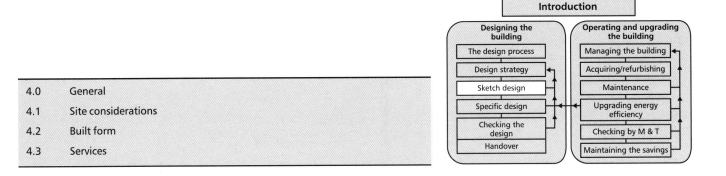

This section highlights some of the issues to be considered in developing an energy efficient sketch design and complements the strategic guidance given in section 3. The principles at the front of this Guide provide a framework for energy efficient design.

4.0 General

The sketch design stage should resolve any issues concerning the interrelationship between architecture and building services whilst confirming their respective contributions to the energy efficiency of the building. Decisions which affect the holistic concept need to be taken during this stage, so that the members of the design team can proceed with detailed design work (covered in the following sections) fully aware of the relationship between the components and the whole.

Site layout, the potential size of the building and the fuels available present both opportunities and constraints. The site conditions influence the built form and can be used to advantage to promote passive ventilation and daylight strategies[1–4]. The sketch design process is shown in Figure 4.1.

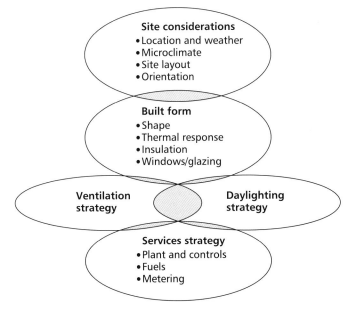

Figure 4.1 Sketch design

4.1 Site considerations

Some of the key site issues that effect energy efficiency are shown in Figure 4.2.

4.1.1 Local weather and microclimate

An effective design will take advantage of any local variations in climate, for instance by using local wind conditions to drive natural ventilation. Geography, topography, landscape, shelter, shading and surrounding buildings can all influence the development of built form and services, sometimes in different ways on different facades. These effects can be further enhanced by building arrangement and added landscape features[5–7].

The level of external pollution and noise, particularly in urban areas, may influence the choice of ventilation system and could exclude natural ventilation as an option. In these cases, careful design can provide acceptable solutions, e.g. by placing areas requiring low noise levels furthest away from noise and pollution sources.

4.1.2 Site layout and shape

The nature of the site will have a strong effect on built form and orientation, as well as a knock-on effect on services design. Planning requirements, local and national bye-laws and fire protection requirements may further restrict the building shape and orientation, affecting its services and energy performance. The position of approach roads and the requirements for vehicle parking could also influence

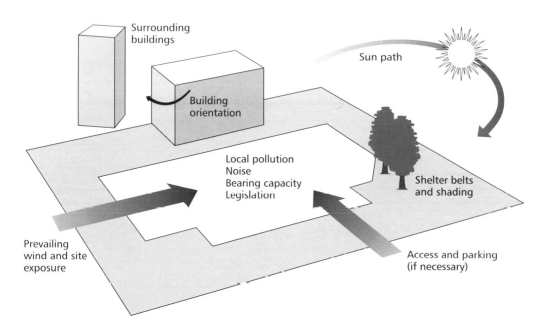

Figure 4.2 Site considerations

the energy efficiency of the design. Often, such features can be used to advantage, e.g. by using a parking structure to form a noise barrier.

4.1.3   Building orientation

Choosing the optimum orientation to maximise daylight and to minimise summer heat gain and winter heat loss can have a significant impact on energy efficiency, particularly if it avoids or minimises air conditioning. For example, north-facing windows suffer very little solar gain and benefits are often gained by having the major building axis pointing east/west. East or west-facing glazing is harder to shade from direct sunlight, as the sun angles are low at some times of year. South facades receive both direct and diffuse radiation and are relatively easy to control.

4.2   Built form

The building envelope should be considered as a climate modifier rather than solely a means of excluding external climatic conditions. The envelope generally has four main functions:

—   In cold weather, to reduce heat loss through the fabric, to maximise the benefits of solar and internal heat gains, and reduce losses associated with uncontrolled air infiltration.

—   In warm weather, to minimise solar heat gain and avoid overheating, also to use window shading and thermal mass to attenuate heat gain.

—   To allow optimum levels of natural ventilation.

—   To allow optimum levels of daylighting.

Relatively simple adjustments to built form at the sketch design stage can have a substantial effect upon future energy performance. If left until later stages, more complex and costly solutions may be necessary to make similar energy savings. Energy efficiency can be influenced through built form via:

—   shape

—   thermal response

—   insulation

—   windows and glazing

—   ventilation strategy

—   daylighting strategy.

These interrelated items, discussed below, need to be fully integrated during the sketch design process.

4.2.1   Shape

4.2.1.1   Building form

Compact building forms have a relatively small exposed surface area for a given floor area, thus reducing the influence of the external environment. A compact design may also benefit by requiring less space for the distribution of horizontal and vertical services, particularly for air ductwork. However, if commercial pressures and/or a compact design lead to a deep plan, i.e. over 15 m in depth, there may be a greater complexity of servicing. The core of the building may then require continuous electric lighting[8] and internal activities may prompt mechanical ventilation or air conditioning[9]. The energy efficiency benefits from natural ventilation and daylight penetration are most easily obtained up to 6 metres inwards from the windows. Taller constructions can increase energy consumption due to greater exposure and the need for lifts. Figure 4.3 shows examples of how building shape may affect energy efficiency.

4.2.1.2   Atria

Atria are rarely incorporated in designs for the main purpose of energy saving. The most likely motivation is architectural or the desire to make effective use of the site but their impact on the building services design can be significant. Energy efficient atria work best as a buffer between the inner and outer environments and should be

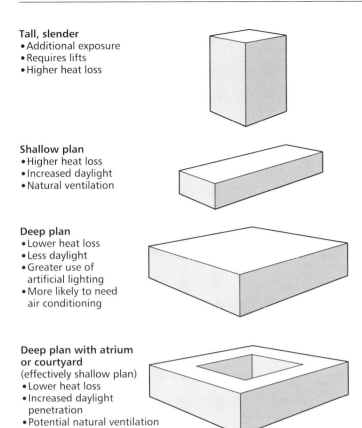

Tall, slender
- Additional exposure
- Requires lifts
- Higher heat loss

Shallow plan
- Higher heat loss
- Increased daylight
- Natural ventilation

Deep plan
- Lower heat loss
- Less daylight
- Greater use of artificial lighting
- More likely to need air conditioning

Deep plan with atrium or courtyard
(effectively shallow plan)
- Lower heat loss
- Increased daylight penetration
- Potential natural ventilation strategy

Figure 4.3 Examples of built form and its effect on energy

Table 4.1 Possible advantages and disadvantages of atria

Advantages	Disadvantages
Conversion of open courts to daylit and protected spaces	Added fire and smoke risks
Reduced conduction losses	Need to make provision for ventilating spaces which may otherwise be open to ambient air, e.g. light well construction
Possible use of the atrium as a sink for warm extract air	
Enhanced use of daylighting in the building core	Cost of glazing - total building costs can be less, depending on the form of atrium
Possible use of the atrium as a thermal flue to promote air flow through the rest of the building	Risk of overheating
Ability to pre-heat ventilation air	Delicate plants may require precise lighting and temperatures, increasing energy consumption
	Loss of daylighting compared with courtyards

carefully integrated into the sketch design and related to the heating, ventilation and daylighting strategies. Various forms of atria are shown in Figure 4.4.

To ensure that an atrium does not increase overall energy consumption, the following points are suggested:

— The daylighting levels should be maximised by using reflective finishes and clear glazing to reduce the need for daytime electric lighting. The electric lighting must then be controlled to gain the benefits.

— The atrium should be used as a heat recovery/buffer space, e.g. pre-heating incoming fresh air or passing exhaust air through the atrium on its way out of the building.

— Shading and high rates of ventilation should be provided in summer to prevent overheating.

The advantages and disadvantages of atria are shown in Table 4.1. Atrium design is also covered by Buckley[10]; the LT Method[11] provides a detailed design methodology and atrium ventilation is discussed in CIBSE Applications Manual AM10[12].

The daylight performance of an atrium is complex and depends on:

— its orientation and geometry

— the character of its wall and floor surfaces

— the nature of its roof and glazing.

In addition, the proportions of the atrium determine the amount of direct daylight reaching the floor; wide, shallow,

square atria perform better in this respect than do deep, narrow, rectangular ones.

The design of atrium walls significantly affects the distribution of light once it has entered the atrium. Dark finishes reduce internal reflectance and, the deeper the atrium, the more important this becomes. Windows in the atrium wall also reduce internally reflected daylight. Spaces facing into the atrium should have requirements corresponding with those of the atrium; rooms at the upper levels tend to receive plenty of light but need protection from glare while those at the base need to maximise the amount of light they receive. Other design strategies include making rooms near the base shallower, increasing their floor to ceiling heights, or successively stepping back the upper floors so that all rooms have some view of the sky.

Putting a glass roof over an open court reduces daylight levels in the court by at least 20%. The structure of an atrium roof, therefore, should minimise obstructions to the glazing area, and its connections to the building should ensure that light is allowed to wash the atrium walls.

Poorly designed atria can present problems with glare and excessive solar gains, leading to occupant dissatisfaction and sometimes higher energy consumption. Careful design of shape, orientation, room reflectance and shading can avoid these problems[10].

4.2.2 Thermal response

The dynamic thermal response of a building can be used to reduce energy consumption[13]. This response is a measure of the ability of the building to exchange heat with the environment when subjected to cyclic variations. It depends on the admittance of the contents and components of the structure and their surface areas. This ability smoothes out transient temperature variations and is especially important in reducing maximum summer time temperatures[2,3], thus avoiding or minimising the use of air conditioning. Increasing admittance also smoothes out transient heating/cooling loads and results in longer heat-up and cool-down periods. The thermal response can be different depending upon where the mass is placed e.g. floors, facades, internal walls, contents, etc. To make effective use of this mass it is necessary to ensure a good

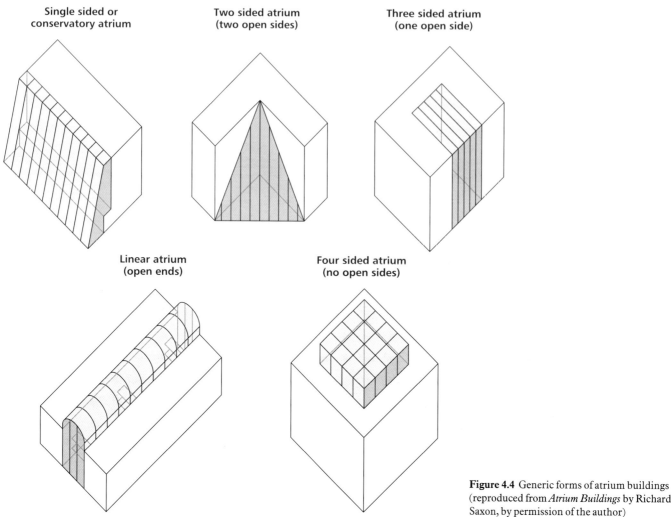

Figure 4.4 Generic forms of atrium buildings (reproduced from *Atrium Buildings* by Richard Saxon, by permission of the author)

heat transfer to and from the structure, for example by using embedded coils or ducts[1].

A well managed heavyweight building with high admittance can cope with a wide variation in gains and can often provide a robust solution if effective natural or mechanical night ventilation or cooling of the structure can be ensured (see 4.2.5.2). However, a high thermal mass does not guarantee a comfortable environment and night ventilation is critical to avoiding summer overheating. If the building could be subject to high heat gains, it may benefit from a high thermal response to slow down temperature swings, reducing cooling energy. If an intermittent heating regime predominates, a less thermally massive building would have shorter preheat periods and use less heating energy, provided that any tendency to overheat is well controlled.

If night ventilation cannot be assured a lower thermal mass should be chosen, although mass can still be useful in restricting peak temperatures and air conditioning loads. Attempts should then be made to minimise solar and internal gains, and maximise useful daytime ventilation.

Where a heavyweight structure and significant night ventilation are considered necessary, the operation of windows should be explained to the management and other building occupants, and possibly automated. Effective automatic control would need to be integrated with the rest of the control system (see section 5) and provide management feedback.

Intuitive manual control by the occupants depends on the feedback they receive. In a low thermal response building, internal and external heat gains would prompt window opening for cooling, although the temperature swings could be so large that cooling would not be achieved without excessive air movement. On the other hand, in a thermally massive building, the structure would absorb heat and delay the time when conditions would become uncomfortable. However, the structure's ability to absorb heat gains depends on it being cooled down at some time before the gains occur. Occupants will be unable to anticipate this, and so will need to be educated on how to undertake manual night cooling. Once they have learned this technique, feedback (in the form of discomfort) will prompt corrective action on days when overheating is likely.

Internal partitions and furniture increase the thermal response of the building. Cellular buildings often have a high thermal mass, regardless of the admittance of the materials used, as the extra surface area increases the thermal response. This can balance the effect of a lack of cross-ventilation, but effective night ventilation still needs to be assured. However, a full fit-out by interior designers can reduce the thermal response by covering exposed slabs and walls, changing their admittance. Thus the occupants of the building also need education so that they are aware of this when they brief initial and future fit-out contractors.

Heavyweight buildings may have areas that perform as lightweight buildings; for example, a large glazed entrance hall. Such areas may receive excessive solar gain and also be subject to higher heat losses than the remainder of the building, so they will need to be zoned separately using appropriate fast response zone controls.

4.2.3 Insulation

Reducing the thermal transmittance of the building envelope by adding insulation can help reduce heating demand and result in lower heating energy consumption. Insulation is much cheaper to include at initial construction stage than later in the building's life. Greater insulation in a building can simplify and reduce the capacity of its heating system. The resultant capital cost saving should be balanced against the additional insulation cost.

The location of insulation has a strong effect on the admittance and thus the thermal response. In intermittently heated buildings, it is sometimes preferable to place the insulation close to the interior surface of the wall. This will modify the thermal response of the room by reducing the ability of the masonry to absorb or emit heat and thus allow the heating system to track rapid changes in heating requirement. This may be desirable with intermittent heating, but may lead to rapid overheating if heat gains change rapidly. Insulation located on the external surface tends to de-couple the mass of the structure from the influence of the external environment and hence enables it to stabilise the internal environment.

In buildings with high internal heat gains[9], the effect of insulation on total energy use requires careful assessment. Removal of heat gains will become more reliant on ventilation if the building fabric cannot readily dissipate internal heat gains. This will require more careful design and will increase the need for, or capacity of, mechanical cooling systems.

Design issues include:

— *Internal insulation*: the structure is cold leading to greater likelihood of interstitial condensation or frost damage. Condensation can be avoided with extra ventilation and/or extra heating to raise surface temperatures, but this has an energy cost.

— *Interstitial insulation*: there is the possibility of thermal bridging at openings or junctions with internal walls and floors, with the risk of condensation or excess heat loss.

— *Composite structure*: fixing details are critical to avoid thermal bridging, particularly where masonry penetrates insulated components for structural reasons.

— *External insulation*: the structure remains warm, with less risk of surface condensation. The full benefit of the thermal capacity of the structure is obtained.

4.2.4 Windows and glazing

The amount and type of glazing, along with the shape, location and functionality of the windows, are key factors in

Table 4.2 Advantages and disadvantage of windows in terms of energy performance

Advantages	Disadvantages
Provide daylight, avoiding the use of electric lighting at certain times	Possible source of glare requiring screening and additional use of electric lighting
Openable windows can provide natural ventilation, avoiding the need for mechanical ventilation in some cases	Source of uncontrolled air infiltration/drafts causing additional heating demand e.g. badly fitting frames
Removal of internal heat gains	
Transmission of beneficial spring, autumn and winter solar gain which can reduce heating demand	Allows high heat loss through conduction, increasing heating demands
Openable windows permit occupant control of local environment which can reduce heating and cooling demands	May cause overheating due to solar gains possibly creating a need for mechanical cooling
	Control of natural ventilation is influenced by noise and pollution with no possibility of heat recovery

the effective control of heat losses and gains to the building with consequent effects on ventilation, daylight and control strategies, see 4.2.5 and 4.2.6.

Strategic decisions at concept design require early collaboration between architects and building services engineers to review the factors that influence the glazing design. In particular, the percentage of glass, the likely user reaction, the provision of daylighting and the implications for the design and control of heating, lighting and cooling systems. CIBSE Applications Manual AM2[8] provides a design methodology including the visual and energy performance of windows, although this does not cover natural ventilation or window control systems.

4.2.4.1 Windows and window systems

Modern integrated window systems can offer good control of openable areas of glazing, built-in noise reduction and solar protection measures. These should be investigated as part of the strategic design intention of obviating the need for air conditioning. Types of opening windows are described in CIBSE Applications Manual AM10[12].

In terms of energy performance, windows have the advantages and disadvantages shown in Table 4.2.

The design of window/glazing systems must achieve a balance between:

— providing daylight (controls which integrate electric lighting with daylight and occupancy are essential to minimise energy consumption)[14]

— effective use/control of heat gains and losses

— providing natural ventilation (the usability of the window mechanisms/furniture are crucial)

— providing external views, controlling glare and privacy

— allowing some degree of occupant control over local environment.

Many types of window design are available, the relative ventilation characteristics varying significantly. There are a number of criteria to consider:

— *Ventilation capacity*: i.e. how much air can flow through a given window area of different designs. This will depend on the ratio of the effective open area to the facade area taken by the window unit. It will, in turn, depend on how the window opens (side, top/bottom, or centre pivot, sliding etc.) and the distribution of the open area in the vertical plane. In some cases, it may be possible to induce local stack ventilation via say low to high level windows.

— *Controllability*: i.e. how the air flow capacity changes with opening. Good control at small openings is particularly important for winter comfort.

— *Impact on comfort*: i.e. what effect will the position of the room air inlet have on such factors as draughts?

— *Integration with solar control strategies*: in particular the use of blinds. The physical movement of the window may be restricted by an independent blind. The blind elements can provide an obstruction to the free area of the opening or the effectiveness of the blind may alter with window position.

The relative benefits of different types of window design are as follows:

— *Horizontal pivot windows*: produce very effective ventilation because large open areas are created at a separation equivalent to the window height. Air will tend to enter at the lower level and exit via the top of the window. They are easily adjustable to provide control of the ventilation rate.

— *Vertical pivot windows*: less efficient ventilators than horizontal pivot windows because the open area is uniformly distributed through the height of the window rather than concentrated at the extremes; but they can work well in combinations.

— *Top/bottom hung windows*: even less effective as ventilators than pivot windows as all the opening area is concentrated at one end, the top or bottom of the window.

— *Sliding windows*: similar characteristics to the corresponding horizontal or vertical pivot windows. A good seal is important in reducing draughts and energy loss when closed.

— *Tilting top vents*: provide smaller opening areas than the other systems as they occupy only a relatively small proportion of the window height. However, they can provide good draught-free ventilation, especially in cross-ventilation mode.

Useful rules of thumb for opening window design are:

— high level for cross ventilation

— low level for local ventilation

— trickle ventilation for winter time

— large openings for still summer days.

Windows are the most obvious controllable opening for natural ventilation, especially in summer. *Building Regulations Part F*[15] recommends an openable area of at least 1/20th of the floor area for rapid ventilation. Windows should:

— ventilate effectively (see Figure 4.5) but not cause draughts

— provide sufficient glare-free daylight and adequate view out of the building

— keep out excessive solar gain but allow a contribution during any heating period

— provide good insulation and avoid condensation

— allow occupants to adjust finely the openable area

— be simple to operate and make secure.

There can be a conflict between security and good ventilation, compromising energy performance, particularly for night ventilation. This can be alleviated by careful selection of window opening or by separating the ventilation element from the window.

Selection of window areas must accommodate the factors which influence the health and well being of the occupant. Occupants generally prefer to work adjacent to a window for the external view and natural lighting on the working plane. Any restriction of glazed areas to less than 30% of the external wall area must, therefore, be considered with care. However, case studies[16] suggest buildings with greater glazed areas may often operate with blinds down and the lights on because of the effects of glare. A balance must be drawn between these needs.

4.2.4.1 Glazing

The energy efficiency of glazing depends on the following:

— Single, double or multiple glazing: the more layers, the less light transmittance but the better the thermal performance.

— Window frame construction and detailing: the area of the frame, its material and whether a thermal break is included, have a substantial effect on the composite thermal transmittance of the complete window system[8,13].

— Type of coating: modern coatings can have a greater effect on the energy consumption than the type of glass. Thin plastic films are used in some multi-layered windows to reduce weight and provide anti-reflective qualities. However, to reduce significantly heat transfer through multi-layered windows they must control radiation heat transfer. Ideal glazing is transparent to short-wave radiation and reflective to long-wave radiation, allowing daylight and useful solar gains to enter while resisting radiative heat loss. 'Reflective glass' and solar control film reduce solar transmission, but at the expense of daylight and useful solar gain in winter. They can also create problems by reflecting sun onto other buildings or onto the northern facades of the same building.

— Type of glass: some tinted glass reduces solar heat gain but also cuts down daylight transmission and distorts the colour of the landscape. Heat absorbing glass does not reduce daylight transmission to quite the same degree and it only reduces heat gain by

Deeper windows can ventilate better....   .... but avoid draughts at working level   Consider controllable opening lights

Figure 4.5 Effect of window shape on ventilation performance[25] (reproduced from BRE Digest 399 by permission of the Building Research Establishment)

10% since a large percentage of the heat absorbed by the glass is re-radiated into the interior.

— Insulating layer in sealed glazing: heavy gases such as argon have lower thermal conductivity than air. Vacuum and translucent insulating fills are also becoming available.

It is always more cost effective to include energy efficient glazing at the initial construction stage rather than retrofitting. CIBSE Applications Manual AM2[8] shows some of the available combinations. Selective low-emissivity double glazing, with a heat loss equivalent to that of triple glazing, has a light transmission factor of approximately 80% and can provide a robust solution.

4.2.5 Ventilation strategies

Establishing a clear ventilation strategy is key to reaching an integrated energy efficient design. The strategy should provide:

— control over unwanted ventilation

— the correct quantity of fresh air for health and odour/moisture control, and for the rejection of excessive heat gains, if needed

— a driving force to move air into and around the building

— a means of controlling the air movement to and from the right place and at the right time, preferably involving the occupants so that it can match their needs.

Figure 4.6[12] provides a flow chart to assist in the design process, indicating a strong dependence on the depth of the building (see 3.3). A move towards air conditioning or mechanical ventilation is likely to increase consumption significantly and, although this may be unavoidable in some circumstances, it can be mitigated by energy-efficient fabric, systems, controls and the effective operation of the building.

4.2.5.1 Control of unwanted ventilation

Part L of the *Building Regulations*[17] calls for measures to minimise air leakage in both domestic and non-domestic buildings. The building fabric should be as airtight as possible to take advantage of a well-designed ventilation strategy. 'Build tight, ventilate right' is true for both mechanical and naturally ventilated buildings[18].

Background ventilation can be provided by trickle ventilators.

The reduction of infiltration relies on good building details[19] and on the quality of the building construction. The architect and builder must collaborate in implementing this part of the strategy because the performance of ventilation systems, and particularly the achievement of energy efficiency and comfort conditions, is dependent on the amount of infiltration occurring through the building envelope. Leaky buildings will interfere with the performance and energy efficiency of mechanical systems and will greatly reduce the net efficiency of heat recovery devices.

Typical infiltration openings include:

— the openable perimeter of windows and doors

— the window/door frame to wall interface

— wall to wall, wall to ceiling and wall to floor junctions

— porous and semi-porous building materials

— perimeter leaks around penetrations such as service ducts

— open flues

— open doorways.

Good attention to sealing is needed to minimise leakage routes. The leakage performance of openable windows and doors, and the performance of weather-stripping components for windows and doors, is covered by *BS 6375*[20] and *BS 7386*[21]. However, the greatest leakage has often occurred at the perimeter of the window assembly, particularly in buildings that are ostensibly sealed.

Particular attention should be paid to detailing at the junctions of building elements, e.g. the junction of curtain walling panels with mullions, window frames with openings in the external wall, junctions at eaves and in prefabricated structures. At these junctions, components built to factory tolerances often meet elements that are subject to site accuracy. The use of sealants and gaskets may provide a solution, provided that suitable materials and procedures are specified.

4.2.5.2 Natural ventilation

Naturally ventilated buildings generate the driving force for air movement by relying on a range of techniques which maximise the potential of the stack effect, using air passages

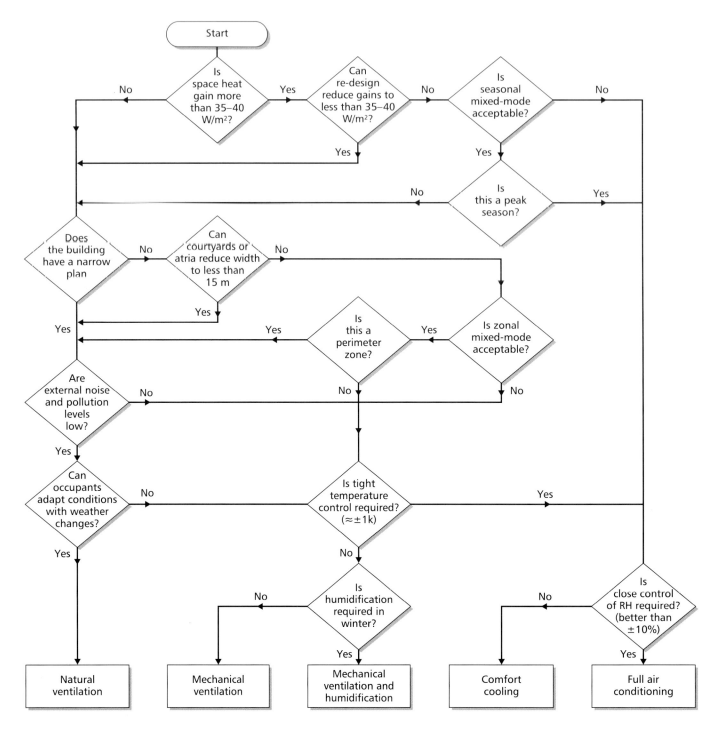

Figure 4.6 Selecting a ventilation strategy[12]

at differing heights and wind effects, often by ventilating from at least two facades. Guidance and case studies on the control of natural ventilation are provided in BSRIA Technical Note TN11/95[22]. CIBSE Guide A4: *Air infiltration and natural ventilation*[23] and *BS 5925*[24] give simple equations to estimate ventilation flows. Figure 4.7 shows various natural ventilation strategies[25].

The design of a naturally ventilated building should reflect the different requirements for winter and summer occupancy. In winter, excess ventilation should be minimised with background ventilation controlled by trickle ventilators or low level mechanical ventilation to meet occupants' needs for health and comfort. In summer, ventilation rates may need to exceed what is required for moisture and odour removal to satisfy occupants' needs to

avoid overheating. As part of this process, the careful distribution of fresh air within the space is important to achieve the objectives without causing draughts.

Ventilation controls should be ergonomically efficient and respond rapidly; their use should also be explained to the occupants. Where ventilation controls do not work properly (e.g. inaccessible window catches or insufficient fine control), occupants will often undermine the original strategy by taking alternative steps, e.g. introducing desk fans or making requests for air conditioning.

Trickle ventilation

Trickle ventilators are designed to provide the required minimum fresh air rate, particularly in winter, but without

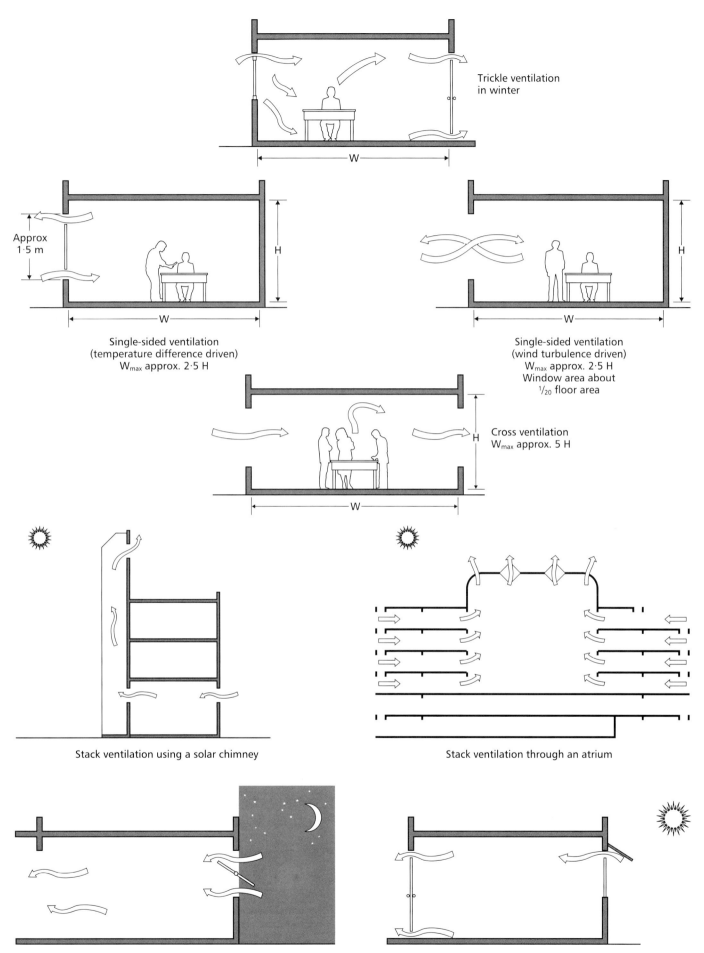

Trickle ventilation
in winter

Approx
1·5 m

Single-sided ventilation
(temperature difference driven)
W_{max} approx. 2·5 H

Single-sided ventilation
(wind turbulence driven)
W_{max} approx. 2·5 H
Window area about
$1/20$ floor area

Cross ventilation
W_{max} approx. 5 H

Stack ventilation using a solar chimney

Stack ventilation through an atrium

Night ventilation to restrict temperature rise next day

Figure 4.7 Ventilation strategies[25] (reproduced from BRE Digest 399 by permission of the Building Research Establishment)

Table 4.3 Advantages and disadvantages of trickle ventilation

Advantages	Disadvantages
Low cost	Variable rates of air change
Little maintenance needed	Little or no control of air flow pattern
Provides a safe level of background ventilation	No possibility of heat recovery
	Poor control can result in unnecessary heat loss

Table 4.4 Advantages and disadvantages of passive stack ventilation

Advantages	Disadvantages
Possible to achieve a consistent flow pattern that can remove pollutants at source	Only limited control of the rate of air flow rate is possible; unless the building is very well sealed (i.e. airtight), the combination of passive stack ventilation and infiltration may lead to excessive air flow rates, particularly during the heating season
No electrical power needed	
	Poor installation (such as bends in ductwork or excessive duct lengths) can result in low air flow rates

the increase in heating energy loss caused by opening windows. Part F of the *Building Regulations*[15] recommends a provision of 400 mm^2 per m^2 of floor area, with a minimum provision in each room of 4000 mm^2. These should be placed at a high level (typically 1.75 m above floor level) to avoid draught problems (see Figure 4.7).

The advantages and disadvantages of trickle ventilation are shown in Table 4.3.

Single-sided ventilation

This occurs when large, natural ventilation openings (such as windows and doors) are situated on only one external wall. Exchange of air takes place by wind turbulence, by outward openings interacting with the local external air streams and by stack effects driven by temperature difference. The rules of thumb shown in Figure 4.7 apply for moderate to high heat gains.

Single-sided ventilation should only be used when the building form or location limits ventilation to one facade. Until recently, the practical limits of single sided natural ventilation have been considered to be 6 m. However, recent research[25] concludes that, for low-heat gain, single-sided ventilation may be effective over a depth of up to 10 m, and may even be incorporated into open plan offices. Care should be exercised to minimise draughts for occupants at the perimeter when fresh air is required deep into the space. Also, people remote from the window can exercise less control and are therefore less tolerant of adverse conditions.

Cross ventilation

Cross ventilation occurs when inflow and outflow openings in external walls have a clear internal flow path between them (see Figure 4.7). Flow characteristics are determined by the combined effect of wind and temperature difference. Cross ventilation depends on the co-operation of occupants on opposite sides of the building to open windows appropriately, but can also be affected by internal partitions.

Stack induced ventilation

Ducts, shafts, solar chimneys etc. can be used to create a column of air at higher temperature thus generating pressure differences that give rise to the stack effect (see Figure 4.7). Passive stack effects can also be promoted through an atrium that will additionally act as a buffer to reduce fabric heat losses.

Stack ventilation can be controlled by automatic vents at the top of the stack, operated by temperature sensors in the space. Advantages and disadvantage of passive stack ventilation are shown in Table 4.4.

Night cooling

Increased ventilation at night can help remove heat that is stored in the building structure during the daytime to avoid high summer temperatures. A range of passive and active night cooling strategies can be used to achieve this objective, the simplest generally relies on good window design to allow ventilation at night (see Figure 4.7).

Solutions include using the thermal capacity of the building (see 4.2.2) by passing air through the building structure, e.g. hollow core slabs. In this way, the building envelope can be used to dissipate at night heat that has been absorbed during the day. Thus, the fabric provides a reservoir for incidental heat gains. These can be used for space heating in cold weather, or dissipated to ambient air using a night purge in warm weather. However, it is important to take account of the fan energy used to move the air through the structure.

Night ventilation in well insulated buildings with high thermal response factors can reduce the maximum daytime temperatures by 2–3°C, provided the thermal mass is exposed and a good control strategy deployed, see BSRIA Technical Notes TN 11/95[22] and TN 5/96[26].

4.2.5.3   Mixed mode ventilation

If a complete mechanical or natural ventilation strategy is not feasible, a mixed mode approach may be considered rather than full air conditioning[27–29]. Mixed mode alternatives can stretch the performance of natural ventilation by using mechanical systems only when and where necessary. Mixed mode designs can be seen as a logical extension to shell-and-core, as mechanical cooling only needs to be added where the occupants confirm that it is required. Over-design can be avoided, capital expenditure reduced and adaptation to meet changes in use can be allowed.

Mixed mode design strategies

There are three distinct approaches: contingency, complementary and zoned. Each of these can be developed in a wide variety of ways:

— *Contingency designs*: make provision for future addition or removal of mechanical systems. For example, a naturally ventilated building may be planned to allow mechanical ventilation and/or air conditioning to be added easily (locally or generally). Equally, an air conditioned building may be planned so that natural ventilation, or a combination of natural and mechanical systems, could easily be used if the air conditioning was no longer needed. This approach is particularly useful where occupancy/activity may change. Although there is a premium due to the space set aside, this is less than the capital cost of installing air conditioning.

— *Complementary designs*: have natural and mechanical systems present together. This may seem like a 'belt and braces' solution — and sometimes it is — but appropriate combinations can achieve an effective result at less cost than full air conditioning.

— *Zoned designs*: have different systems, or combinations of systems, in parts of the building which differ in their requirements for ventilation and cooling, owing to either their occupancy and usage or to their planning and location. Zoning is particularly efficient where problems can be grouped; for example, where a building is poorly located for passive cooling but has high occupancy and high equipment gains co-existing with relatively high solar gains. In this case, local air conditioning can do several jobs. However, studies suggest that the cooled areas may acquire higher status and 'concurrent' or 'changeover' approaches may then be preferable.

Mixed mode operating strategies

In complementary designs, it is important that natural and mechanical systems work together without clashing. In principle, there are three ways of achieving this:

— *Concurrent operation*: where the natural and mechanical systems operate together, for example in a building with openable windows and background mechanical ventilation. With some care, this can be an effective and energy efficient solution. For example, a building designed for high thermal stability, background ventilation (typically in the range 1–3 air changes per hour), with efficient fans, heat recovery and night cooling, may be able to maintain a steady temperature economically. The mechanical ventilation may also be used to extract hot or polluted air at source. Even if the mechanical system seldom makes it necessary to open the windows, the ability to do so increases tolerance and choice for occupants, provides additional ventilation if required and can permit the mechanical systems to be more modestly sized.

— *Changeover operation*: where the natural and mechanical systems can operate together in a variety of different ways that may alter with the seasons, the weather, occupancy levels or even the time of day. The intention is to maximise the use of natural ventilation but to introduce the necessary mechanical systems as and when required. A simple example would be a building that is naturally ventilated during the day but, if it becomes too hot by the evening, can use a mechanical system to pass night air to extract heat and pre-cool the structure. Another is where room cooling units, such as fan coils or chilled panels, have interlocks that permit them to operate only when the window is shut.

— *Alternate operation*: like changeover operation but with a much longer timescale. The building, or zone, operates in one mode for a long period, typically years, but certainly months. For example, part of a building may be air conditioned with the windows locked shut to suit one type of occupancy or use. However, if the occupancy and use were to change, natural ventilation or some hybrid could be used instead. Another example is where a cooling system is activated only in very hot weather, when the occupants would be alerted and asked not to open the windows while the cooling was running.

A flowchart to help select mixed mode strategies is shown in Figure 4.8.

4.2.5.4 Mechanical ventilation and air conditioning

There are instances where some form of forced ventilation system is unavoidable e.g. deep plan buildings, high internal gains, exacting environmental conditions etc. Even then, designers should seek to make effective use of ambient conditions with a view to minimising demand. Good zoning and controls are a key factors in making any mechanical ventilation strategy energy efficient, see sections 5 and 6, although controlling humidity will always increase energy consumption. Variable flow systems are preferable for energy efficiency, see section 10.

4.2.6 Daylighting strategies

The daylight strategy will have a significant influence on built form and, hence, the overall design concept. Strategies can vary significantly from say a building incorporating an atrium and light wells, with daylight for a large percentage of the year, to deep plan buildings that can only provide daylight around the perimeter of each floor. These different approaches hinge on the nature of the site (including the surrounding building etc.) and using the available daylight to its full extent, together with any necessary shading to avoid overheating and glare. CIBSE Applications Manual AM2[8] and BS 8206[30] provide simplified design guidance.

4.2.6.1 Using daylight

Good lighting design maximises the use of natural daylight to provide illumination, minimising installed lighting loads and lighting consumption and, thereby, reducing internal heat gains[31]. Daylight strategy, therefore, has a strong effect on the requirement for mechanical ventilation and air conditioning. The additional capital cost of improving daylighting should be offset against the running cost savings in lighting, and the capital and running costs of mechanical ventilation or air conditioning to remove the

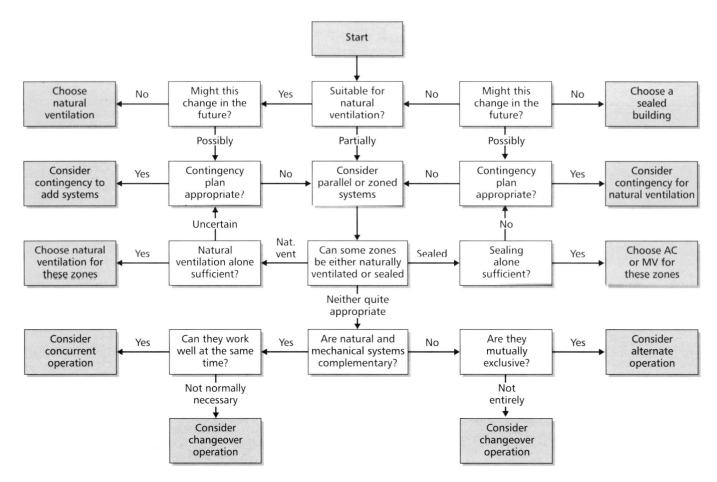

Figure 4.8 Selecting mixed mode strategies[27,28] (reproduced from DETR General Infromation Report *Mixed-mode buildings and systems.* Crown copyright)

heat it produces. The LT method provides a 'ready-reckoner' for optimising daylight penetration[11].

The amount and distribution of daylight depends on the size and position of the windows, the window construction, the external and internal obstructions and the type of glazing material. To maximise the use of daylight, high room surface reflectances should be used to promote good distribution[8,30–32]. Effective control of the electric lighting is the key to realising the potential energy saving from daylight. The electric lighting control system should reduce light output when daylighting levels are adequate and when the space is unoccupied[14,33], see 8.5.

Figure 4.9 shows a range of daylighting solutions that can be employed to fully utilise and control the use of natural light[4,32,34].

4.2.6.2   Daylighting levels

The level and availability of daylight varies with time, season and weather conditions[35]. In temperate climates, where an overcast or diffuse sky predominates, it is quantified in terms of 'daylight factor' which is a measure of the amount of daylight reaching the working surface in the room[8,30]. The amount of daylight illuminance for particular tasks will be the same as for electric lighting[32].

The average daylight factor indicates the appearance of the interior in daylight. For example, a room with an average

daylight factor of not less than 5% will appear 'light' and many tasks will not require electric lighting during daytime. However, a room with an average daylight factor of 2% or less will require electric lighting for most of the day[32,36]. A regular schedule for cleaning windows and internal room surfaces is necessary to ensure that daylighting levels are maintained, thus avoiding energy waste.

The variation of daylight throughout the day, and the year, affects the length of time it can be used to offset the use of electric lighting energy. These can be established using calculation procedures laid down in CIBSE Applications Manual AM2[8], *BS 8206*[30], BRE Digest 309[37]. CIBSE Guide A2: *Weather and solar data*[35] also provides values of probable sky illuminance hours for Kew. To prevent summer overheating, it is generally preferable to keep out the high sun of summer by good fabric and window design[8,30,32,35].

4.2.6.3   Zoning for daylighting

To maximise daylighting, the electric lighting installation should be zoned to take account of occupancy patterns and daylight distribution. Zones should start at the perimeter and work towards the central area. They should be parallel to windows and depending on the glazing ratio of the building facade, solar shading etc., the daylit zone may vary in depth to over 6 m. The number of zones and complexity of the lighting system should be balanced against the value

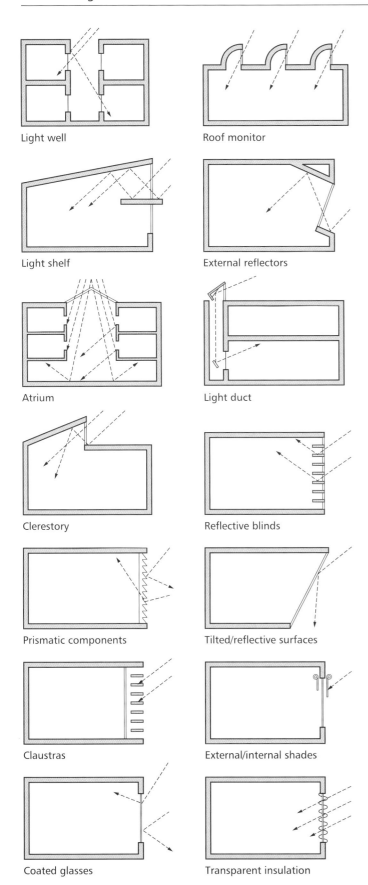

Light well

Roof monitor

Light shelf

External reflectors

Atrium

Light duct

Clerestory

Reflective blinds

Prismatic components

Tilted/reflective surfaces

Claustras

External/internal shades

Coated glasses

Transparent insulation

Figure 4.9 Daylighting devices[4] (reproduced from Thermie Maxibrouchure *Daylighting in buildings*. Crown copyright (1994))

4.2.6.4   Shading

Daylight can be controlled either actively, e.g. with external adjustable manual or automatic blinds, or passively using architectural features such as orientation and overhangs to reduce solar gains when the building may be susceptible to overheating. Figure 4.10 shows a range of external shading devices.

The appropriate type, size and positioning of any shading device will depend on climate, building use and the source of the light to be excluded (high or low angle direct sunlight; diffuse sky light; or perhaps reflected light from paving on the street outside). Deciduous trees or vines can be used to screen the solar heat and glare in summer and filter light in winter, and planting can sometimes solve the problem of reflected light from neighbouring structures, water or ground finishes. Designers should balance the benefits of having moveable external blinds against the relative robustness of fixed external shading.

Interior shades protect occupants against the immediate effects of direct sunlight and against glare. But when infra-red radiation penetrates the glazing most of it is trapped in the room and must be dissipated by ventilation or mechanical cooling. Mid-pane blinds are often a useful compromise and tend to require less maintenance and cleaning.

Horizontal shading elements are effective in reducing peak summer solar gain where high solar attitudes are experienced, primarily on southerly facades. Vertical elements are effective for restricting solar gain to facades subject to lower solar attitudes, i.e. east and west.

Fixed external shading devices include permanent facade features such as overhangs and window reveals. Unlike external blinds, the shading effect cannot be adjusted and the obstruction to daylight is permanent.

Reveals can be used to set back the window/glazing systems from the building envelope's opaque fabric to provide both vertical and horizontal shading effects, for east/west facades and south facades respectively. Overhangs can also be used to shade and are most effective on apertures that have a southerly orientation. Horizontal overhangs are not as effective on east or west facing walls, where reveals are more suitable.

Where large overhangs are used, the daylight factor is reduced and the result may be a greater use of electric lighting; this may offset the energy savings made on the HVAC systems. In air conditioned buildings, the investment in fixed external shading devices will also reduce central plant size and capital costs.

Automatically controlled shading devices can provide improvements by shading when there is excessive solar gain, and retracting to utilise daylight and winter solar gain. Control is a critical element and, in particular, the integration with electric lighting control is essential. Systems that default to a condition of 'blinds down' and 'lights on' must be avoided. However, a 'seamless' variation between daylight and electric lighting can be difficult to achieve. Large step changes prompted by automatic controls should be avoided as this can prove irritating to occupants[14,33]. Individual control, rather than fully automatic modulation, is generally preferred by occupants.

of the likely electricity saving. Infra-red or similar hand held controllers should be investigated to reduce wiring costs. The control or switching system also needs to be fully integrated with these zones in order to achieve potential savings, see 8.5.

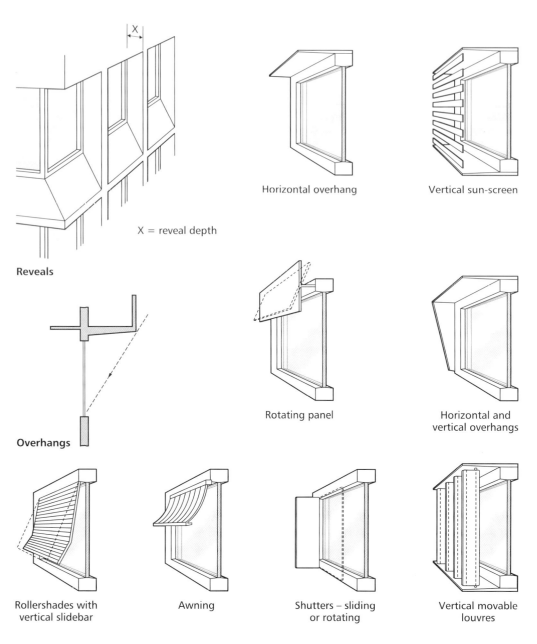

Figure 4.10 External shading devices

Horizontal overhang

Vertical sun-screen

X = reveal depth

Reveals

Rotating panel

Horizontal and vertical overhangs

Overhangs

Rollershades with vertical slidebar

Awning

Shutters – sliding or rotating

Vertical movable louvres

Automatic external shading devices need to be provided with overrides to permit manual adjustment by the occupants, and automatic retraction to prevent wind damage.

4.3 Services

4.3.1 Concepts for services

Selecting the most appropriate and energy efficient systems is fundamental to the overall sketch design. Good selection of zones and effective means of control is also vital to energy efficiency. At times when passive natural ventilation and daylight can not alone meet the needs of occupants, the building services should meet the remaining demands as simply and effectively as practicable, in harmony with the occupants and the building as a whole.

The following points should be considered during design:

—   Select the most efficient source, e.g. boiler, chiller, lamp etc.

—   Use the most environmentally friendly fuel, see 4.3.2.

—   Ensure that plant is not oversized and output can be matched to demand e.g. using a modular approach.

—   A 'keep it simple' approach is often best to ensure that design intentions can be achieved and energy consumption kept under control.

—   Do not simply employ 'add-on' energy saving features; ensure they are part of an integrated strategy.

—   Always consider part load conditions and efficiencies, and provide modulating systems where appropriate.

—   Zone the building carefully to meet the needs of occupants. Select appropriate controls for each zone to allow, for example, the building manager to isolate unoccupied areas. These should ensure services only operate when, where, and to the level required.

—   Select effective controls for the central plant to minimise plant running hours and cycling.

Table 4.5 Factors to consider when choosing fuels

Factor	Coal	Waste-derived fuel	Natural gas	Fuel oil	Electricity	Multi-fuel	Waste heat
Local availability							
Security of supply		✔				✔	✗
Fuel cost	✔	✔	✔	✔	✗✗	✔✔	✔✔
Flexibility/ controllability	✗	✗	✔	✔	✔	✗	✗
Capital cost of plant	✗	✗			✔	✗✗	
Space and civil works required	✗	✗	✔		✔	✗	
Complexity of ancillary plant	✗	✗				✗	✗
Attendance and maintenance	✗	✗	✔		✔✔	✗	✗
Chimney requirements	✗		✔		✔✔	✗	
Noise	✗	✗				✗	
Environmental emissions	✗				✗		✔

Key: ✗ unfavourable; ✔ favourable (double ticks/crosses emphasise favourability/unfavourability)

Controls should be designed to give priority to natural resources, e.g. daylight, before electric lighting.

— Ensure that large central systems do not operate to meet small loads, e.g. if summer hot water demand is low, install separate heating and hot water systems rather than a combined central system.

— Consider a mixed mode approach to avoid having one large system operating all year round. Demands can be met using different design strategies (contingency, complementary, or zoned) and/or different operating strategies (concurrent, change-over or alternate) (see 4.2.5.3).

— Special needs, e.g. additional lighting, should be met locally and not used for the entire area.

— The temperatures of the heating and cooling media supplied to heat exchangers should be kept at the minimum and maximum values, respectively, that are able to achieve the necessary performance.

— Provide some element of user control and, thereby, assist in promoting comfort. Controls should be sufficiently flexible to satisfy different occupancy levels and activities, e.g. the necessary switching to allow a half level of lighting for cleaners or security staff outside normal working hours.

— Systems should revert to safe and energy-efficient 'off' or 'standby' levels after use rather than automatically left on.

— Controls should be appropriate to the user, e.g. building management systems (BMS) can be very effective in large buildings or estates with resident engineers, whereas less complex controls may be more appropriate in smaller buildings.

— It is essential that feedback mechanisms are put in place to monitor the status and operation of the building. These mechanisms should ensure that building managers know if energy consumption is greater than expected.

Further details on the selection and design of particular systems is provided in sections 6 to 11.

4.3.2 Fuel selection

Fuel selection is a strategic decision, which can drive the choice and design of building services and hence future energy efficiency. The decision is often dominated by practical issues, such as the availability of fuels on site, access for delivery, as well as the space and cost of fuel storage. Fuel costs are a significant driving force and environmental emissions are a growing influence.

Typical fuel specifications and combustion details are shown in CIBSE Guide C5: *Fuels and combustion*[38]. Conversion factors are provided in Appendix A2. Table 4.5 summarises the factors to consider when choosing different fuels.

Electricity

Electricity is generally a premium fuel but relatively expensive (currently 2.5 to 7 p/(kW h)). Although it is usually easy and cheap to install electricity supplies, and it is clean at the point of use, some forms of generation cause high CO_2 emissions (see 4.3.2.1). High voltage transformer losses can be around 1% of energy consumed on larger installations and therefore transformer efficiency should be considered at the design stage.

Lower power factors lead to higher electricity costs, greater energy consumption and larger switchgear and cables. It is desirable to keep power factors above about 0.9 and this should be addressed when selecting equipment, particularly lighting, electronics and motors. Where necessary, power factor correction equipment should be installed. For example, improving the power factor of a 100 kW demand from 0.75 to 0.93, the current would be reduced from 186 A to 150 A. Typically, a payback period of less than two years could be expected depending upon the supply contract and usage.

Natural gas

Natural gas is a convenient, cheap and clean fuel, but it is not available on all sites and connection costs can be significant. Where gas is supplied at high pressure, temperature and pressure adjustments usually need to be made to establish the actual volume used. Care should also be taken to ensure that the true calorific value is used in any energy calculation.

Fuel oil

Fuel oil is supplied in a range of densities and calorific values from kerosene to heavy fuel oil. Heavier fuel oils are generally cheaper but have lower calorific values and require heating to ensure that they have the correct viscosity at the burner. They also produce more harmful emissions when burnt. Monitoring fuel deliveries does not provide an accurate reflection of consumption and integrating meters should be installed for monitoring and targeting purposes.

Solid fuels

Solid fuels are normally inexpensive although they require more handling, boiler management and storage space. They also have significant environmental impact, see 4.3.2.1. These fuels are normally delivered by weight and come in various sizes and calorific values. Unless there is a recording meter on the grate or screw feed to the boiler, accurate measurement of consumption can be difficult. A crude arrangement using storage bays can be employed to estimate usage.

Liquid petroleum gas (LPG)

Liquid petroleum gas (LPG) is a clean fuel (normally propane or butane) but comparatively expensive. It is usually delivered by tanker (requiring access) and stored as a liquid under pressure. Consumption is normally measured using a standard gas meter.

4.3.2.1   Environmental emissions of fuels

Burning fossil fuels results in emissions to the environment and contributes to the threat of climate change, primarily through carbon dioxide emissions. Table 4.6 shows a comparison of the different fuels and their relative CO_2 emissions. Electricity production causes emissions at the power station, although the factor is generally falling as power stations become more efficient and use fuels with lower CO_2 emissions. By comparison, renewable sources of energy produce little or no greenhouse and acid gas emissions.

Boilers running on fossil fuels generally produce NO_x and/or SO_x. Emissions are specific to the type of fuel and plant but low NO_x boilers are now widely available.

4.3.2.2   Renewable sources of energy

The use of naturally renewable energy resources is becoming more common in buildings. Waste incineration, bio-fuels, wind, bio-gas and hydroelectric schemes should all be considered at the design stage, depending upon local

Table 4.6 Carbon and carbon dioxide equivalents (1997 data)

Fuel	CO_2 equivalent (kg/(kW h))	Carbon equivalent (kg/(kW h))
Coal	0.34	0.093
Coke	0.43	0.12
Other solid fuel	0.41	0.11
Gas	0.20	0.055
Oil	0.29	0.079
Electricity	0.52	0.142

conditions and availability. Active and passive solar energy systems are becoming more common in buildings although the economics still require careful assessment. Photovoltaic cells to produce electricity are becoming cheaper and are beginning to have applications in buildings. Simple solar systems for heating domestic hot water have been used extensively in hot climates although they have not generally provided a high rate of return on investment in the UK.

4.3.3   Metering

Most sites have main accounting meters for electricity and gas provided by supply authorities. These meters can provide accurate demand patterns for energy management purposes. Whilst these give a measure of total consumption, designers should always include sub-metering to monitor where energy is actually being used; in particular, to identify individual building consumption on multi-building sites. A good maxim is: 'if you can't measure it, you can't manage it'.

Sub-metering allows the cause of increased energy use to be diagnosed more readily and, therefore, should be provided in all buildings to improve building management. It is generally cheaper to install sub-meters as part of the design than to retrofit at a later stage. Sub-metering is particularly important where there are large process loads which may mask the true performance of the building, e.g. a computer suite or kitchen. It will also enable fair billing for energy use where a building may be subdivided for occupation by more than one organisation, or where one occupant has a variety of cost centres.

The justification for sub-metering is highly dependent on energy type. Electricity has a high unit cost but metering is cheap, reliable and accurate, relative to other fuels, making a good case for monitoring. Energy used in main plant, e.g. gas, oil or electricity, is often easy to meter. However, metering of services, such as heat, chilled water and air conditioning can require more complex meters than fuels. Hours run meters on significant items of equipment can help to deduce the breakdown of energy use by different services. It is also important to develop a coherent metering strategy to avoid the problems shown in Figure 4.11.

4.4   Summary

The sketch design can be regarded as complete only when:

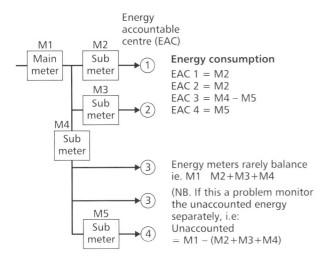

Figure 4.11 Providing a coherent sub-metering strategy[39] (reproduced from *Energy — containing the costs* by permission of the Department of the Environment, Transport and the Regions)

— the overall strategy is clearly stated and understood by all those involved

— the interrelationships between the architectural and services aspects of the design have been resolved

— the contributions to energy efficiency made by each aspect of the design have been established

— decisions which affect the holistic concept of the design have been made, e.g. whether mechanical ventilation or cooling is needed, whether the building form will encourage the usc of daylight and how the lighting will be controlled

— all members of the design team appreciate the impact that their components have on the whole.

References

1   *A performance specification for the energy efficient office of the future* GIR 30 (London: Department of the Environment, Transport and the Regions) (1995)

2   *Avoiding or minimising the use of air-conditioning — A research report from the EnREI Programme* GIR 31 (London: Department of the Environment, Transport and the Regions) (1995)

3   Baker N V *Energy and environment in non-domestic buildings. A technical design guide* (Cambridge: Cambridge Architectural Research/Building Research Energy Conservation Support Unit) (1994)

4   *Daylighting in buildings* Thermie Maxibrochure (Building Research Energy Conservation Support Unit/OPET) (1994)

5   *Climate and site development. Part 1: General climate of the UK* Digest 350 (Garston: Building Research Establishment)

6   *Climate and site development. Part 2: Influence of microclimate* Digest 350 (Garston: Building Research Establishment)

7   *Climate and site development. Part 3: Improving microclimate through design* Digest 350 (Garston: Building Research Establishment)

8   *Window design* CIBSE Applications Manual AM2 (London: Chartered Institution of Building Services Engineers) (1987)

9   *Internal heat gains* CIBSE Guide A7 (London: Chartered Institution of Building Services Engineers) (1986)

10   Buckley M, Field J and Lloyd Jones D *Low energy atria* (Garston: Building Research Establishment Energy Conservation Support Unit) (To be published)

11   Baker N V and Steemers K *The LT Method 2.0. An energy design tool for non-domestic buildings* (Cambridge: Cambridge Architectural Research/Building Research Energy Conservation Support Unit) (1994)

12   *Natural ventilation in non-domestic buildings* CIBSE Applications Manual AM10 (London: Chartered Institution of Building Services Engineers) (1997)

13   *Thermal properties of building structures* CIBSE Guide A3, (London: Chartered Institution of Building Services Engineers) (1980)

14   *Electric lighting controls — A guide for designers, installers and users* GPG 160 (London: Department of Environment, Transport and the Regions) (1997)

15   *The Building Regulations Part F: Ventilation* (London: Stationery Office) (1995)

16   Bordass W T, Bromley A K R and Leaman A J *Comfort, control and energy efficiency in offices* IP3/95 (Garston: Building Research Establishment) (1995)

17   *The Building Regulations Part L: Conservation of Fuel and Power* (London: Stationery Office) (1995)

18   Perera E and Parkings L Build tight — ventilate right *Building Services Journal* (June 1992)

19   Perera E S, Turner C H C and Scivyer C R *Minimising air infiltration in office buildings* BR265 (Garston: Building Research Establishment) (1994)

20   *BS 6375: Performance of windows* (London: British Standards Institution) (1989/95)

21   *BS 7386: 1997: Specification for draughtstrips for the draught control of existing doors and windows in housing (including test methods)* (London: British Standards Institution) (1997)

22   Martin A J *Control of natural ventilation* TN 11/95 (Bracknell: Building Services Research and Information Association) (1995)

23   *Air infiltration and natural ventilation* CIBSE Guide A4 (London: Chartered Institution of Building Services Engineers)

24   *BS 5925: 1991 (1995): Code of practice for ventilation principles and designing for natural ventilation* (London: British Standards Institution) (1995)

25   *Natural ventilation in non-domestic buildings* Digest 399 (Garston: Building Research Establishment) (1994)

26   Martin A *Night cooling control strategies* TN 5/96 (Bracknell: Building Services Research and Information Association) (1996)

27   *Mixed-mode buildings and systems* GIR (London: Department of Environment, Transport and the Regions) (to be published)

28   Jaunzens D and Bordass W T Building design for mixed mode systems *CIBSE National Conference 1995* (London: Chartered Institution of Building Services Engineers) (1995)

29   Bordass W T, Entwisle M J and Willis S Naturally ventilated and mixed mode office buildings — Opportunities and pitfalls *CIBSE National Conference 1994* (London: Chartered Institution of Building Services Engineers) (1994)

30   *BS 8206: Lighting for buildings: Part 2: Code of practice for daylighting* (London: British Standards Institution) (1985)

31   Bell J and Burt W *Designing buildings for daylight* BR288 (Garston: Building Research Establishment) (1995)

32   *CIBSE Code for interior lighting* (London: Chartered Institution of Building Services Engineers) (1994)

33   *People and lighting controls* IP6/96 (Garston: Building Research Establishment) (1996)

34   Littlefair P J *Designing with innovative daylighting* BR305 (Garston: Building Research Establishment)(1996).

35   *Weather and solar data* CIBSE Guide A2 (London: Chartered Institution of Building Services Engineers)(1982).

36   Gould J R, Lewis J O and Steemers T C *Energy in architecture: The European passive solar handbook* EUR 13445 (1992)

37   *Estimating daylight in buildings: Part 1* Digest 309 (Garston: Building Research Establishment)(1986)

38   *Fuels and combustion* CIBSE Guide C5 (London: Chartered Institution of Building Services Engineers)(1976)

39   *Energy — containing the costs* (London: Department of Environment, Transport and Regions/Chartered Institute of Management Accountants)(1992)

Bibliography

General

Bordass W T, Bunn R, et al. PROBE: Some lessons learned from the first eight buildings *CIBSE National Conference* 1997 (London: Chartered Institution of Building Services Engineers)(1997)

Fundamentals ASHRAE Handbook (Atlanta, GA: American Society of Heating, Refrigeration and Air Conditioning Engineers)(1997)

HVAC Applications ASHRAE Handbook (Atlanta, GA: American Society of Heating, Refrigeration and Air Conditioning Engineers)(1995)

Atria case studies LB50/88 (Bracknell: Building Services Research and Information Association)(1988)

Gregory D P *Future fuel prices and competitiveness to the year 2005* TN 2/86 (Bracknell: Building Services Research and Information Association)(1986)

Smith M H *Maintenance and utility costs — results of a survey* TM 3/91 (Bracknell: Building Services Research and Information Association)(1991)

Pike P *Weather data* RR 10/95 (Bracknell: Building Services Research and Information Association)(1994)

Environmental code of practice for buildings and their services — Case studies CS4/96 (Bracknell: Building Services Research and Information Association)(1996)

Building services and environmental issues: the bibliography LB 74/92 (Bracknell: Building Services Research and Information Association)(1992)

Selecting windows by performance Digest 377 (Garston: Building Research Establishment)

Energy efficiency in dwellings Digest 355 (Garston: Building Research Establishment)

Comparative life cycle assessment of modern commercial buildings SC98 (Garston: Building Research Establishment)(1997)

Thermal response of buildings CIBSE Guide A5 (London: Chartered Institution of Building Services Engineers)(1979)

Barnard N Fabric energy storage of night cooling *CIBSE National Conference 1994* (London: Chartered Institution of Building Services Engineers)(1994)

Mills F A Atrium building performance *CIBSE National Conference 1995* (London: Chartered Institution of Building Services Engineers)(1995)

Archard and Gicquel *European passive solar handbook — Basic principles and concepts for passive solar architecture* CEC DG XII for Science Research and Development (Brussels: Commission of European Communities)(1986)

Passive solar design — Netley Abbey Infant School GIL 12 (London: Department of Environment, Transport and the Regions)(1996)

Passive solar design — Looe Junior and Infant School GIL 33 (London: Department of Environment, Transport and the Regions)(1996)

The benefits of including energy efficiency early in the design stage — Anglia Polytechnic University GPCS 334 (London: Department of Environment, Transport and the Regions)(1997)

Energy efficiency in offices. A guide for the design team GPG 34 (London: Department of Environment, Transport and the Regions)(1993)

Designing energy efficient multi-residential buildings GPG 192 (London: Department of Environment, Transport and the Regions)(1997)

Irving S J Air-to-air heat recovery *CIBSE National Conference 1994* (London: Chartered Institution of Building Services Engineers)(1994)

Best Practice in the specification for offices (Reading: British Council for Offices)(1997)

Ventilation

Potter I N *Ventilation effectiveness in mechanical ventilation of dwellings* TN 1/88 (Bracknell: Building Services Research and Information Association)(1988)

Liddament M *Building air tightness and ventilation — an overview of international practice* TN 5/86 (Bracknell: Building Services Research and Information Association)(1986)

Jackson A J Air conditioning and energy efficiency *CIBSE National Conference 1995* (London: Chartered Institution of Building Services Engineers)(1995)

Liddament M W *A guide to energy efficient ventilation* (Coventry: Air Infiltration and Ventilation Centre)(March 1996)

Leaman A, Cohen R R and Jackman P J Ventilation of office buildings: Deciding the appropriate system *CIBSE National Conference 1995* (London: Chartered Institution of Building Services Engineers)(1994)

Design guide for free cooling RR16/96 (Bracknell: Building Services Research and Information Association)(1996)

Daylighting

Thompson M W and Mucibabic Model studies of daylight factor: light shelves, curved ceilings and external obstruction *CIBSE National Conference 1995* (London: Chartered Institution of Building Services Engineers)(1995)

Loe D Interior lighting quality and the potential for energy saving *CIBSE National Conference 1995* (London: Chartered Institution of Building Services Engineers)(1995)

Crisp V H C, Littlefair P J, Cooper I and McKennan G *Daylighting as a passive solar option: an assessment of its potential in non-domestic buildings* BR129 (Garston: Building Research Establishment)(1988)

Lighting controls and daylight use Digest 272 (Garston: Building Research Establishment)(1983)

Hunt D R G Predicting lighting use — a method based upon observed patterns of behaviour *Lighting Research and Technology* 12(1)(1980)

Lynes J A and Littlefair P J Lighting energy savings from daylight estimation at the sketch design stage *Lighting Research and Technology* 22(3)(1990)

Littlefair P J Innovative daylighting: review of systems and evaluation methods *Lighting Research and Technology* 22(1) 1990

Hildon A and Byrd H Daylighting: appraisal at the early design stages *Lighting Research and Technology* 11(2) 1979

Baker N, Franchotti A and Steemers K *Daylighting in architecture — a European reference book* (London: James and James)(1993)

Site planning for daylight and sunlight BR209 (Garston: Building Research Establishment)(1991)

5 Control strategies

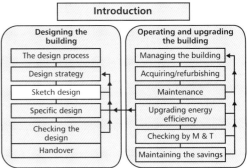

This section sets out some of the key issues to be considered in developing energy efficient control strategies for building services, in line with the principles at the front of this Guide. Guidance on designing specific controls is given in sections 6 to 10. Upgrading controls is covered in section 19 and maintenance of controls in section 17. Further guidance on controls can be found in the CIBSE Applications Manual AM 1[1], in CIBSE Guide B3: *Ventilation and air conditioning (systems, equipment and control)*[2], Fuel Efficiency Booklet No. 10[3], the *Standard Specification For BEMS*[4] and DETR General Information Reports 41[5] and 40[6].

5.0   General

Good control is essential to maintain the desired levels of service, comfort and safety in an energy efficient manner[7]. Even well designed systems can perform badly if the controls are inadequate or incorrectly installed. Good controls can:

— increase the comfort of occupants

— prevent systems from being on when not needed

— switch systems on just early enough to achieve comfort by occupancy time, and off early enough to minimise consumption

— ensure that services are provided at the right level, e.g. at an appropriate temperature

— minimise maintenance requirements by preventing over use of services

— reduce energy consumption, running costs and minimise emissions to the atmosphere.

Whatever strategy is devised, the following are some basic guidelines for controls:

— User interactive controls should be territorial, i.e. their operation should influence the space occupied by one person (if possible), and they should be near the area that they control.

— They should be intuitive, i.e. as obvious as reaching for a light switch; there should be a clear indication that control action has been initiated.

— User interactive controls should be located in obvious places, not where they will be difficult to reach or obscured by furnishings.

— Systems should be robust and capable of being easily re-configured, e.g. when office layouts change.

— Automatic systems should have simple overrides, although management should always be aware when these are being used.

— Management should understand how the systems interact, and how to avoid possible conflicts.

— Where possible, the default state should be the low-energy state, and systems should switched off automatically when there is no further need for them.

— All services should be controllable. For example, unsuitable hydraulic arrangements can lead to systems that are uncontrollable no matter how sophisticated the control system. Hydraulic interaction between systems is a major cause of control stability problems and often occurs between primary and secondary circuits (see 9.3).

— Systems should be sized correctly. The stability of controls can be adversely affected if primary plant is oversized, leading to energy waste and, often, poor reliability. Conversely, generously sized distribution systems can significantly reduce transport losses and aid control stability, particularly with variable flow systems, as there is less variation in differential pressure throughout the system.

— Where possible, controls should monitor themselves for efficient operation in accordance with the design intentions, and alert management if they detect problems, e.g. simultaneous cooling and heat recovery in an air handling plant.

5.1 Developing a strategy

Establishing a practical control strategy that is appropriate to the structure, occupancy, activity and services is an essential step in achieving energy efficiency and ensuring that the building and its services work in harmony. The design team needs to establish this in outline at an early stage. It is essential that they ultimately pass this strategic overview to the building contractor and the operator to ensure that the design concept can be put into practice correctly.

Occupants should enjoy reasonable comfort under automatic control, but should also be able to alleviate discomfort manually when necessary. Designers need to seek a balance between central control and local occupant control. Staff satisfaction and comfort can also be linked to better health and productivity, so that in well designed and well managed buildings, 'virtuous circles' begin to emerge, where comfort, control, productivity and energy efficiency all go together[8].

Studies[8] show that improved controls for temperature, lighting and ventilation will lead to energy savings. A successful control strategy addresses issues well beyond simply the selection of automatic controls for heating and cooling etc.

The more complex a building, the more difficult it can become to manage. There is a requirement, therefore, for a strategy with clearly stated objectives which do not conflict and which provide an achievable balance between energy and comfort.

Unfortunately, if the complex technical systems designed to increase comfort or reduce energy consumption are too complicated, they can actually bring about a situation where the management loses control of the building. Consequently, comfort levels can reduce or energy consumption can increase and the building is in a vicious circle. It is, therefore, better to introduce a few well-chosen techniques into the design correctly, rather than to smother a building with energy-saving features which require complex and elaborate controls.

Control systems should have good interfaces with management and users, particularly in more highly serviced buildings and where responsibilities are divided between landlord, tenant and contractors.

Energy efficient buildings are not automatically comfortable. In buildings where comfort and energy efficiency go together successfully, the unifying reason appears to be good management, not just of energy, but also of the entire process of procuring, designing, building, occupying, operating and maintaining the buildings.

Designers should seek to make their intended operating strategies obvious, convenient, and effective. It is especially important not to ignore the original control strategy when spaces are being fitted out and refurbished. For example, access to perimeter controls for windows, blinds or HVAC systems is often blocked by furniture[8].

5.1.1 Avoiding conflicting controls

It is essential that interaction between individual systems and their controls is considered at the design stage to ensure that the whole building is controllable, maintainable, and can be commissioned successfully. Unwanted interaction between systems, e.g. cooling and heating, can cause major energy wastage and result in failure to obtain desired comfort conditions. Factors to consider include:

— Control of the system should not cause any effect which upsets the stability or operation of the system's component parts, e.g. compensated circuit valve position should not affect flow through boilers.

— Systems must be designed such that the effect of control on one zone does not affect another zone.

— Systems must be designed such that the effect of control on one system does not affect other systems.

— Wherever possible, designers should aim for simple and understandable control strategies, capable of producing the conditions required. However, elements of these strategies (such as optimum start) will inherently be sophisticated.

— Regardless of the underlying complexity of control, local and central user interfaces should be as intuitive and easy to understand as possible.

— It could be uneconomic to provide controls that operate with a degree of accuracy to which a plant or building is unable to respond, or to select equipment that is capable of producing more precise control than the application requires.

— Controls should be appropriate to the thermal response of the building and its services, e.g. lightweight buildings need services and controls that can respond rapidly to changes externally and internally, as there is no capacity to store heat or 'coldness' within the building fabric. Heavyweight buildings can be very difficult to control and will need controls to be set up with an inherent lag to avoid excessive cycling, and possibly an element of predictive control to anticipate conditions and avoid overshoot.

5.1.2 Zoning the building and services

Services are often required at different times and levels (e.g. temperatures) in different areas of a building. A successful control system will provide a good match between these requirements on a zone by zone basis. A zone is defined as a part of the building whose services are capable of independent control, either in time or in level of service (e.g. temperature), or in both.

All but the smallest of buildings will require some form of zoning. The choice of zones plays an important part in designing the overall control strategy. The building use, layout and services will influence the choice of controls. Questions to be addressed are:

— Does the layout of the building lend itself to particular zones, e.g. floor-by-floor?

— Is there scope for more zones?

— Is more than one building involved? Can they be treated separately?

— Is more than one tenant involved? Should each tenant's space be one zone?

— Do the services have some obvious circuits, e.g. secondary heating circuits?

— Is it possible to integrate the building layout zones with the services zones?

— Are there different activities, occupancy patterns, temperature and lighting requirements?

Good zone control can provide greater comfort and save energy. Objective zoning of services can add to the controllability of systems where load profiles vary between areas of the building. Zones should also be chosen to meet the needs of occupants. It is particularly important to avoid large systems defaulting to 'on' when there is little or no local demand to be met.

Multiple zone control is most advantageous:

— in larger buildings

— in poorly insulated buildings or parts of buildings

— where a section of the building is not often used

— where the rooms have different uses and requirements

— where different systems are used

— depending on orientation, buildings that are subject to wide variations in sunlight throughout the day.

Buildings that receive solar gain on one side in the morning and the opposite side in the afternoon should have the heating for each facade zoned separately. Lighting controls should be zoned parallel to windows in order to compensate for additional daylighting. Where small areas, such as cellular offices are intermittently occupied, occupancy sensing control in individual rooms would provide more economical operation.

Multi-zone air conditioning systems, with a common cooler battery and zone re-heater batteries, should avoid over-cooling the primary air. Where possible, zones should have a similar load profile to prevent wasteful common cooling and zone reheat. Separate air handling units, or zone cooler batteries, are desirable for areas with a higher cooling load profiles.

There is normally little benefit in zoning tempered air systems unless occupancy varies considerably between zones. Hydraulic systems serving fan coils and induction units may benefit from zoning where load profiles or usage hours vary significantly between zones.

VAV systems will benefit from zoning where load profiles vary significantly[9]. However, this should not compromise duct sizes or flow measurement. Preference should be given to reducing duct losses, ensuring good time and temperature control of the VAV units and good control of the supply and extract fans.

Where perimeter heating is used in conjunction with internal zones which are predominantly in need of cooling, consideration should be given to linking the controls in adjacent internal and perimeter areas to minimise simultaneous heating and cooling.

5.1.3 Accuracy of control

Excessively tight specification of acceptable temperatures and humidities can waste energy and may not be essential to achieving comfort conditions. It is normally acceptable to allow for some float in space conditions. A float of 2–3°C is common although a greater variation is often acceptable, particularly where space temperatures are reset with respect to external conditions. Seasonal variations, e.g. higher summer temperatures, should also be catered for.

Far greater variations in humidity are acceptable, as very few buildings require control to ±5% relative humidity, and occupants will normally tolerate a range of say 30% to 70%. In the UK, it is usual to maintain minimum humidity levels during cold spells in winter when the moisture content of the outside air is very low.

Float is inherent with proportional control, which in a closed loop requires an offset from set point to provide a control action. On/off control also allows for variation in space temperature due to switching differentials. However, to prevent excessive swings in temperature, thermostats should incorporate accelerator heaters.

For systems with both heating and cooling, a dead-band should be incorporated when no control action takes place. Although rarely necessary, proportional plus integral (P+I) control can be used, when the dead-band between heating and cooling can be increased to allow an acceptable variation in space temperature and minimise energy consumption.

For main plant where the supply condition is directly controlled, such as for VAV systems, control accuracy and energy efficiency normally go together. This also applies to heating systems such as compensated circuits. Both of these systems should normally be controlled in a P+I mode, which eliminates offset.

5.1.4 Variable flow control

Variable flow control of air and water based services can give very considerable savings in fan and pump energy, and variable flow control can be used on most distribution systems. For example, controlling heating pump speed to respond to variations in load caused by two-port valves and TRVs is highly cost effective. Equally, VAV systems have potentially significant air distribution savings over other central plant systems, provided that pressures are well controlled and air handling plant and drives are intrinsically efficient.

Variable speed drives also allow rapid matching of pump and fan duties during commissioning and will provide significant savings compared with manual system regulation. Typical energy savings are 20% at 10% regulation and 40% at 20% regulation dependent upon characteristics. Manual system regulation increases system resistance and is inherently inefficient.

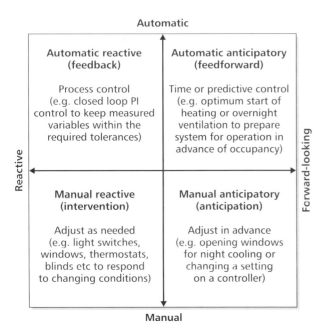

Figure 5.1 Strategic features of controls[8] (reproduced from BRE Information Paper IP3/95 by permission of BRE)

5.2   Strategic control functions

Figure 5.1 identifies the four main areas in which control systems should aim to perform if they are to combine manual and automatic functions[8]. Control functions are classified as manual or automatic (vertical axis) and as reactive or forward-looking (horizontal axis). Effective control strategies should aim for good performance in all quadrants.

Historically, there has been a tendency to expect that automatic systems alone will cope and, in particular, feedback controls (top left quadrant). Forward-looking items need a good understanding by users of the functions and purposes of systems and good feedback on achieved performance.

Even among automatic controls, anticipatory control (top right) has been the poor relation, and is often limited to time control. Effective anticipation is becoming increasingly important in strategies proposed for energy efficient buildings, but it has often proved difficult to get right, needing careful attention.

Appropriate manual intervention (bottom half) can be effective in avoiding waste, discomfort or dissatisfaction. Occupants who can influence conditions appear to be more tolerant of environments which, in sealed air conditioned buildings, would be unacceptable.

In order to improve both comfort and energy efficiency, the aim should be to:

—   provide comfort with automatically controlled systems that keep people comfortable, without waste, for a high proportion of the time (top left of Figure 5.1)

—   provide facilities that permit the occupants to alter conditions quickly and easily (bottom left), particularly where the comfort band adopted is wide.

More sophisticated systems involving anticipation should have:

—   simple, accessible facilities for occupants to adjust controls in advance (bottom right) and for managers to re-program automatic controls intended to anticipate changing conditions (top right)

—   effective information feedback to management on the performance of these systems, particularly where they operate unseen or outside normal occupancy hours, e.g. the controls of mechanical night ventilation/cooling systems need to alert management if the supply air temperature rises significantly above the outside temperature due to plant or control faults (e.g. damper seizure or unwanted heater battery operation).

The control system objectives should be clearly defined at an early stage alongside the response times for events.

5.3   Control selection

The choice of controls has a direct effect on the operation and energy consumption of a building.

Table 5.1 considers common selection criteria for control systems. Pneumatic controls were used widely in large buildings until the early 1980s since at that time they could provide relatively complex control strategies at low cost. They are still common in many existing buildings but for recent applications they are likely to have been replaced by microprocessor-based controllers.

Simple electric controls such as thermostats providing on/off control actions are still appropriate for basic control functions such as domestic heating and limit functions.

Traditional electronic controllers can be effectively used for a range of control functions although most controllers are now microprocessor based. All microprocessor based controllers provide direct digital control (DDC) with digital control algorithms, although the term DDC is most often associated with freely programmable devices.

Dedicated function controllers offer a fixed range of functions such as optimum start and compensator control and can offer a combination of functions in one unit. These controllers normally have in-built keypads and displays providing a comprehensive user interface, and are often very cost effective. Other units are available which offer dedicated functions such as terminal unit control where no in-built local user interface is provided, again they are normally very cost-effective.

Freely programmable controllers are now available in a wide range of sizes. They are able to function independently of any other controllers and local operator interface units are available. Freely programmable controllers are normally used in larger plant rooms and where plant is more complex. They also often referred to as outstations when forming part of a BMS.

One of the major advantages of microprocessor-based controllers is the facility for communication that is available with all but a few of the dedicated function units.

Table 5.1 Control system selection

Feature	Control system type		
	Pneumatic	Electric/electronic	Microprocessor (DDC)
Accuracy	Poor compared with others with high drift	Good with high grade thermistors or resistance sensors	Good with high grade thermistors or resistance sensors
Maintenance requirements	High, with damage to all components in the event of instrument air contamination	Low	Low
Optimum start/stop	No	Possible but now all DDC	Yes
Boiler sequence control	Yes, with limitations	Yes	Yes
Compensator control	Yes	Yes	Yes
AHU control	Yes	Yes	Yes
A/C terminal unit control	Yes	Yes	Yes
Communications for global control strategies	No	No	Yes
Local monitoring	Limited	Limited	Comprehensive available
Communications for integration into BMS	No	No	Yes
Accurate calculations for enthalpy, etc.	Poor	Limited	Yes
Actuator force	High	Can be limited	Can be limited

Communication between units allows for global time and reset functions, etc. It also permits supervision from an on-site, or remote, central facility (BMS) or from another controller, dependent upon the system selected. The use of such controllers as part of an integrated control strategy has the potential for energy savings through tighter control and monitoring of the building. However, since there are capital cost implications, and staff need to be trained in their use, it is best not to complicate the system unnecessarily.

5.4 Building management systems

A building management system (BMS) can significantly improve the overall management and performance of buildings, promoting an holistic approach to controls and providing operational feedback. Energy savings of 10–20% can be achieved by installing a BMS compared with independent controllers for each system[10]. However, BMSs cannot compensate for badly designed systems, poor management or incorrect maintenance, although user experiences[11] show that even the earliest systems were normally of significant benefit. A BMS also needs to be well specified and engineered, with good documentation and user interfaces if it is to be used effectively.

Deleting the BMS supervising computer to save a small fraction of the overall capital cost happens quite often. However, it is a false economy and will undoubtedly increase energy consumption and total life-cycle cost.

The monitoring facilities of a BMS allow plant status, environmental conditions and energy to be monitored, providing the building operator with a real-time understanding of how the building is operating. This can often lead to the identification of problems that may have gone unnoticed, e.g. high energy usage. Energy meters connected to a BMS, providing real-time energy consump-

tion patterns and ultimately a historical record of the buildings energy performance, can be logged and analysed in a number of ways both numerically and graphically. BMSs can, therefore, improve management information by trend logging performance, benefiting forward planning/costing. This can also encourage greater awareness of energy efficiency among staff.

Alarms are also monitored providing instantaneous indications and records that plant has shut down, maintenance is required, or environmental conditions are outside limits.

Most modern microprocessor-based control systems have communication facilities that permit the addition of a BMS central facility at relatively low cost. Additional monitoring is often desirable, as are additional points for individual control of pumps and fans, etc. However, these may add to overall cost compared with more basic control strategies. BSMs that integrate security, access control and lighting control are now available. These can, where appropriate, reduce the total cost of incorporating a range of services and, hence, help to justify the additional cost.

As with controls, staff must be trained in the use of BMSs and over-sophistication should be avoided.

The following issues need to be considered when a BMS is to be included in a design:

— The BMS supplier should be given a clear brief and a full functional specification, together with input/output schedules, monitoring requirements and schematic drawings[4]. Many functions can be incorporated at little or no cost when specified initially, but can be expensive to incorporate at a later stage.

— A formal handover demonstration procedure should be agreed. The greater the understanding, the more likely are the energy savings.

— A significant level of support should be provided by the BMS supplier during commissioning[12] and to prove systems software[13].

— The scope for system expansion at each outstation should be considered. Often the addition of a single point may require a complete outstation if all points on the original are occupied.

— The provision for future retraining in the event of staff changes. To minimise day-to-day reliance on suppliers for simple maintenance measures, suitable user documentation should be made available for system fault finding and maintenance.

— The ability of the system to integrate with other hardware and software should be considered when selecting a BMS. In particular, the integration of a BMS with an energy monitoring and targeting software package can benefit energy management.

— A graphical user interface, provided it is clear, informative and usable can promote better understanding and use of a BMS and, hence, energy savings. Colour dynamic displays can provide useful aids to fault diagnosis, as well as visual indication of plant status and relationships between points.

— The financial justification for a BMS should ideally include a full life-cycle costing calculation based on discounted cash flow. Estimates of potential savings should, where possible, account for contributions from improved maintenance and increased reliability, in addition to reduced energy consumption.

— The ability to interrogate local outstations should be carefully considered when selecting a BMS. Some systems provide a communication interface to allow local override control and local checking of functional integrity following maintenance action.

5.5   Occupant controls

User interaction with control systems is important for the long-term success of a building and therefore requires careful consideration at an early stage in the design. Occupants often feel more comfortable when there is a general perception of being in control. This can be as important as having objectively good comfort conditions.

People like control and rapid response, particularly when they experience a 'crisis of discomfort'[14]. Current trends, however, can tend to take control away from occupants. These trends include open-plan spaces with interlocked furniture which does not allow the working position to be moved (to avoid local glare or draughts), and choosing automated systems with poor, or no manual over-rides. This can create a dependency culture in which management has to solve problems which individuals might have been able to deal with themselves. Without good, attentive and responsive management, this culture can start to spread in any building in which the occupants are unable to make their own adjustments, not just in relation to air conditioning[15]. However, an effective response does not always require good and well placed individual controls. A skilled and committed building manager with a well-configured BMS can give similar results in response to a telephone request.

Air conditioned buildings are usually better at providing controlled comfort conditions for most occupants for most of the time. However, they are difficult to adapt to people who may wish to alter conditions. Naturally ventilated buildings are usually better equipped for alleviating discomfort quickly when it does occur, albeit sometimes only marginally. For example, local control of TRVs can provide good comfort conditions in an energy efficient manner, with occupant interaction via the TRV settings.

Local control problems are generally more prevalent in open-plan areas than in cellular offices where a small number of people can make choices relatively easily. For example, case studies[8] show how lighting in open-plan offices is often left on, whereas lighting in cellular offices is switched off (and then remains off) more frequently.

More sophisticated control systems offer many occupant interaction options. These include local user reset of temperature, user hand-held remote control, telephone-based systems, systems linked with security and occupancy control, all of which can help save energy if applied correctly. However, lack of clarity and over-complexity can often negate the potential savings and care must be taken to ensure that these facilities are intuitive and easy to use.

Where buildings are randomly occupied, such as village halls, a simple push button that runs the heating for a predetermined period (via a timer) is desirable with suitable frost and low temperature protection facilities. Anything more complicated can lead to unnecessary operation.

Where buildings have regular occupancy plus intermittent evening use, such as schools, simple user interfaces should also be provided for use out of normal hours. This will often require interfacing with an optimiser; some manufacturers provide pre-configured override options. User interfaces to change occupancy periods or check temperatures should be as easy to use as possible with each function clearly identified. Poor user interfaces can lead to poor control and in some cases to controls being disabled causing energy waste.

References

1   *Automatic controls* CIBSE Applications Manual AM1 (London: Chartered Institution of Building Services Engineers) (1985)

2   *Automatic controls* CIBSE Guide B11 (London: Chartered Institution of Building Services Engineers) (1986)

3   *Controls and energy savings* Fuel Efficiency Booklet No. 10 (London: Department of Environment, Transport and the Regions) (1993)

4   *Standard specification for BEMs* Volume 2 Version 3.1 AH 1/90 (Bracknell: Building Services Research and Information Association) (1990)

5   *Variable flow control* General Information Report 41 (London: Department of Environment, Transport and the Regions) (1996)

6   *Heating systems and their control* General Information Report 40 (London: Department of Environment, Transport and the Regions) (1996)

7   *Controls for building services, an introductory guide* (Slough: Satchwell Control Systems Ltd) (1992)

8   Bordass W T, Bromley A K R and Leaman A J *Comfort, control and energy efficiency in offices* IP3/95 (Garston: Building Research Establishment) (1995)

9   *Selecting air conditioning systems: A guide for building clients and their advisers* Good Practice Guide 71 (London: Department of Environment, Transport and the Regions) (1993)

10   *Centralised energy management in buildings* Thermie Maxibrochure (Building Research Energy Conservation Support Unit/OPET)

11   Levermore G J *Staff reaction to building energy management systems* DLP 4 (Bracknell: Building Services Research and Information Association) (1989)

12   Pike P and Pennycook K *Commissioning of BEMs — a code of practice* AH 2/92 (Bracknell: Building Services Research and Information Association) (1992)

13   Pike P G *BEMs Performance Testing* AG 2/94 (Bracknell: Building Services Research and Information Association) (1994)

14   Haigh D User response in environmental control, in Hawkes D and Owers J (eds) *The Architecture of Energy* pp 45–63 (London: Construction Press/Longman) (1981)

15   Bordass W, Bunn R, et al. PROBE: Some lessons learned from the first eight buildings *CIBSE National Conference 1997* (London: Chartered Institution of Building Services Engineers) (1997)

Bibliography

HVAC Applications ASHRAE Handbook (Atlanta, GA: American Society of Heating, Refrigeration and Air Conditioning Engineers) (1995)

Howlett A *A survey of national and international standards applicable to building energy and management systems* RN 1/88 (Bracknell: Building Services Research and Information Association) (1988)

Barnard N and Starr A *BEMs as condition based maintenance tools* TN(S) 4/95 (Bracknell: Building Services Research and Information Association) (1995)

Levermore G J *Building energy management systems — The basics* DLP 1 (Bracknell: Building Services Research and Information Association) (1988)

Levermore G J *Control with a building energy management system* DLP 2 (Bracknell: Building Services Research and Information Association) (1988)

Martin A J *Control of natural ventilation* TN 11/95 (Bracknell: Building Services Research and Information Association) (1995)

Holmes M J *How boiler selection and controls affect annual energy consumption* AG 1/78 (Bracknell: Building Services Research and Information Association) (1978)

Pike P G *Improved fresh air control* TN 3/94 (Bracknell: Building Services Research and Information Association) (1994)

Intelligent buildings LB 51/89 (Bracknell: Building Services Research and Information Association) (1989)

Martin A *Night cooling control strategies* TN 5/96 (Bracknell: Building Services Research and Information Association) (1996)

Brown R *Radiant heating* AG 3/96 (Bracknell: Building Services Research and Information Association) (1996)

Fitzgerald D *Room thermostats — choice and performance* LR 42 (Bracknell: Building Services Research and Information Association) (1968)

Martin A J *Sensors — which way now?* RN 2/88 (Bracknell: Building Services Research and Information Association) (1988)

Colthorpe K J *The control of pre-heating time* LR 5 (Bracknell: Building Services Research and Information Association) (1960)

King A *UK domestic controls market* SR 55210/2 (Bracknell: Building Services Research and Information Association) (1990)

Ventilation and air conditioning (requirements and systems, equipment and control) CIBSE Guide B2/3 (London: Chartered Institution of Building Services Engineers) (1986)

Banyard C P Developing a library of system control strategies *CIBSE National Conference 1995* (London: Chartered Institution of Building Services Engineers) (1995)

Martin A Control of natural ventilation *CIBSE National Conference 1995* (London: Chartered Institution of Building Services Engineers) (1995)

Controls to reduce electrical peak demands in commercial buildings CADDET Analyses Series: 7 (Sittard: Centre for the Analysis and Dissemination of Demonstrated Energy Technologies) (1991)

Automatic controls CIBSE Commissioning Code C (London: Chartered Institution of Buildings Services Engineers) (1973)

Energy efficiency in refurbishment of industrial buildings — Strategy One Ltd, Nelson, Lancashire GPCS 192 (London: Department of Environment, Transport and the Regions) (1994)

Saving energy in schools — the local authority chief officer's guide to energy efficiency ECON 17 (London: Department of Environment, Transport and the Regions) (1991)

Energy audits for buildings Fuel Efficiency Booklet No. 1 (London: Department of Environment, Transport and the Regions) (1993)

Energy efficiency in offices: A guide for the design team Good Practive Guide 34 (London: Department of Environment, Transport and the Regions) (1993)

Smith G P Specifying control systems and BMS *Heating and Air Conditioning Journal* (May/June 1994)

6   Ventilation and air conditioning design

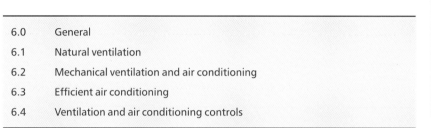

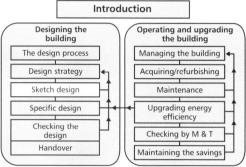

This section sets out some of the key issues for designing energy efficient ventilation and air conditioning systems, in line with the principles at the front of this Guide. Energy issues related to the maintenance of ventilation systems are covered in section 17. Further information on ventilation is provided in CIBSE Applications Manual AM10[1], CIBSE Guide sections B2/B3[2], ASHRAE Handbook: HVAC Applications[3], DETR General Information Report 31[4] and BRE Digest 399[5].

6.0   General

The form of the building will influence the ventilation strategy as discussed in sections 3 and 4. Ventilation is often responsible for the largest energy loss from buildings and has grown in relative importance as improved levels of insulation have reduced conduction losses. Designers should:

— minimise uncontrolled air infiltration by designing a tight envelope; 'build tight — ventilate right'

— minimise demand by avoiding over-design which leads to high air change rates

— use 'passive' before 'active' solutions by giving preference to natural ventilation[1,4,5]

— choose efficient primary plant where mechanical ventilation is essential

— consider energy recovery between air streams

— distribute air effectively by avoiding excessive duct lengths, system resistance and duct heat loss

— use effective controls through good zoning, effective time control, and variable flow control where possible.

An energy efficient design aims to provide thermal comfort and acceptable indoor air quality with the minimum use of energy. Mechanical ventilation is a primary energy intensive process, and air conditioning is even more so. Therefore, an energy efficient building will provide the desired internal conditions by relying on natural means where possible.

A ventilation system (whether natural, mechanical, or a combination of the two) should be able to satisfy health, comfort and cooling needs, with a good degree of local control. Defining the optimum ventilation rate is crucial to energy efficiency. Too little fresh air will result in the internal air quality becoming unsatisfactory; too much causes excessive energy consumption. The minimum required is 5 l/s per person (or 0.5 l/(s m²)) while the recommended rate is 8 l/s per person (or 0.8 l/(s m²)). Cigarette smoking can double or quadruple this requirement. A good strategy should be, therefore, to avoid smoking in buildings or to provide separately ventilated rooms for smokers.

6.1   Natural ventilation

Designs which rely on natural ventilation can provide the following advantages:

— lower running costs through lower energy consumption[1,6]

— decreased capital cost[1]

— decreased maintenance costs[1,7]

— reduced transport energy associated with fans[1]

— fewer problems due to plant noise[1].

It is desirable, therefore, to begin by examining the provision of fresh air requirements by natural means (see section 4).

Heat gains are a critical factor in the success of natural ventilation strategies, as shown in Table 6.1.

Design tools, such as the LT method[8] can help establish a balance between internal/solar heat gains, the need for heating and cooling, daylight and fresh air by optimising glazing, built form etc.

Any external environmental conditions which may limit or preclude the use of natural ventilation, e.g. high levels of

Table 6.1 The relationship between design features and heat gains

Design feature	Total heat gains† (W/m² floor area)			
	10	20	30	40‡
Minimum room height (m)	2.5	2.7	2.9	3.1
Controllable window opening (down to 10 mm)	E	E	E	E
Trickle vents for winter	E	E	E	E
Control of indoor air quality (may be manual)	?	?	E	E
Design for daylight to reduce gains	?	E	E	E
Daylight control of electric lighting	?	?	E	E
100% shading from direct sun	?	E	E	E
Cooling by daytime ventilation only	E	E	P	P
Cooling by day and night ventilation	N	?	E	E
Exposed thermal capacity	N	N	E	E

Key: (E) essential; (N) not necessary; (P) potential problem; (?) may be required

† Sum of solar gains plus gains from people, lights and office machines

‡ The guidance in this table is indicative of scale only and will vary depending on the characteristics of a particular building. In particular, heat gains greater than 40 W/m² can be catered for by careful design of building form but will require very detailed analysis

noise or pollutants, should be identified at an early stage. When it is necessary to keep windows shut to exclude noise, fumes, smoke and dirt, it may force a move to a mechanical ventilation system with the consequence of higher energy consumption. Pollution levels that may force a mechanical ventilation system are shown in CIBSE Applications Manual AM10[1].

Even if some of these limitations are encountered, it may still be possible to design the building to take advantage of natural ventilation. This may require a re-assessment of the ventilation strategy and sketch design (see section 4), or may suggest a mixed-mode approach could be appropriate.

6.2 Mechanical ventilation and air conditioning

Mechanical ventilation rates should be kept to a minimum commensurate with acceptable levels of indoor air quality. Therefore, the size of fan, fan power usage and ventilation heating/cooling loads should be kept to a minimum. Designers are also advised to consider the possibility of meeting comfort requirements using mechanical ventilation alone without mechanical cooling.

Fan capacities larger than those shown in Table 6.2 suggest oversizing of plant[9].

Specific fan power should be 2 W/(l/s) or less to achieve good practice in offices[6]; very energy efficient systems can sometimes be around 1 W/(l/s).

Mechanical ventilation systems resolve a number of problems associated with natural systems. They require much smaller openings, they can be easier to control and they also provide sound absorption and security. However, they consume electricity and heat the air. Fans can in theory operate at better than 80% efficiency, but in practice less efficient units tend to be specified to save money or

Table 6.2 Basic fan capacity benchmarks

Building	Fan capacity ((litre/s)/m³ of ventilated space)
Offices	1.4
Retail stores, halls and theatres	2.1
Restaurants	3.5

provide a design safety margin. The loss of efficiency is dissipated as heat. Systems can have fan gains of up to 2 K, which can make the difference between a comfortable building and one that is too warm.

If a building is sealed and mechanically ventilated, occupants may react to the loss of individual control by demanding a high degree of environmental stability that might not be possible without mechanical cooling. Full mechanical ventilation also tends to require significantly higher air change rates than where natural ventilation is also available, increasing HVAC capital and running costs. In order to minimise these costs, designers should consider the possibility of a mixed-mode approach before opting for a fully air conditioned building,

6.2.1 Mixed-mode buildings

Mixed-mode design (see 4.2) can involve a variety of ventilation and cooling systems, possibly supplying different areas or at different times. It is essentially the provision of the least amount of mechanical air movement and cooling that can still achieve the conditions required. For example, it may be advantageous to turn off the air conditioning system for parts of the season, and rely on ventilation and cooling by opening windows. This so-called 'mixed-mode' approach requires the design rigours of both natural and mechanical ventilation.

Table 6.3 Advantages and disadvantages of balanced ventilation

Advantages	Disadvantages
Contaminants removed at source	Building must be effectively sealed to prevent air ingress by infiltration.
Incoming air can be conditioned and cleaned.	
	Expensive, requiring two complete duct work systems.
Potential for heat recovery from exhaust air.	
	Regular cleaning and maintenance is necessary.
Weather independent, provided structure is moderately airtight	
	Electrical energy consumed in fans.

6.2.2   Efficient ventilation

Fresh air rate is only one parameter in the design of a successful ventilation system, the second being ventilation efficiency which has a range of definitions[10]. These relate to the way in which fresh air is distributed within the occupied space, and its consequent ability to remove pollutants. The various ventilation techniques are summarised in CIBSE Application Manual AM10[1].

Figure 6.1 shows three different patterns of airflow within a space. In general terms, piston flow is the most efficient ventilation flow pattern, followed by mixed flow and then short-circuiting. Piston flow removes the pollutant directly to the extract point, mixed flow disperses the pollutant through the whole space and short circuiting results in the pollutant not being removed at all.

Displacement ventilation attempts to provide piston flow by introducing 'fresh' air gently at a low level and at a temperature just slightly below the room ambient, with a view to providing a local environment and eliminating the need to temper the entire space, e.g. a theatre. Any local heat sources in the lower part of the room create convection currents that also contribute to the general upward movement. The warmed air and contaminants are then exhausted at high level.

Displacement systems operate with lower airflow than traditional methods, thus saving energy. However, supply air has to be warmer than for mixing ventilation, thereby increasing heating requirements. Further information about displacement ventilation can be found in BSRIA Technical Note TN 3/93[11].

It is generally desirable and energy efficient to adopt a balanced ventilation system, comprising independently ducted supply and extract. The advantages and disadvantages of balanced ventilation are shown in Table 6.3.

Care must be taken in selecting the ratio between the supply and exhaust airflow volumes. For spaces where there are no noxious fumes and where moisture ingress is unlikely to be a problem it is generally recommended that the extract be slightly (10–20%) less than the supply. Conversely, where fumes or moisture problems exist, the supply flow rate should be 90% to 95% of the extract rate to encourage fumes to pass through the plant.

Energy efficiency will be improved by the following measures where appropriate:

— Provide heat recovery via thermal wheels, run-around coils, etc. on full fresh air air handling

Piston flow

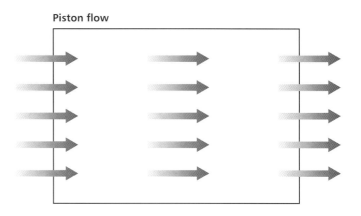

Mixed flow

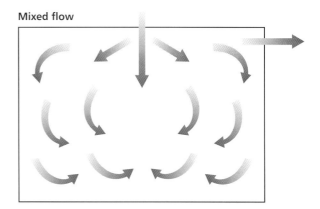

Short circuiting

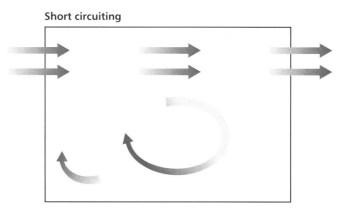

Figure 6.1 Ventilation efficiency

units, including tempered air systems. Supply and extract systems must be designed such that heat recovery can be easily facilitated.

— Provide effective control of dampers for minimum fresh air and free cooling on recirculation systems.

— Ensure that fresh air and exhaust dampers are closed when the building is not occupied.

— Ensure that only the minimum fresh air required is treated, preferably automatically by varying the minimum fresh air content during occupied periods with respect to air quality.

— Provide effectively-controlled 'free' cooling wherever possible

— Minimise duct lengths and bends and providing adequately sized ducts (case studies[12] have shown that with careful design fan energy can be halved compared with the norm)

— Correctly select and size the most efficient fans.

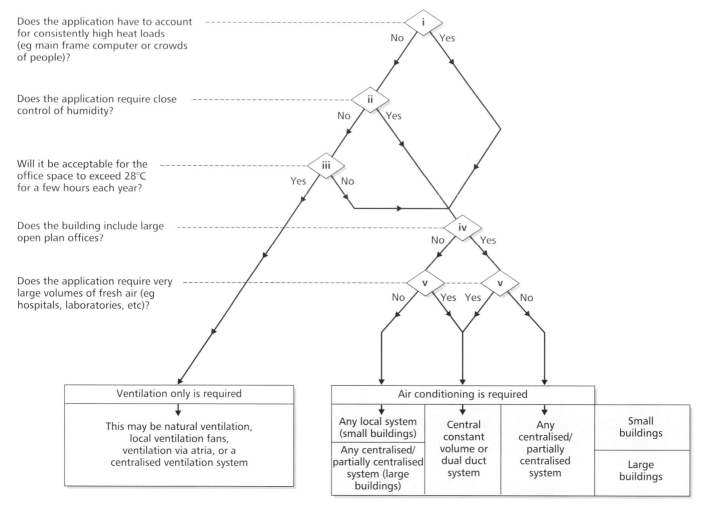

Figure 6.2 Assessing the need for air conditioning (adapted from BRECSU Good Practice Guide 71[13]. Crown copyright (1993))

— Ensure that the control strategy considers all full and part load conditions, and is fully described and correctly configured.

6.2.3   Need for air conditioning

Introducing full air conditioning into a design can often add around 50% to the eventual running costs of the building and should therefore be avoided where possible.

Although full air conditioning involves humidity control, in the UK the term is commonly used for the provision of cooling to the conditioned space, the cooling being supplied by mechanical means. In the UK, there is a limited set of circumstances in which a building will require air conditioning. However, it can be necessary in certain circumstances due to pollution, external noise and high heat gains.

When designing mixed-mode or mechanically ventilated buildings, a balance should be sought between moving small amounts of cool air rather than large amounts of tempered or ambient air.

Figure 6.2 provides useful guidance in assessing the need for full air conditioning, comfort cooling or mechanical ventilation[13].

6.2.3.1   Avoiding mechanical cooling

Avoiding the need for mechanical cooling is a function of integrated service and fabric design as discussed in section 4[4]. There are several steps to be taken to minimise the energy need for air conditioning:

— Minimise the heat gains to the space by careful design of the building envelope.

— Minimise internal heat gains from lighting, office equipment etc.

— Wherever possible, meet the cooling requirements with free or passive cooling sources (see below).

— Ensure the systems and controls are able to match the cooling requirements efficiently.

— When mechanical cooling is required, limit where it is employed and ensure that the cooling plant operates as efficiently as possible.

In general, the liberation of more than about 40 W/m^2 from lighting and other sources may be regarded as excessive and will constitute grounds for re-assessing the design to minimise these heat gains.

The main problem in avoiding mechanical cooling is that the period when heat gains are greatest usually coincides with periods when outside air temperatures are at a maximum, thus reducing the cooling potential. It is

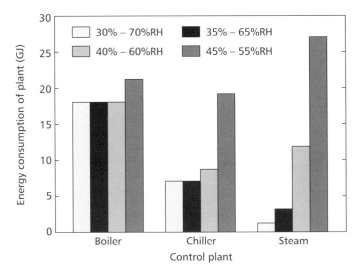

Figure 6.3 Effect of humidity control on energy use

necessary, therefore, to consider ways in which stored 'coldness' can be exploited.

Using night air to cool the building fabric can avoid the need for mechanical cooling. The building fabric can be used as a thermal store acting as a heat sink during the occupied hours by absorbing the incidental gains.

The thermal mass of the building then needs to be directly available for heat exchange. Exposed concrete ceilings are widely used and can achieve an additional 2–3°C reduction of the daytime internal temperature. The reduced surface temperature of the exposed concrete also influences the radiant thermal environment and enhances the effect (see 4.2.5).

6.2.3.2 Need for humidity control

Full air conditioning with humidity control is even more energy intensive than systems providing heating and cooling only. It is essential, therefore, to question the requirements, tolerances and need for humidity control[1,4]. For most human comfort applications, relative humidity can drift between 40% and 70%[14]. Where humidity needs to be controlled within much tighter bands, both capital and running costs will be increased. In general, the closer the design humidity tolerances, the greater the energy consumption (see Figure 6.3).

Close control of humidity is sometimes required for specialist applications such as the protection of exhibits in a museum. Designers should carefully evaluate whether both humidification and de-humidification are required to maintain conditions within acceptable limits[15].

De-humidification is generally only required in summer. The most common method of removing moisture is by cooling the air to its dew-point using a chilled water cooling coil so that moisture condenses out. This commonly occurs when air is being cooled for comfort conditioning. For close control of relative humidity the air may be cooled further to

the required moisture content, then re-heated to bring it back to the required temperature. Cooling then reheating makes de-humidification an energy intensive process that should be avoided where possible, unless heat rejected from the cooling process can be used for re-heat.

Desiccants offer an alternative method to de-humidify air. Exposure of the air to chemicals such as calcium chloride or silica gel will remove moisture. In order for the desiccant to be re-used, it has to be regenerated by heating to drive off the moisture. Often much more air is dehumidified and reheated than is necessary, avoidable by using a by-pass plant. The cost of the regeneration plant and the cost of providing heat for the regeneration process have so far limited the take-up of this technology. However, it may become more attractive if a local source of waste heat exists for regeneration. It is also particularly appropriate if there is a need for de-humidification without the need for significant sensible cooling, e.g. clean rooms.

Humidification is mainly required in winter and can be achieved by either steam injection, water spray or ultra sound humidifiers. Spray humidifiers are now less common due to health concerns. The characteristics of different types of humidification equipment are discussed in CIBSE Guide B3[2].

Steam injection systems, whether direct from a steam distribution system or from local electrode boilers, give rise to very significant energy consumption. Where steam is available on site, it is sensible to make use of it and directly inject steam to humidify. However, this will add significantly to the winter demand on the boiler plant. More commonly, local electrode humidification units are used to inject steam into the air stream. These units generally have independent controls and can cause significant increases in electricity consumption.

Ultrasonic humidification systems are now becoming more common, using up to 90% less energy than electrode systems and, hence, provide a cost-effective alternative. Lower electrical consumption results in reduced electrical wiring costs, although a water purification plant is required to operate the system. Ultrasonic humidifiers require little energy themselves, although the air temperature will decrease due to the evaporative cooling effect. Re-heating is then necessary to bring the air up to the required supply temperature.

6.3 Efficient air conditioning systems

There is a wide range of air conditioning plant, including some that offer greater scope for energy efficiency. For a more detailed description of the systems, see Guide section B3[2] and BSRIA TN15/92[16]. DETR Good Practice Guide 71[13] gives a useful summary of the relative advantages and disadvantages of the various systems. Figure 6.4[13] and Table 6.4[13] below list the systems and indicate the capital and running costs of some of options, based on gross floor area and 1992 prices.

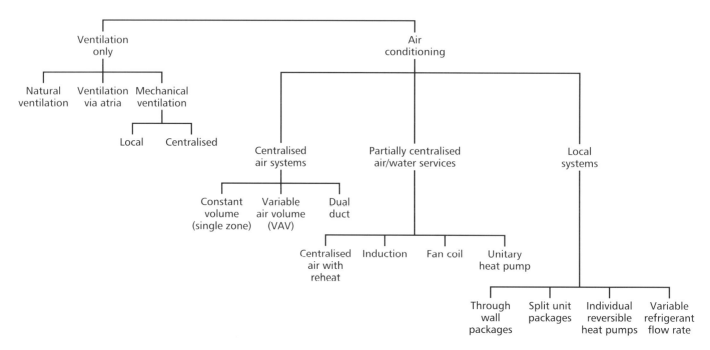

Figure 6.4 Types of air conditioning system[13] (reproduced from DETR Good Practice Guide 71. Crown copyright (1993))

Table 6.4 Air conditioning system costs in offices

System type	Costs			CO_2 emisssion (kg/m^2) p.a.
	Capital (£/m^2)	Energy (£/m^2) p.a.	Maintenance	
Centralised 'all-air' systems				
Ventilation and heating - no air conditioning	100	1.9	Medium	30
Constant volume (single zone)	160	3.0	Medium	50
Variable air volume (VAV)	180	2.4†	Medium to high	40†
Dual duct	210	3.4	Medium	55
Partially centralised air/water systems				
Centralised air with reheat	200	3.1	Medium to high	50
Induction units	160	3.2	High	50
Fan coil units	170	3.2	Medium to high	50
Unitary heat pump	130	3.2	Medium to high	55
Local systems				
Heat and local ventilation-no air conditioning	90	1.1	Low	17
Through wall packages	70‡	3.5	Low	75
Split unit packages	85‡	3.5	Medium to high	75
Individual reversible heat pumps	110	3.0	Medium to high	55
Variable refrigeration flow rate	130	2.8	Medium to high	50

† System fitted with variable speed fan; ‡ Excludes separate provision of heating

Note: Figures are indicative only and based on gross floor area and 1992 costs; capital costs exclude related building work and cost of BMS

6.3.1 Central all-air systems

6.3.1.1 Constant volume

In centralised constant volume single zone systems the heating and cooling loads of the conditioned space are met by changing the temperature of the supply air. Comfort requirements determine the supply temperature, which results in large air volumes and large ductwork consuming considerable transport energy, even when only small amounts of cooling are required.

These systems should only be used for single zones with common heating/cooling load characteristics such as large rooms, lecture theatres etc. where they can provide a well controlled and efficient system. Single zone systems must not be used for multiple zones with different heating/cooling loads because control of conditions will be very poor and operation very inefficient. However, correctly applied single zone systems are one of the few types of air conditioning system where simultaneous heating and cooling of the same air is not necessary except during dehumidification.

Centralised constant volume multiple zone systems are also available. However, multiple zone systems with local re-heats are more common (due to plant and duct space requirements) and characteristics are similar (see 6.3.2.1).

6.3.1.2 Dual duct

Dual duct systems have high transport energy, heating and cooling loads. The heated and cooled air are required to be circulated separately and the two air streams then combined to produce an intermediate comfort temperature, thereby wasting heating and cooling energy. Such systems should not be used except where reclaimed energy can be applied. Where they are used, it is important that they have controls to automatically reset temperatures at the central air handling unit to provide minimum heating and cooling to satisfy the hottest/coolest zone. Dual duct variable air volume systems are available and offer significantly improved energy efficiency.

6.3.1.3 Variable air volume

In general, energy efficiency is improved by moving to variable air volume (VAV) systems to minimise transport energy. However, VAV systems should be matched to suitable applications. They are primarily suited to applications with a year round cooling load such as deep plan office buildings and can also have other limitations to their application such as ceiling height due to box throw etc. The VAV boxes for each zone should be individually controlled, making it necessary for appropriate locations for temperature sensors to be available. VAV systems can provide flexibility for future fit out and partition changes, provided the locations of supply and extract grilles and sensors are carefully considered.

VAV systems reduce the airflow rate in relation to the demand, rather than change the supply air temperature. The air handling unit (AHU) supplies cooled air (normally at 10–18°C but this can be at 6°C from ice storage) to VAV boxes which vary the volume with respect to space temperature. The supply fan is normally controlled with

Table 6.5 Advantages and disadvantages of variable air volume systems

Advantages	Disadvantages
Often the most efficient form of airconditioning	Complex in comparison with other types of air conditioning system
Highly flexible for initial/future fit-out requirements	Integration of controls from concept stage essential
Opportunity to reduce AHU and duct size compared to multi-zone system if diversity allowed on cooling load	Special diffusers may be required for good room air distribution at low loads
VAV systems, using DDC controls with communications, will generally require less maintenance in occupied areas than multi-zone systems with reheat coils	VAV systems with conventional controls, or additional VAV box coils/fans, could require greater maintenance than multi-zone systems
	Additional sound attenuation may be required for maximum velocity

respect to static pressure and it responds to demand by varying volume. The extract fan volume is controlled with respect to the supply fan volume. The AHU fans achieve variable volume by variable speed drive (VSD), variable pitch or the less efficient inlet guide vane control. VAV boxes with reheat and fan assisted boxes are available but care must be taken to ensure that these are only used where necessary to avoid wasting energy. The advantages and disadvantages of VAV systems are shown in Table 6.5.

Care needs to be taken to maintain stable airflow patterns in the room at reduced flows, using fan or induction assisted terminals to maintain the total flow to the room by mixing re-circulated room air with the primary air from the plant. Fan assisted terminals are commonly used with low temperature systems, sometimes in co-operation with ice storage because of the requirement for low chilled water temperatures. Local mixing with the room air is then used to achieve acceptable supply temperatures.

The energy consumed in the terminal fans or, in overcoming the extra pressure of induction terminals, should be taken into account when assessing overall energy consumed by fan assisted, or induction terminals.

6.3.2 Partially centralised air/water systems

Systems in which the air does not transport all the cooling and heating may offer energy savings due to reduced flow rates from the plant room to the spaces served.

To satisfy zones that have variable requirements, both heating and cooling pumped water circuits are needed. Three-pipe systems with a common return must be avoided at all costs as cooling and heating energy will be wasted when the return water is mixed.

Tempered fresh air systems limit the humidification and de-humidification capacity. However, this is normally adequate for most applications and discourages attempts at unnecessary close control of humidity, which is very wasteful of energy.

Savings due to reduced air flows must be balanced against the restricted free cooling from fresh air, the additional energy used due to higher pressures and local fan energy, and the energy required for heating and chilled water distribution pumps.

The AHU should be sized for minimum fresh air duty only, to reduce transport energy. The minimum fresh air volume can be controlled with respect to air quality via VSDs to minimise the amount of heating and cooling of fresh air. Turndown may be limited, dependent upon application. Varying fresh air volume is unlikely to be satisfactory with induction systems due to the minimum pressure required at the induction terminal units. Heat recovery via thermal wheels or run around coils should be considered at the AHU.

Where the building is likely to require cooling in one area and heating in another, or where common cooling coils are used with multiple re-heater batteries, heat recovery from the chillers to supply the terminal unit heating coils, or re-heat batteries, should be considered. This will require a low temperature (warm water) heating circuit. Top-up heat can be provided by condensing boilers, which will always operate in the condensing mode.

All partially centralised systems should have local controls with communication to provide demand-based control of main plant.

6.3.2.1　　Centralised air with reheat

These systems (commonly known as multi-zone) require the full volume of air necessary for heating and cooling loads to be transported to and from the AHU. The AHU should incorporate a controlled re-circulation system via dampers (or other means of heat recovery) and free cooling (enthalpy) control to minimise energy use.

Most systems incorporate a common cooling coil, which must be controlled with respect to the zone requiring the greatest amount of cooling. Additional re-heating for the other zones is therefore required, necessitating simultaneous heating and cooling of the same air. This increases energy consumption compared with correctly applied multiple single zone systems.

Systems with minimum air treatment at the AHU and local heating and cooling coils are likely to be far more efficient than systems with a common cooling coil at the AHU, although capital costs will be increased.

Dew-point systems provide saturated air at the cooling coil at all times to provide very stable humidity conditions when air is reheated to the desired space temperature. However, these systems are only necessary for special applications, such as laboratories, and should normally be avoided since they can be very inefficient. Systems with the cooling coil controlled in relation to the zone requiring greatest cooling are much more efficient and should normally be used.

6.3.2.2　　Induction

In order to produce the air jet velocity needed to induce room air through the casing and over water coils, induction systems need to operate at higher pressures than those of low velocity systems. Also, having high pressure sufficient to drive room circulation in the furthest zone means that the extra pressure needs to be removed from other branches in an induction system. Typically, this is achieved by careful sizing of the ductwork, together with dampers for the final trimming. Restrictions such as jet nozzles and dampers for flow regulation inherently absorb fan power and thus it is important to consider how much energy is used compared with other means of creating room air circulation.

Two coil induction units should be used where both heating and cooling are required at the terminal. Systems with one coil terminal units require much higher air volumes from the AHU to provide the heating, increasing transport energy. Even where the common heating coil is effectively controlled, simultaneous heating and cooling is inevitable. This can be reduced by effective zoning of the AHUs serving areas with different load profiles such as facades with different orientations. Single-coil systems should have the supply temperature reset in a similar manner to multi-zone systems; they also require a sophisticated control system. Where this is not possible, such as in existing systems, the supply temperature should be scheduled in relation to ambient temperature.

6.3.2.3　　Fan coil

Fan coils place the motive power for distributing heat and cooling within or close to the zone being served. This means that fan power is not used to move this air down ducts from the central plant. However, additional power is required at fan coil units to circulate the room air. The cross-flow and tangential fans used in fan coil units typically have an efficiency of around 40% — around half that of the most efficient AHU fans.

The energy consumption by these alternative routes should be assessed. Fan units with free cooling are suitable for some applications (on outside walls of low-rise buildings) and can provide additional economy of operation.

6.3.2.4　　Chilled beams and ceilings

Cooled ceilings have chilled water supplied either to pipes, clipped into metallic ceiling panels, or to 'beams'. The main difference between these approaches is the ratio of radiant to convective output (the panels giving a higher radiant component). The ceiling surface temperature must remain above the room air dew-point to ensure that condensation does not occur. To avoid this risk, a separate fresh air system normally provides de-humidification as well as temperature control. Operating at a higher chilled water temperature than conventional systems offers the possibility of using passive cooling instead of mechanical cooling. This system also requires less fan power due to the lower air flow requirements.

Cooled ceilings have also been used with upward or positive displacement distribution systems as discussed in 6.2.2. The use of a cooled ceiling reduces the room height for which this type of system will work and also increases the heat gain that can be dealt with to 30–40 W/m^{2}[17]. However, the limitations on the temperature difference between supply and room temperature and the inlet velocity remain.

Due to the temperature control being provided by a separate fresh air system, simultaneous heating and cooling may occur and reduce the overall efficiency of operation.

6.3.2.5 Unitary heat pumps

For buildings where there is a significant spatial variation in load, especially if there is a need for simultaneous heating and cooling in different zones, the use of localised reversible heat pumps connected to a circulating water system can be advantageous. This provides the opportunity to transfer energy around the building, i.e. by carrying heat from a cooled zone into a zone requiring heat. This effectively recovers heat or coldness from different parts of the building. Controls should be linked where more than one unit is used in a common zone, to avoid individual heat pumps simultaneously heating and cooling the same space.

A boiler and cooling tower are normally connected to the water system to top up or reject heat as necessary. This system also has reduced transport losses by circulating low temperature water as the heat source/sink. Also, because there are several items of plant around the building, areas with several heat pumps will not lose the service completely during individual unit breakdowns. Conversely, main-tenance is costly and can cause considerable disturbance in occupied areas.

The efficiency of the main heating and cooling source, the local heat pumps, is reduced compared with other types of air conditioning due to the common circuit being used as both a heating and cooling source. This reduction in efficiency can be minimised by scheduling the circuit temperature in relation to outside temperature so that it increases when cold and vice versa.

Typically, the cooling COP for smaller individual units is 2.4 to 2.6[18], although it is important to consider the energy consumption by the other components in the system, such as the boiler, cooling tower and pumps for the low temperature water circuit. A tempered fresh air system will also be needed for minimum fresh air requirements.

6.3.3 Local air conditioning

Local air conditioning systems include through-the-wall packaged units and split systems to provide comfort cooling, or heating and cooling, but not humidity control. Ventilation air needs to be handled separately, and thus there is little scope for controlled free cooling. Whilst it is not common to base a major new design on individual local air conditioning units, they are commonly used to introduce air conditioning in major refurbishment of naturally ventilated buildings.

Individual local units have lower COPs than centralised plant and often lack a coherent control strategy. However, they provide scope for energy savings through:

—   avoiding multiple heat exchange (into/out of chilled water and condenser water) and fouling at each water heat transfer surface

—   avoiding pumping large volumes of chilled and condenser water

—   simpler heat rejection equipment (i.e. direct air cooled condensers instead of cooling towers with their energy consumption and water treatment consequences)

—   plant operating only in those areas that need cooling at a given time.

Although more localised plant may increase maintenance costs, this approach may provide greater standby in areas served by a number of local units.

Where it has been decided that air conditioning is unnecessary in the building as a whole, it may be appropriate to use highly localised units to cool hot spots in a mixed-mode approach, thus avoiding larger cooling systems. A similar approach may be appropriate where cooling requirements are more stringent in one small area than in the building as a whole.

6.3.3.1 Through-the-wall packages

These units are difficult to integrate into a coherent system, but may be applicable where a single room of a building needs to be cooled, either to different temperatures, or at different times, from the remainder which has a co-ordinated system. Cooling COP lies in the range 1.5 to 2.3. Heating is sometimes provided by electric resistance heaters, which should be appraised carefully in life cycle cost terms. Care should be taken to ensure that they do not operate in conflict with any separate space heating system, or with other similar units in the same zone, and that they are time controlled to function only when required. Where possible, free cooling by directing fresh air through the unit without mechanical cooling should be adopted.

6.3.3.2 Individual reversible heat pumps

Packaged heat pumps have much the same limitations as through-the-wall packages except that heating can be provided more efficiently by reversing refrigerant flow through the indoor and outdoor coils. This saves energy in comparison with electric resistance heating, but care needs to be taken to compare the total running cost of heat from this source with other alternatives such as a separate central heating system.

6.3.3.3 Split unit packages

Split units have a separate outdoor unit to house the compressor and condenser thus avoiding noise problems in the space being served. Some units offer variable speed compressors that enable cooling to be modulated, and thus the energy use can be matched more closely to cooling requirements. Split systems provide cooling COPs of 2.5 to 3.0 whereas through the wall units only give 1.5 to 2.3. Otherwise, they should only be used in the same context as individual packaged units, with extra care taken to avoid the prospect of leaks from the connecting refrigerant lines.

6.3.3.4 Variable refrigerant flow rate

Variable refrigerant flow rate (VRF) multi-split systems are generally regarded as local systems but are increasingly used as distributed cooling systems. More than one indoor unit can be connected to the same outdoor unit. However, it is important to comply with the manufacturer's recom-mendations on horizontal pipe runs, number of bends and vertical lift, in order to minimise energy losses.

In each circulation loop, the refrigerant flow rate can be varied to match the heat transport requirements, thus making energy savings. Some suppliers offer heat recovery between zones on the same circulation loop, and it is in this mode that the system operates at its peak COP of 3.1[19]. In heating only, or cooling only, modes the best system COPs lie in the range 2.3 to 2.5.

In some installations, several outdoor units for individual refrigerant loops have been located in a bank adjacent to each other, but not connected, which can give the false impression of a co-ordinated system. Care should be taken to ensure a coherent control strategy with this approach. In particular, controls for multiple units serving the same space should be linked to avoid simultaneous heating and cooling. Dead-bands between heating and cooling set points should be adequate to avoid individual units cycling between heating and cooling modes.

6.3.4   'Free' cooling

Before considering a system that depends on mechanical cooling, every opportunity should be taken to use 'free' cooling, of which fresh air is the most obvious source. In systems where sufficient air quantities can be delivered to the space, it can be used to reduce demands on mechanical cooling when ambient temperatures are sufficiently low. All-air recirculation systems are ideal applications where savings can be achieved. However, care must be taken to consider the resulting relative humidity, as the energy used for humidification, particularly electric, can offset the refrigeration savings. Additional energy used for air transportation should also be compared with the mechanical cooling savings.

Effective controls for free cooling, linked with system demand and fresh air high limit override or enthalpy control, are essential for efficient operation (see 6.4.4).

6.3.5   Heat recovery

Integrating heat recovery systems into the design of air conditioning and ventilation systems is essential for energy efficiency. Including heat recovery as an integral part of an overall design will always be more cost effective than retrofitting at a later stage. In some cases, this can reduce the capacity of primary plant required and may also reduce the overall capital cost of the building services.

There must be sufficient energy being rejected to justify the added complications and running costs of installing heat recovery devices (see 19.3.4). With some equipment, the likelihood of cross-contamination between air streams is a key consideration. The extra power consumption of pumps or fans to overcome additional air resistance should always be taken into account. This is particularly important where system operating hours are much greater than heat recovery hours.

Effective controls for heat recovery, linked with system demand and fresh air high limit override or enthalpy control, are essential for efficient operation.

Heat recovery systems are most applicable and cost effective in ventilation systems that reject large amounts of heat, e.g. where high moisture content air is exhausted from swimming pools, or where there is no possibility of re-circulating air (e.g. in full fresh air hospital theatre systems). In both these cases, cross-contamination must be avoided.

A further method of recovering heat is to extract air through luminaires to recover a proportion of the energy consumed by the lamps. The heat in this air may be reclaimed and re-used where needed. This system also reduces the cooling load in the room by preventing a large part of the lighting heat load entering the room; the system can also increase the light output of fluorescent lamps.

6.3.6   Minimising transport losses

Keeping air transport losses to a minimum is an essential part of an energy efficient design. BRECSU Good Practice Guide 33[20] shows that for typical air conditioned offices, energy used by fans is comparable to that used by the refrigeration plant itself. Many of the 'passive' technologies, which offer reductions in refrigeration load, can cause an increase in fan power requirements. A balance needs to be struck between this additional fan power and reduced refrigeration loads.

The four main ways of reducing fan energy consumption are:
—   optimising the fan characteristic
—   efficient system regulation (see 10.4)
—   reducing air transport losses
—   switching off the system when not required.

6.3.6.1   Fan power

The selection of a fan type is primarily determined by the application and, where a choice is available, the most efficient should be chosen. In general, centrifugal fans are more efficient, controllable and quieter. Aerofoil-bladed centrifugal fans can be up to 30% more efficient than a forward curved centrifugal fan for a typical application. The additional capital cost is normally recovered within two years.

All mechanical ventilation fans should be sized as close to the actual demand as possible in order to keep capital and running costs to a minimum. Motors should not be significantly oversized as efficiency and power factor will reduce.

Fan characteristics should be matched to the chosen method of volume control[16]. This can be achieved through various means, such as variable speed motors and variable pitch fans to optimise fan performance at part load. Variable speed drives are covered in 10.4 and BRECSU Good Practice Guide 2[21]. Inlet guide vanes, disc throttles and dampers are not generally recommended for energy efficiency due to the 'throttling' effect.

Specific fan power should be kept to a minimum and energy efficient systems should achieve around 2 to 3 W/(l/s).

6.3.6.2   Air transport losses

Transport energy losses can also be minimised by reducing resistance to air movement through good ductwork design. This is constrained by increased capital costs and by the space requirements for the larger ductwork, but careful consideration at the design stage can reduce energy

Table 6.6 Selection of controls for mechanical ventilation systems

Plant	Control function
Ventilation systems start/stop up to 30 kW heating	Time switch; resolution better than 15 minutes, spring reserve/battery back up
Ventilation systems start/stop 30 – 100 kW heating	Optimum start/stop recommended
Ventilation systems start/stop over 100 kW heating	Optimum start/stop required by current *Building Regulations*
Fresh air and exhaust dampers; tempered air systems	Open/closed linked with time control of plant
Fresh air, re-circulation and exhaust dampers; central air handling units; minimum fresh air	Full re-circulation when unoccupied; minimum fresh air position when occupied; minimum fresh air preferably controlled with respect to air quality
Fresh air, re-circulation and exhaust dampers; central air handling units; free cooling	Free cooling override of minimum fresh air from heating/cooling sequence; fresh air temperature high-limit or preferably enthalpy control
Tempered air systems	Heating/cooling sequence for constant supply temperature; possible reset supply condition according to ambient temperature or summated demand if appropriate
Single zone air handling units	Heating/cooling sequence from space or return air temperature; possible minimum supply air temperature to prevent dumping of cold air; systems for large spaces (lecture theatres, etc.) reset supply air temperature from return air
Multi-zone air handling units; common cooling coil	Re-heater batteries controlled with respect to space or return air temperature. Common cooling coil controlled from zone requiring most cooling; do not control cooling coil at constant off coil temperature, except in rare case of dew-point system
VAV air handling units: temperature	Heating/cooling sequence for constant supply temperature; possible reset supply temperature according to ambient temperature or summated demand if appropriate
VAV air handling units; supply fan	Speed or pitch control with respect to duct pressure 2/3 way along supply duct
VAV air handling units; supply fan, alternative methods	Speed or pitch control with respect to point near supply fan with reset from summated system demand, plus low limits; demand based control strategies based on VAV box positions can be used but can be unduly influenced by poorly sized boxes
VAV air handling units; extract fan	Control with respect to supply/extract differential volume
VAV boxes	Control velocity between minimum and maximum with respect to space temperature
Dual duct air handling units	Control hot and cold decks for a constant temperature. Possible reset according to outside temperature or summated demand
Dual duct mixing boxes	Mix hot and cold duct supplies according to space temperature
VAV dual duct	Fans as for VAV; temperature as for dual duct
Fan coil units	Return air (or space) temperature control of heating and cooling in sequence
Induction units	Heating and cooling control in sequence from space or return air temperature; segregation of heating and cooling hydraulic distribution essential for efficient operation
Intermittently occupied areas	Occupancy sensing controls with appropriate default values dependent upon system response
Humidification	Control from space or return RH, supply modulating high limit
De-humidification	Over-ride temperature control of cooling coil to cool air below dew-point; re-heat via re-heater batteries as per normal temperature control; supply temperature low limit may be required

consumption significantly. The following guidelines should be followed:

— Ductwork should be designed to achieve minimum pressure loss. This requires the use of low-loss fittings (swept bends rather than elbows etc.) and to undertake pressure loss design to minimise damper requirements.

— Central plant filters provide a significant resistance to airflow. A careful balance must be struck between filtration efficiency and pressure drop which both vary with time for a given installation.

— The length of ducts should be minimised by carefully siting the plant room and air-handling units. Excessive ductwork increases pressure drop, and increases fan duty and consumption.

6.4 Ventilation and air conditioning controls

Air systems generally provide a more rapid response than wet systems, so good control is essential for comfort conditions and energy efficient operation. DDC or BMS controls are generally recommended as they provide more accurate control of temperature and volumes (see section 5). The control of ventilation and air conditioning is covered in CIBSE Guide B3: *Ventilation and air conditioning (systems, equipment and control)*[2], CIBSE Applications Manual AM1[22] and DETR General Information Report 41[23].

Table 6.6 provides guidance on the selection of controls for mechanical ventilation systems.

6.4.1   Plant start/stop

Air systems should generally be started and stopped in accordance with the guidance given in 5.5. Due to the faster response of air systems, optimum start control has a lesser effect but should still be used. Optimum stop is not normally used with ventilation systems due to the need to maintain minimum fresh air rates. Night purge systems pre-cool the building structure overnight to limit the daytime peak cooling requirement and require operation at night.

Heater and cooler batteries, humidifiers, etc. should always be interlocked with the fan to ensure they are only able to operate when required. Terminal units such as fan coil units, fan assisted VAV boxes, etc. should all have effective time control. Demand based control systems to operate central plant only when required should be considered to minimise energy consumption.

6.4.2   Set points, dead-bands and summated signals

Temperature and humidity set points must be selected for the minimum energy consumption consistent with comfort conditions. Adequate dead-bands between heating and cooling are essential to minimise energy consumption and avoid simultaneous heating and cooling.

Where DDC is used with P+I control, the results of the heating and cooling calculations should be summated and a common signal produced to avoid simultaneous heating and cooling due to the integral action. The signal should then split into heating, free cooling (where appropriate) and mechanical cooling.

6.4.3   Sensor location

Sensors must be located in representative positions for the services being controlled. Where multiple terminal units are used in air conditioning systems, such as VAV systems, one sensor per terminal unit is normally required.

6.4.4   Free cooling control

Free cooling can significantly reduce the running costs of air conditioning systems. Central air handling units should have the supply, re-circulation and extract dampers controlled in parallel to provide fresh air as the first stage of cooling. The dampers should be overridden to minimum fresh air in the event of high fresh air temperature. Free cooling control is improved by enthalpy control which compares fresh air and return air enthalpy, controlling the fresh air to meet demand. Enthalpy control is essential where controlled humidification and/or de-humidification are provided by the AHU.

Free cooling is available with some packaged air conditioning units and should be used wherever possible. Free cooling is also available via cooling towers providing cooled water without chillers operating (see 7.1.3). Complex control strategies and additional filtration are necessary for effective operation, although significant savings are claimed.

6.4.5   Humidity control

Most comfort cooling applications do not require close control of relative humidity in the occupied space (see section 5) and do not require controlled de-humidification.

Humidification may be required with air conditioning systems to provide a minimum relative humidity in winter. A relative humidity limit in the supply air is required to prevent saturation in the distribution ductwork.

Energy efficient humidifiers should be used, preferably with modulating control rather than control in stages or simple on/off control.

Where both humidification and de-humidification is essential, a wide dead-band between humidification and de-humidification set points is recommended to minimise energy consumption.

Humidistats or humidity sensors can suffer from drift causing inaccurate relative humidities and possibly higher energy consumption. Specifying a high quality sensor and regular calibration can help avoid this.

6.4.6   Multi-zone systems

Multi-zone systems with a common cooler battery must have the cooler battery effectively controlled with respect to the space requiring the greatest amount of cooling, as poor control can lead to excessive energy use. These systems must not be controlled at a constant supply temperature, except in the rare case of a dew-point system.

6.4.7   Air quality control

Air quality control can provide significant energy savings for both full fresh air and re-circulation systems.

Air quality can be controlled with respect to CO_2, e.g. the concentration of metabolic carbon dioxide due to increased occupancy or multiple contaminants, to provide economy of operation where occupation levels vary in buildings. CO_2 control is more expensive but can be set up more easily. Multiple contaminant control needs to be set up with empirical values. However, it often has a rapid payback.

The minimum fresh air quantity is normally controlled via the supply, re-circulation and extract dampers in relation to air quality. This is particularly effective for VAV systems where fixed minimum damper positions would provide varying fresh air content.

The air volume can be controlled on full fresh air systems in relation to air quality via variable speed drives or variable pitch axial fans. However, minimum ventilation rates may be required to provide adequate heating and cooling, air distribution, etc. Significant energy savings can still result even where turndowns in volume are limited (see DETR General Information Report 41[23]).

BSRIA Technical Note TN 12/94[24] suggests that significant energy savings may accrue from the use of CO_2 control. However, each application has to be judged on the ventilation requirements based on predicted occupancy profiles for the particular building and TN 12/94 contains the means of assessing the viability of given schemes. In general, the energy benefits of a CO_2 controlled ventilation system manifest themselves in buildings with spaces subject to variable occupancy.

6.4.8 VAV control

The control of VAV systems is far more complex than other air conditioning systems. VAV systems should normally only be used where the load is predominantly cooling throughout the year, such as a deep plan office building. Good space and duct sensor locations are essential for energy efficient operation.

Proportional space temperature control is preferable for stability, ease of commissioning and efficient operation. A dead-band between heating and cooling is necessary where reheat occurs.

Most modern VAV systems use velocity reset VAV boxes. Primary air volume is reset between minimum and maximum settings in relation to space temperature. These are pressure dependent and the system is substantially self-balancing. Reheat is normally at minimum volume to prevent energy wastage. Fan-assisted VAV boxes generally have greater energy consumption, additional maintenance and higher capital costs.

Supply fans are normally controlled in relation to static pressure, two thirds of the way along the supply duct. Care must be taken to ensure the static pressure setting is not higher than necessary as this will waste energy and possibly cause increased noise at the terminal units at low loads. Extract fans are normally controlled in relation to differential volume. Difficulties can arise due to velocity sensor locations from which the volumes are calculated. A wide range of VAV controls is discussed in detail in DETR General Information Report 41[23].

References

1   Natural ventilation in non-domestic buildings CIBSE Applications Manual AM10 (London: Chartered Institution of Building Services Engineers) (1997)

2   Ventilation and air conditioning (systems, equipment and control) CIBSE Guide B2/B3 (London: Chartered Institution of Building Services Engineers) (1986)

3   HVAC Applications ASHRAE Handbook (Atlanta, GA: American Society of Heating, Refrigeration and Air Conditioning Engineers) (1995)

4   Avoiding or minimising the use of air-conditioning — A research report from the EnREI Programme GIR 31 (London: Department of the Environment, Transport and the Regions) (1995)

5   Natural ventilation in non-domestic buildings Digest 399 (Garston: Building Research Establishment) (1994)

6   Energy efficiency in offices — a technical guide for owners and single tenants ECON 19 (London: Department of Environment, Transport and Regions) (1997)

7   Office service charges analysis 7th edn (London: Jones, Lang and Wootton) (1992)

8   Baker N V and Steemers K The LT Method 2.0. An energy design tool for non-domestic buildings (Cambridge: Cambridge Architectural Research/Building Research Energy Conservation Support Unit) (1994)

9   Oversized air handling plant GN 11/97 (Bracknell: Building Services Research and Information Association) (1997)

10   Allen C Air Infiltration Glossary Coventry: Air Infiltration and Ventilation Centre) (1981)

11   Alamdari F et al. Displacement ventilation performance — office space application TN 3/93 (Bracknell: Building Services Research and Information Association) (1993)

12   Energy efficiency in offices — 1 Bridewell Street GPCS 21 (London: Department of Environment, Transport and the Regions) (1991)

13   Selecting air conditioning systems. A guide for building clients and their advisers GPG 71 (London: Department of Environment, Transport and the Regions) (1993)

14   Environmental criteria for design CIBSE Guide A1 (London: Chartered Institution of Building Services Engineers) (1979)

15   Cassar M Environment management: Guidelines for museums and galleries (London: Museums and Galleries Commission)

16   Refrigeration and the environment — typical applications for air conditioning TN 15/92 (Bracknell: Building Services Research and Information Association) (1992)

17   Butler D J G Chilled ceilings and beams — BRE research CIBSE National Conference 1997 (London: Chartered Institution of Building Services Engineers) (1997)

18   Jones W P Air conditioning applications and design (2nd edition) (London: Edward Arnold) (1997)

19   Smith M Split personalities Building Services Journal (June 1997)

20   Energy efficiency in offices. Understanding energy use in your office GPG 33 (London: Department of Environment, Transport and the Regions) (1992)

21   Guidance notes for reducing energy consumption of electric motors and drives GPG 2 (London: Department of Environment, Transport and the Regions)

22   Automatic controls CIBSE Applications Manual AM1 (London: Chartered Institution of Building Services Engineers) (1985)

23   Variable flow control GIR 41 (London: Department of Environment, Transport and the Regions) (1996)

24   Carbon dioxide-controlled mechanical ventilation systems TN 12/94.1 (Bracknell: Building Services Research and Information Association) (1994)

Bibliography

Raw G J, Roys M S and Leaman A J Further findings from the office environment survey Proc. 5th International Conf. Indoor Air Quality and Climate, Canada Housing and Mortgage Corporation, Toronto (1990)

Calculation of energy demands and targets for the design of new buildings and services CIBSE Energy Code Part 2 (a) Heated and naturally ventilated buildings (London: Chartered Institution of Building Services Engineers) (1981)

Leighton D J and Pinney A A A set of standard office descriptions for use in modelling studies BEPAC TN/90/5 (Reading: Building Environmental Performance Analysis Club) (1990)

BS 5422: 1990: Method for specifying thermal insulating materials on pipes, ductwork and equipment (in the temperature range −40°C to +700°C) (London: British Standards Institution) (1990)

Levermore G J Building energy management systems (London: E and F N Spon) (1992)

Martin P L and Oughton D R Faber and Kell: Heating and air-conditioning of buildings (7th edition (Oxford: Butterworth Heinemann) (1989)

Energy efficiency handbook (Penrith: Heating and Ventilating Contractors Association) (1987)

Alexander R For best boost vary velocity *Heating and Air Conditioning Journal* 24–27 (December 1988)

Wall G Optimisation of refrigeration machinery *Int. Journal of Refrigeration* **14**[6] 336–340 (1991)

Eto J H and de Almeida A Saving electricity in commercial buildings with adjustable speed drives *IEEE Trans. on Ind. Applications* **24**[3] (1988)

Addy M Cooling it *Energy Manager* 25–26 (July/August 1988)

Mills M Variable speed drives *Refrigeration, Air Conditioning and Heat Recovery* 19–20 (February 1987) (See also Parts 2, 3 and 4 in March, April and May issues)

Cooper P J Cutting refrigeration energy costs in supermarkets *Refrigeration, Air Conditioning and Heat Recovery* 44–48 (February 1987)

Creaner M and Morse R CVC — A speed and capacity control system *Refrigeration, Air Conditioning and Heat Recovery* 57–60 (May 1987); 65–75 (June 1987)

Steer J W and Doig R The specification of efficient ventilation systems in the decommissioning of redundant plant at Sellafield *CIBSE National Conference 1995* (London: Chartered Institution of Building Services Engineers) (1995)

Green R H, Taylor M S and Fletcher P G The performance of a prototype, commercial building, balanced ventilation, heat pump *CIBSE National Conference 1995* (London: Chartered Institution of Building Services Engineers) (1995)

Riffat S B, Shao L and Shehata Mop fan for removal of air-borne pollutants *CIBSE National Conference 1995* (London: Chartered Institution of Building Services Engineers) (1995)

Leaman A J, Cohen R R and Jackman P J Ventilation of office buildings: deciding the appropriate system *CIBSE National Conference 1994* (London: Chartered Institution of Building Services Engineers) (1994)

Channer G R A mixed mode ventilation system for an office tower which addresses the problems of infiltration, internal comfort and energy consumption *CIBSE National Conference 1994* (London: Chartered Institution of Building Services Engineers) (1994)

Edwards M, Linden P and Walker R R Theory and practice — natural ventilation modelling *CIBSE National Conference 1994* (London: Chartered Institution of Building Service Engineers) (1994)

Jones W P *Air conditioning engineering* (London: Edward Arnold) (1982)

Stoecker W F and Jones J W *Refrigeration and air conditioning* (London: McGraw-Hill) (1989)

Chilled ceilings and beams CIBSE Research Report RR5 (London: Chartered Institution of Building Services Engineers) (1998)

Air-to-air heat recovery CIBSE Research Report RR2 (London: Chartered Institution of Building Services Engineers) (1995)

Pre-cooling in mechanically cooled buildings TN16/95 (Bracknell: Building Services Research and Information Association) (1995)

Design guide for free cooling RR16/96 (Bracknell: Building Services Research and Information Association) (1996)

7　Refrigeration design

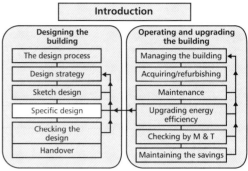

This section sets out key issues to be considered when designing energy efficient refrigeration systems and should be read in conjunction with section 6, which covers mechanical ventilation and air conditioning. There is considerable potential at sketch design stage to minimise or even avoid the need for mechanical cooling and this is addressed in section 4. Energy issues related to the maintenance of refrigeration systems are covered in section 17. For further detail on refrigeration, refer to the CIBSE Guide section B14[1], DETR Fuel Efficiency Booklet No 11[2], BSRIA TN15/92[3], and DETR Good Practice Guides 36[4], 37[5], 38[6], 44[7], and 42[8].

7.0　General

Most refrigeration plant is electrically driven and can add significantly to energy costs and CO_2 emissions. Moreover, the need for cooling is increasing, due to the greater use of computers and increasing comfort expectations.

7.1　Minimising cooling requirements

Minimising the need for cooling can reduce energy costs and, in some cases, the capital cost of plant. The need for cooling can be minimised by:

— reducing cooling loads

— raising cooling supply temperatures

— using 'free' cooling.

7.1.1　Reducing cooling loads

Cooling loads can be reduced in many ways, as discussed in section 4, for example by:

— selecting office equipment with lower power use

— improved management (e.g. turning off lights and personal computers when not in use)

— optimising set points (e.g. space temperature, air supply temperature, recirculation rate and humidity)

— improved, but not necessarily closer, control of temperatures, flows and humidities.

7.1.2　Raising supply temperatures

Raising the temperature at which cooling is delivered allows higher evaporating temperatures which increases refrigeration efficiency and, therefore, reduces energy consumption. It may also increase the cooling capacity of a given size of refrigeration plant. For example, the energy cost of delivering water at 6°C is some 10% more than at 10°C. Furthermore, the capital cost of the central plant is likely to be lower, although this may be offset by higher costs of fan coil units, distribution systems, terminal units and other emitters. Temperatures at which cooling is delivered can be raised by:

— installing larger, more efficient heat exchangers for cooling air, but with increased capital cost

— increasing chilled water or supply air volume flow rates, and increasing pipe and duct sizes to maintain the same pump or fan power

— increasing chilled water flows through heat exchangers and increasing pipe sizes to avoid increasing pumping energy

— separating cooling duties that require low temperatures (e.g. de-humidification or areas where cooling loads are exceptionally high) from more general cooling duties that can be achieved with higher temperatures

— raising set points at times of lower cooling demand (e.g. compensating chilled water temperatures).

7.1.3　'Free' cooling

'Free' cooling using ambient air to cool a secondary fluid, usually water or glycol, can also be used to cool air in the

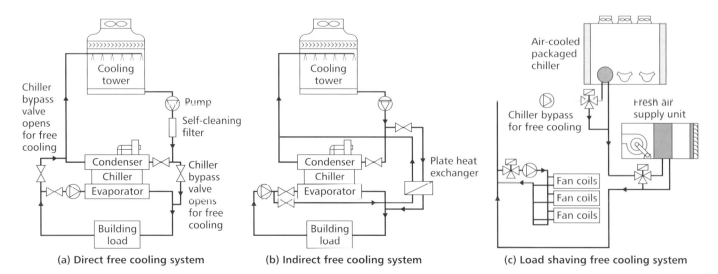

Figure 7.1 Options for free cooling[9] (reproduced from Premises and Facilities Management by permission of the publisher)

building. The secondary fluid can be cooled via cooling towers, air-cooled heat exchangers (dry air-cooling coils) or evaporative heat exchangers. Some options are shown in Figure 7.1[9]. Free cooling systems such as these can be effective in situations where the cooling demands are high and unrelated to ambient temperature, for example in computer suites and telephone exchanges.

The direct system or 'strainer cycle' circulates water directly through a cooling tower without running the chiller. The potential for this 'free' cooling is demonstrated by the fact that, in London, the ambient wet bulb temperature is below 8°C for more than 40% of the year. A diverter valve causes cooled water to circulate directly from the cooling tower to the cooling coils in the chilled water system. A strainer is provided in the circuit so that the cooling tower water can be kept sufficiently clean to prevent blockage of the small waterways in the cooling coils. The pressure drop across the strainer will increase the pumping pressures, and this has to be balanced against the free cooling provided. The potential for contamination and fouling of the chilled water circuit can also be a significant problem.

To avoid some of the drawbacks, indirect systems are available, incorporating a plate heat exchanger with a closed-circuit cooling tower[10]. However, use of this system reduces the amount of potential free cooling due to the temperature difference across the heat exchanger.

7.2 Designing efficient systems

Oversizing refrigeration plant increases capital and running costs unnecessarily. Chiller capacities greater than those shown in Table 7.1 suggest oversizing[11].

The lower the chilled water (evaporator) temperature, the more energy used and the greater danger of freezing. Therefore, arrangements that segregate chillers used for low temperature circuits will improve energy efficiency. Direct expansion (DX) cooling can more easily provide lower air temperatures, and it can be worthwhile installing separate DX systems for specific dehumidification duties.

Table 7.1 Basic chiller plant capacity benchmarks

Building	Chiller capacity (cooling load) (W/m^2)
Offices, health-care, retail stores	140
Restaurants	220
Computer suites	400

Note: Indicated capacities on equipment nameplates may not be applicable; actual cooling loads may be significantly lower than those shown in table

Designs should deal with common problems to maintain efficiency[4,8]. For example, in large chiller plant, an automatic air purging system will prevent the build-up of air and other non-condensable gases in the condenser, and effective oil separation and recovery systems will prevent evaporator fouling.

Instrumentation should be incorporated for monitoring the performance[12] of large chiller plant. As a recommended minimum, power use, condensing and evaporating temperatures, chilled fluid and ambient temperatures should be measured. Leakage of refrigerant and oil usage should also be monitored. Refrigerant leakage can cause a significant increase in energy consumption and should, therefore, be minimised through adherence to good practice[13].

7.2.1 Thermal storage

Thermal storage techniques can smooth out the peaks and troughs in cooling demand, improving the loading and efficiency of chillers[14]. The economics are highly dependent on the electricity tariff. Opportunities include:

— chilled water storage during periods of low demand

— ice storage, where ice is formed on plates or tubes and subsequently defrosted to provide chilled water

— other phase change and eutectic materials that freeze at certain temperatures depending on the particular substance (they can be frozen during

Table 7.2 Advantages and disadvantages of thermal storage systems

Advantages	Disadvantages
Smaller chiller required, running or longer hours at or near its design duty, thus maximising its COP and therefore improving overall system efficiency	Mixing losses in the storage vessel
	Increased conduction losses from the system because of the lower temperatures and the larger surface area
Reduced operating cost e.g. ability to operate for longer periods on low cost tariffs and reduced maximum demand charges	Increased plant room space required to allow for the storage vessel
Steadier load operation increases reliability and reduces maintenance cost (i.e. reduced plant cycling)	Ice systems operate at lower evaporating temperatures to enable ice production, thus reducing COP (new phase-change materials that 'freeze' at higher temperatures may overcome this)
Operation at lower condensing temperatures because of reduced night time temperatures, thus enhancing COP	

periods of low load e.g. night-time, and then defrosted at peak periods)

— use of the building's thermal inertia (see section 4).

The main advantages/disadvantages of thermal storage systems are shown in Table 7.2.

A further advantage of ice thermal storage systems is the ability to use the low temperature store to cool air to lower levels (say 5°C). This can result in reduced primary air volumes and subsequently reduced fan power in normally sized ducts.

The chiller and thermal store can be used for partial or full storage. Partial storage provides load levelling, with the chiller still operating during the day to meet the peak cooling load. Full storage eliminates the daytime operation of the chiller altogether, thus reducing electrical energy costs, but increasing the store size. These various operational modes are discussed in CIBSE Technical Memoranda TM18[14].

Short term thermal storage, where cooling is smoothed out over say half an hour to a couple of hours, provides a number of benefits:

— it allows plant to be operated more efficiently by not exactly matching demand (e.g. compressors may be operated at full load and then switch off, rather than to run continuously at part load)

— it allows high electricity charges to be avoided (e.g. maximum demand)

— it may allow plant sizes and capital costs to be reduced.

Longer term thermal storage, over several hours, can take advantage of off-peak electricity prices. However, refrigeration efficiency can be reduced because the production of ice and the over cooling of a building require cooling to be delivered at lower temperatures.

7.2.2 Heat recovery

Efficient heat recovery from refrigeration systems in buildings is often difficult to achieve. Heat is available from the de-superheating, condensing and sub-cooling of the high pressure refrigerant, and this heat can be used to supplement space and domestic hot water heating.

Heat recovery is cost-effective where there is a simultaneous demand for heating and cooling and it is feasible to use heat recovered from cooling one area to heat another. Some systems are particularly suited to such situations, e.g. unitary heat pumps (see 6.3.2.5).

Heat recovered from the condenser can be used in those parts of the building that require it. This may often be the case in a deep plan building where the core is in continuous cooling mode, but in winter and mid season the perimeter may require heating. The main drawback is that only low grade heat is available. Heat recovery is usually achieved through a double bundle condenser, which consists of an oversized shell containing two separate tube bundles — one taking water to the open cooling tower, the second to the heating circuit. The energy benefit of this approach has to be offset against the increased pumping costs associated with the recovery system. The likely difference in fuel cost between the electricity for pumping and the fossil fuel for the boiler plant should also be taken into account.

Where air cooled condensers are adjacent to a heating requirement, such as in a warehouse, it may be possible to duct the warm air from the system condensers into the areas requiring heat. The heat generated in plant rooms can also be used for similar purposes, but care must be taken not to raise the plant operating temperatures excessively by doing so as this would reduce COP and increase the plant energy consumption.

De-superheating using a separate heat exchanger can be cost-effective if a suitable heat sink can be found for the recovered heat. There can also be a saving in condenser size and cost, which can help to offset the cost of the heat recovery system.

7.3 Refrigeration efficiency

Many factors can affect the energy efficiency of a refrigeration system. Knowledge of these is essential if an energy efficient design is to be achieved.

7.3.1 Refrigeration cycle efficiency

The higher the coefficient of performance (COP), the better the efficiency[4]. A plant operating with a COP of 4 will use 25% less power to achieve the same cooling than one operating with a COP of 3.

COP depends on condensing and evaporating temperatures, although it is also influenced by compressor efficiency and the choice of refrigerant.

The lower the condensing temperature and pressure, the higher the COP (see Figure 7.2). A drop in condensing temperature of 1 K reduces energy use by around 3%.

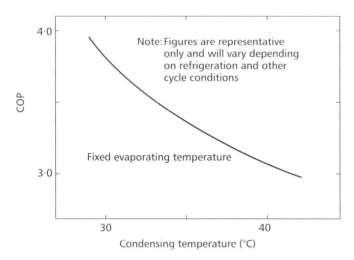

Figure 7.2 Effect of condensing temperature on system performance[8] (reproduced from DETR Good Practice Guide 42. Crown copyright (1992))

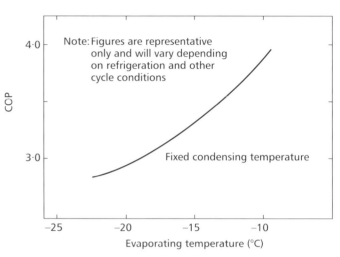

Figure 7.3 Effect of evaporating temperature on system performance[8] (reproduced from DETR Good Practice Guide 42. Crown copyright (1992))

Lower condensing temperatures can be achieved when ambient temperatures are lower, where larger and more efficient condensers are installed and where condenser performance is maintained.

The higher the evaporating temperature, the higher will be the COP, see Figure 7.3. A rise in the evaporating temperature of 1 K will reduce energy use by approximately 3%.

The evaporating temperature is affected by the performance of the evaporator and the expansion valve. Higher evaporating temperatures can be achieved by raising the temperature of the fluid being chilled, installing larger, more efficient evaporators and by maintaining evaporator and expansion valve performance.

The choice of refrigerant can also affect COP, but energy efficiency is likely to be secondary to safety and environmental considerations. Designers should note that the phased withdrawal of many common refrigerants under the 1990 Montreal Protocol may influence their choice of refrigerant[15–19].

7.3.2 System and seasonal performance

Improving the performance of the refrigeration cycle alone will not ensure an efficient design. Energy is also used by the auxiliary equipment, including the condenser, evaporator pumps and fans. The coefficient of system performance (COSP) is generally a more useful measure of energy efficiency than COP and can be defined as:

$$\text{COSP} = \frac{\text{Cooling achieved by refrigeration system}}{\text{Power used by all compressors and auxiliary plant}}$$

Furthermore, it is not sufficient to consider COP and COSP at the plant design conditions alone. COSP should be calculated for all likely conditions, and a seasonal COSP (a weighted average COSP for a year) should be estimated. It is important to recognise that most refrigeration systems will operate well away from the design point for most of the year.

7.4 Primary plant

Where the need for mechanical cooling has been clearly established, designers should select the most energy efficient cooling plant. The plant options, normally vapour compression or absorption chillers, will have a major influence on overall system efficiency.

The COP of vapour compression machines can approach 4.0 and that of absorption chillers up to about 1.0, in terms of delivered energy. When primary energy is considered, the COP's of the different types of plant are much closer, because the vapour compression cycle uses electricity and the absorption process uses heat. It is, therefore, particularly important to consider primary energy and cost when comparing these chillers.

7.4.1 Selecting efficient components

Selection of efficient plant is based on selecting efficient components — condensers, evaporators, expansion valves, compressors, pumps and fans.

7.4.1.1 Evaporators and expansion valves

Evaporators can be 'flooded' or 'direct expansion' types. In general, they should be as large and efficient as is cost-effective to achieve the highest possible evaporating temperature. Raising the evaporating temperature increases the COP and therefore reduces energy costs. A circuit diagram of a single stage vapour compressor and the associated pressure enthalpy diagram are combined in Figure 7.4.

In Figure 7.4, the expansion valve (4–1) controls the flow of liquid refrigerant to the evaporator (1–2), and can have a significant impact on performance. It controls the flow of refrigerant to maintain a level of superheat (1a–2) at the evaporator outlet [2], sufficient to ensure that all the liquid has been boiled before it enters the compressor.

It is important to ensure that these valves are correctly commissioned. They are very often found operating with unnecessarily high superheats, which means that the

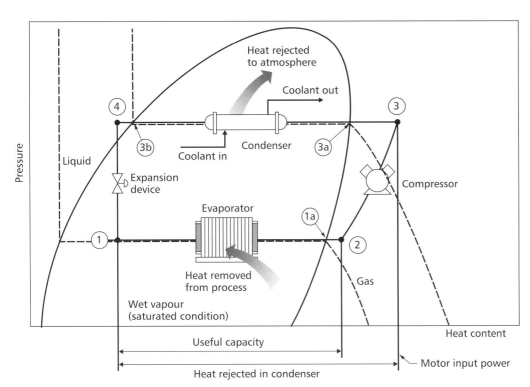

Figure 7.4 Single stage vapour compressor circuit and pressure enthalpy diagram (adapted from DETR Fuel Efficiency booklet No. 11[2]. Crown copyright (1993))

evaporator is starved of liquid and its performance impaired.

Thermostatic expansion valves generally operate within a limited range of pressure drop. For this reason, it is often necessary to install head pressure control to prevent condensing pressures (and corresponding temperatures) falling too low in mild and cold weather. Since this is inefficient, it is vital to ensure that the head pressure set point is set as low as possible.

The electronic expansion valve is a robust and more efficient alternative to the thermostatic expansion valve, the valve opening being controlled electronically. The valve can control superheat far more effectively. Also, it does not have the restricted pressure operating range of the thermostatic valve.

7.4.1.2 Compressors

There are a variety of compressors, including reciprocating, screw, scroll and centrifugal, each with different efficiency characteristics[20]. In selecting compressors, it is important to select machines that will be reliable and easy to maintain, and have a high efficiency under all likely conditions.

The energy efficiency of a compressor can vary between 40 and 85%. Furthermore, manufacturers' data sometimes quote the shaft power into the compressor, while others quote motor input power. For a motor/drive efficiency of 90%, this results in a significant apparent difference in quoted efficiency.

An efficient design will usually consist of multiple compressors in order to meet all demands effectively, avoiding inefficient part load operation. Overall efficiency can often be improved by selecting more compressors of a smaller size and with different capacities.

An efficient control system, combined with the use of effective buffering (thermal storage), will also help avoid poor part-load operation as discussed in 7.2 and DETR Good Practice Guide 59[20]. Hot gas by-pass and suction gas throttling should be avoided as a means of control on all but the smallest plant where very close control of temperature is required.

7.4.1.3 Condensers and heat rejection plant

Heat rejection plant is required to cool the condenser; the efficiency of this process will affect the system COP. Overall seasonal efficiencies are therefore influenced by energy efficient design of heat rejection systems. BSRIA TA 1/93[21] compares the operating costs of the different systems.

The two basic types of condenser are:

— *direct*: air-cooled or evaporative

— *indirect*: condenser heat is rejected via a water system by using cooling towers or dry air coolers.

Evaporative condensers are the basis for the most efficient refrigeration systems since the condensing temperature can closely approach the ambient wet bulb temperature. A cooling tower system achieves a similar performance, although the condensing temperature may be somewhat higher because of the additional heat transfer stage.

Direct air-cooled condensers are less efficient, producing condensing temperatures several degrees above ambient dry bulb temperature. Water-cooled condensers in conjunction with dry air coolers are the most inefficient option, producing even higher condensing temperatures, often with associated high water pumping and fan costs.

Water treatment is also a key issue for cooling towers and evaporative condensers. Effective treatment is essential to avoid legionella, corrosion and fouling[21]. Poor water treatment can greatly increase energy and water costs. Legionella can be controlled if the tower is designed and operated in accordance with CIBSE Technical Memoranda TM13[22].

The larger the condensing system, the better the plant performance, but with correspondingly higher capital costs.

Air-cooled condensers

Air-cooled condensers are the simplest form of condenser heat rejection plant, in which air is blown over finned tubes containing the condensing refrigerant. They are generally found on stand-alone plant such as packaged air conditioners, split systems or some packaged air handling plant. They lose efficiency by having to operate at a relatively high condensing temperature, since they do not have the benefit of evaporative water cooling outside the coil. However, they gain by not having pumping and other auxiliary energy consuming plant associated with condenser water systems.

Evaporative condensers

An evaporative condenser is an extension of an air-cooled condenser. As well as air being blown over the tubes, the tubes themselves are continuously wetted by a re-circulating water system. They are able to achieve a similar performance to water-cooled condensers and open circuit cooling towers, but eliminate the condenser water pumps. The other potential benefit of using evaporative condensers is that they can make use of the thermo-syphon effect to provide 'free' cooling during periods of low demand and low ambient temperature.

The thermo-syphon effect involves the natural circulation of refrigerant without being pumped by the compressor. Thermo-syphoning which requires specially designed chillers can only take place during cold or cool weather when the condensing temperature is lower than the evaporating temperature.

Wet cooling towers

There are two types of wet cooling tower:

— *Open circuit*: water from the condenser is pumped to the cooling tower and is cooled by the evaporation of some of the condenser water. This requires all the water passing through the condenser circuit to be treated and results in increased water consumption due to drift losses.

— *Closed circuit*: condenser water is circulated in a closed loop and a separate water circuit is pumped through the cooling tower, cooling the condenser water by transferring heat through a heat exchanger. This minimises water treatment costs but it also reduces energy efficiency due to the temperature difference across the heat exchanger, although this effect can be minimised by specifying a high-efficiency heat exchanger.

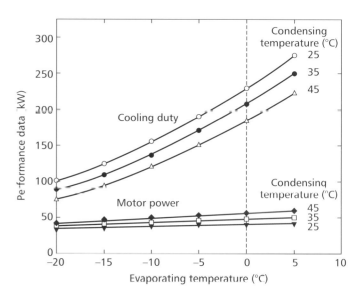

Figure 7.5 Typical compressor performance data[2] (reproduced from DETR Fuel Efficiency booklet No. 11. Crown copyright (1993))

Wet cooling towers minimise condensing temperatures and thus enhance chiller COP since they reduce the water temperature to near the ambient wet bulb temperature. However, the auxiliary power to drive a wet cooling tower is greater than other types of heat rejection system.

Dry coolers

Dry coolers reject heat from the condenser water without making use of evaporative cooling. Since there are two heat exchangers between the refrigerant and the final point of heat rejection, such systems are the least energy efficient.

7.4.2 Vapour compression chillers

Most chillers are based on the vapour compression cycle, using either a positive displacement or centrifugal machine. Whilst machines designed for use with the new zero ozone depleting potential refrigerants[1] can be as efficient as the older technologies, refurbishment of existing machines can result in significant reductions in both refrigeration capacity and efficiency[15–19].

Designers have some flexibility in the selection of temperatures over which the system operates (see Figure 7.5). For example, the condensing temperature will be lower for an evaporative condenser than for an air-cooled condenser.

At part load, the temperature differences in the evaporator and condenser are reduced, and so the evaporating temperature rises and the condensing temperature falls. Part-load COP is, therefore, a balance between increased efficiency due to smaller temperature lift and decreased efficiency due to increased losses[23,24]. Figure 7.6 shows how the balance works for compressor COP alone. However, Figure 7.7 shows the effect of part load operation on system performance, which includes the power taken by the pumps etc. The reduction in compressor COP is particularly significant with screw and centrifugal compressors at low loads.

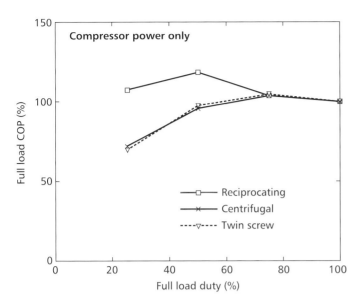

Figure 7.6 Part load compressor performance[2] (reproduced from DETR Fuel Efficiency Booklet No.11. Crown copyright (1993))

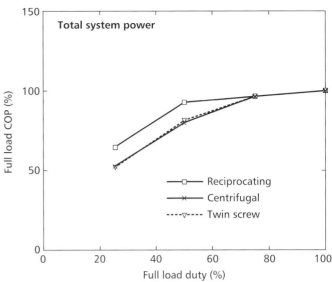

Figure 7.7 Part load system performance[2] (reproduced from DETR Fuel Efficiency Booklet No.11. Crown copyright (1993))

For much of the time, a chiller installation will operate at part-load, so it is important to maintain energy efficient performance. For example, the design duty may require an evaporator temperature of 4°C and a condenser temperature of 40°C, corresponding to an outside design temperature of 28°C. For much of the year, the outside temperature will be lower, so the condensing temperature will also be significantly reduced unless restricted by head pressure control (see 7.4.1.1).

The COP at design full load should not be less than those shown in Table 7.3 and Table 7.4.

7.4.2.1 Reciprocating compressors

Reciprocating compressors are common and often cheaper than other compressor types. However, they have many moving parts and can be more expensive to maintain.

Capacity control to enhance part-load performance can be achieved by cylinder unloading or variable speed control. Cylinder unloading enables output to be reduced in fixed steps, according to the number of cylinders in the machine. For a typical reciprocating compressor, the absorbed power at 25% part load may be about 40% of the full load power.

Variable speed drive gives more flexible control with greater energy savings, although the minimum capacity is much higher because of the need to maintain cylinder lubrication. Compressors are available with improved efficiencies through reduced clearance volumes, better flow through valves and reduced heat transfer. Savings can be up to 20%, although compressor costs are higher.

7.4.2.2 Rotary compressors

In general, rotary compressors are less efficient when operating away from their ideal pressure ratio, but they do not have the valve losses found with reciprocating compressors. They are also more suited to variable speed operation and can sometimes offer a more significant

Table 7.3 Coefficients of performance of reciprocating water chillers

Cooling capacity (kW)	Overall COP	
	Air cooled condensers	Water cooled condensers
<120	2.6	3.2
>120	2.8	3.4

Table 7.4 Coefficients of performance, water chillers with centrifugal compressors

Cooling capacity (kW)	Overall COP	
	Air cooled condensers	Water cooled condensers
< 800	2.2	3.8
> 800	2.3	4.0

operating range than reciprocating compressors due to effective oil cooling.

Screw compressors are expensive and tend to be used in the middle range of compressor sizes, say 150–1500 kW of cooling. The machines are compact and, because of their limited number of moving parts, require less maintenance. Capacity control can be achieved by use of a slide valve to give continuously variable loading down to about 10% of full load. At 25% of full load, the absorbed power will be about 50% of the full load power. Lift valve unloading can be used, but it only provides unloading in discrete steps (usually 25, 50 and 75%). This ability to provide a high turn-down ratio makes them more attractive than reciprocating compressors for larger installations.

Scroll compressors are used in smaller units such as unitary heat pumps and these tend to be up to 10% more efficient than the equivalent sized reciprocating machine.

Centrifugal compressors tend to be used towards the top end of the range (i.e. above 500 kW of cooling). They

Table 7.5 Coefficients of performance, heat operated water chillers

Chiller type	Characteristics			Coefficient of performance† (COP)
	Heat source	Refrigerant	Condenser	
Single effect	Direct fired natural gas	NH_3	Air-cooled	0.5
	Hot water (80–130°C)	H_2O	Water-cooled	0.7
	Steam (0.2–1 bar)	H_2O	Water-cooled	0.7
Double effect	Direct fired natural gas	H_2O	Water-cooled	1
	Steam (3–9 bar)	H_2O	Water-cooled	1.2
	Exhaust gases (280–800°C)	H_2O	Water-cooled	1.1

† ideal rather than achievable

generally have good efficiency at the design condition. Capacity control is usually by inlet guide vanes but this is very inefficient at reduced loads.

7.4.3   Absorption chillers

The COP of absorption chillers tends to be much less than that of vapour compression machines, particularly at part load[23–26].

Table 7.5 shows the range of absorption chillers currently available. Quoted COPs are based on manufacturers' data and are ideal rather than achievable. Their attraction is that they can be operated using waste heat. Where this is readily available, the economics can be very attractive. When combined with CHP, it provides the opportunity to extend the period of the year over which there is a demand for heat, further enhancing the viability of the CHP scheme (see section 9).

7.4.4   Heat pumps

Where there is both a heating and cooling requirement, packaged heat pumps can provide an efficient option[27,28] (see 9.1.5 and 6.3.3).

7.5   Distribution systems

Conventional chilled water systems are covered in CIBSE Guide B14[1]. Most chilled water systems are constant volume, using the same amount of energy for pumping throughout the year, regardless of load. Variable flow systems use modulating two port valves which close on reduced load, thus reducing the total flow of the system. Variable speed pumps respond to the reduced demand and decrease the flow of the pumps to match the load of the system. Considerable energy savings can be achieved with the use of variable flow systems. Coil bypass pipework and regulating valves can be eliminated, thus reducing capital costs and commissioning.

Where there is likely to be a large disparity in load between one zone and another, for instance the north and south facades of a building, separately pumped circuits should be considered. Separate zone circuits can add considerably to the controllability of systems and consequently to the economy of operation, although capital cost may be increased.

Pumps are often selected with a safety margin of around 10% surplus pressure (head) at design flow rates and/or 15% additional flow at design pressure head. The pump with the next highest performance curve is then selected, thereby increasing the oversizing margin. Pumps should be sized close to the actual demand in order to keep power factor, capital and running costs to a minimum[11]. Energy efficiency can be improved by selecting more efficient electric motors (see section 10) and/or introducing variable chilled water flow[29] as shown in Figure 7.8.

7.6   Controls

Good controls can avoid high refrigeration operating costs[30]. Key requirements are as follows:

— Chillers and chilled water systems should only operate when required.

— Maximise full load operation of compressors.

— Keep condensing temperatures low and avoid head pressure control.

— Maintain higher evaporating temperatures.

— Avoid rapid cycling of unloading mechanisms.

— Ensure that auxiliaries can be controlled effectively at low loads.

7.6.1   Individual compressor capacity control

A variety of systems are used to provide compressor capacity control[31]. Nearly all capacity control methods reduce the overall system COP to a greater or lesser extent. Control methods include:

— *On/off operation*: simple and reliable, but frequent on/off cycling of the compressor is potentially harmful and should be avoided.

— *Cylinder unloading of multi-cylinder reciprocating compressors*: the power requirement reduces as the capacity decreases, although not in exactly the same proportion since frictional and other parasitic losses still exist within an unloaded cylinder.

— *Variable speed drives*: can be employed to provide efficient capacity control of reciprocating, vane, screw and scroll compressors. Oil pump performance and avoiding speeds that create critical resonant frequencies should be carefully considered.

— *Slide valves*: used to provide capacity control of screw compressors. The slide valve provides smooth step-less regulation down to 10% of design capacity, although screw compressors consume a significant proportion of full load power when operating at part-load.

— *Variable inlet guide vanes on centrifugal compressors*: capacity reduction is achieved by changing the direction of flow, prior to the refrigerant vapour entering the impeller. This is an extremely inefficient way of providing capacity control, since it reduces the isentropic efficiency of the compressor, and hence system COP.

— *Suction throttle devices*: particularly wasteful as they lower the compressor inlet pressure. This is equivalent to operating with evaporator temperatures lower than design, with all the inherent efficiency penalties.

— *Hot-gas bypass*: circulates high pressure hot-gas from the compressor discharge, through an expansion valve to the low pressure side of the system. This is very inefficient since no useful cooling is undertaken by the by-pass gas and there is no attendant reduction in compressor power input. Also, hot-gas bypass can result in excessive superheating of the suction vapour, which can lead to overheating of the compressor.

7.6.2 Multiple chiller sequence control

It is not uncommon to find large refrigeration systems operating inefficiently while meeting small cooling loads. This often involves multiple compressors all operating at part load and the associated auxiliaries (fans, pumps etc.) operating at full load. Effective sequence control can achieve significant savings in multiple chiller installations by minimising excessive part load operation of compressors and ensuring that associated auxiliary equipment is automatically switched off when not required.

Operating two chillers at three-quarters load can be more efficient than running one at full load and one at half load. The load efficiency characteristics of the chiller should be used to determine the most efficient combination of chillers and chiller stages, for a typical range of loads.

Reciprocating compressors generally demonstrate better part load performance than do screw or centrifugal compressors and should be used, wherever practicable, to provide modulation. Screw and centrifugal compressors are ideally suited to providing the base load of refrigeration, preferably with systems that have reasonably constant evaporating and condensing temperatures.

Sequence control can be used to allow the chiller to operate under its own capacity controls. This is normally less efficient than full capacity control via a common control signal from the sequence control system. Individual capacity control of multiple chillers must only be considered where the total load can be determined at all times, such as from the return temperature on constant flow

systems. Sequence control from the flow temperature, where each chiller operates under its own capacity controls, invariably results in ineffective control, poor operation and reliability.

Good control of multiple chiller installations requires:

— effective hydraulic arrangements

— adequate system water volume capacity (often requiring a buffer vessel)

— high standards of commissioning and maintenance.

Reference should be made to DETR General Information Report 41[29] for details of variable flow control systems.

7.6.2.1 Evaporators connected in parallel

Poor hydraulic arrangements can result in reduced efficiencies. Evaporators connected in parallel should be individually pumped to avoid the chilled water being diluted with that flowing through off-line chillers. Evaporators should also normally be constant flow and separated from the effects of any flow variation in the secondary circuits. Individual chiller primary pumps should be sized for the full duty flow of the chiller, and non-return valves incorporated on each evaporator to prevent reverse flows through off-line chillers.

Secondary circuits should preferably be variable flow to minimise pumping energy and reduce the possibility of freeze-up due to higher differential temperatures. A buffer vessel should be used to separate primary and secondary circuits and add to system capacity (see Figure 7.8). To prevent flow reversal in the buffer vessel and re-circulation of secondary return into secondary flow, primary circuit flow should normally be greater than secondary flow at all loads.

Secondary flow temperature should be used to control the sequence with a low limit on primary flow temperature. P+I control can be used although it is often difficult with stepped outputs from reciprocating chillers and in-built time delays. Floating control can be used with the chiller loading slugged more than chiller unloading. In-built chiller time delays between stages should preferably be deleted, with the slugging from the floating control providing the delay between all stages.

Constant-flow secondary circuits can be used where there is less danger of freezing, but with a greater seasonal pumping energy cost. Where constant-flow secondary circuits are used, sequence control can be with respect to return water temperature in a proportional manner.

An alternative to temperature control is to enable chillers, with individual capacity control, with respect to secondary circuit flowrate. Total heat load of the secondary circuit can be used, but slight inaccuracies in temperature sensing can give significant errors due to the low differential temperature. Therefore, accurate flow metering via magnetic flow meters or vortex meters, etc. should provide an adequate indication of total load based on design differential temperature and should also ensure flow is not reversed in the buffer vessel.

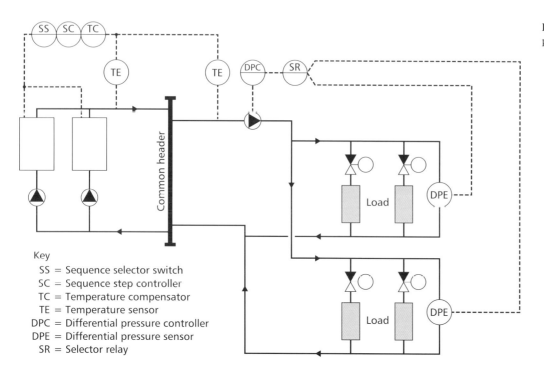

Figure 7.8 Connecting chillers in parallel with variable flow

Key
SS = Sequence selector switch
SC = Sequence step controller
TC = Temperature compensator
TE = Temperature sensor
DPC = Differential pressure controller
DPE = Differential pressure sensor
SR = Selector relay

7.6.2.2   Evaporators connected in series

Chillers connected in series can be used where evaporator pressure drop is relatively low and does not cause excessive pumping losses. This will normally limit the number of chillers to two, although three have been used in some instances. Bypass pipes and manual isolation valves may be provided for maintenance purposes.

Secondary circuits should preferably be variable flow to minimise pumping energy and reduce the possibility of freeze-up due to higher differential temperatures. Series connected evaporators should normally be constant flow and separated from the effects of flow variation in the secondary circuits via a buffer vessel (see Figure 7.9). Sequence control should be proportional to primary circuit return water temperature.

Where constant flow chilled water systems are used, a simple hydraulic layout results, as shown in Figure 7.10. However, seasonal pumping energy costs will be higher.

7.6.3   Condenser control

The control of condensers is an important issue. Condensing systems should ideally be operated to reject heat at the lowest possible condensing temperatures. However, there can be a minimum condensing temperature, corresponding to a particular refrigerant pressure, below which plant will not operate. Head pressure controls are implemented in these cases to prevent the condensing pressure falling below the minimum value in cool weather (see 7.4.1.1). The most common and effective technique is to cycle condenser/cooling tower fans on and off. Alternatives include the use of variable speed fans and the less efficient use of dampers to restrict airflow. In some

cases, water flow can be restricted, using a valve or variable speed pump, or the cooling tower can be bypassed (which is wasteful). The efficient control of fans and pumps is discussed in section 10.

7.6.4   Cooling tower control

Cooling towers are normally controlled by modulation of the water flow over the tower, and up to one third of the cooling can be provided without the fan operating. Beyond this point the fan is switched on and off to provide control of the water temperature. More sophisticated systems have two speed fan motors on centrifugal fans which give better control and reduce energy consumption. Variable speed fans give much better control than two speed fans and are much more energy efficient than inlet dampers.

7.6.5   Distribution system control

There is a range of standard controls that can be included in the design of a typical chilled water system. At the very least, time control should be provided using a time switch, but an optimum start/stop control will provide greater savings. Weather compensation (to vary chilled water temperature in relation to outside conditions) can also be beneficial, producing savings from increased operating temperatures and improvements in COP. System temperatures can also be set back during periods of low load, similar to the use of reset control on weather compensators in heating systems.

Pumping power can be significant in chilled water systems, although it can be reduced by introducing variable speed pumps (see 7.5).

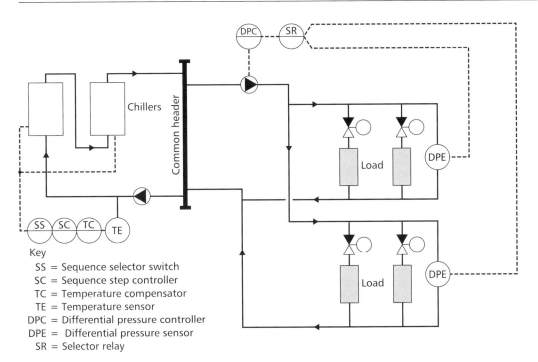

Key

SS = Sequence selector switch
SC = Sequence step controller
TC = Temperature compensator
TE = Temperature sensor
DPC = Differential pressure controller
DPE = Differential pressure sensor
SR = Selector relay

Figure 7.9 Chillers connected in series with variable flow

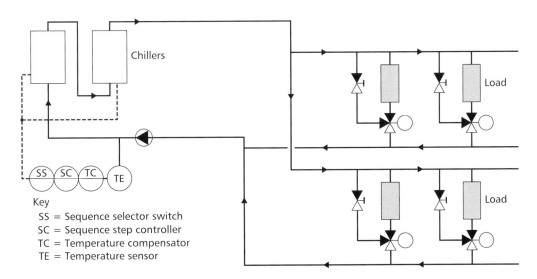

Key

SS = Sequence selector switch
SC = Sequence step controller
TC = Temperature compensator
TE = Temperature sensor

Figure 7.10 Chillers connected in series with constant flow

References

1   *Refrigeration and heat rejection* CIBSE Guide B14 (London: Chartered Institution of Building Services Engineers) (1986)

2   *The economic use of refrigeration plant* Fuel Efficiency Booklet No. 11 (London: Department of Environment, Transport and Regions) (1993)

3   *Refrigeration and the environment — typical applications for air conditioning* TN 15/92 (Bracknell: Building Services Research and Information Association) (1992)

4   *Commercial refrigeration plant: energy efficient operation and maintenance* GPG 36 (London: Department of Environment, Transport and Regions) (1992)

5   *Commercial refrigeration plant: energy efficient design* GPG 37 (London: Department of Environment, Transport and Regions) (1992)

6   *Commercial refrigeration plant: energy efficient installation* GPG 38 (London: Department of Environment, Transport and Regions) (1992)

7   *Industrial refrigeration plant — energy efficient design* GPG 44 (London: Department of Environment, Transport and Regions) (1992)

8   *Industrial refrigeration plant — energy efficient operation and maintenance* GPG 42 (London: Department of Environment, Transport and Regions) (1992)

9   Retrofitting for free cooling *Premises and Facilities Management* (June 1997)

10   De Saulles T Free cooling revisited *Building Services Journal* **17**[(12)] (December 1995)

11   *Oversized cooling and pumping plant* GN 13/97 (Bracknell: Building Services Research and Information Association)

12   Calder K *Practical chiller system monitoring* TN 7/94 (Bracknell: Building Services Research and Information Association) (1994)

13   *Cutting the cost of refrigerant leakage. An introductory guide for users of small to medium sized refrigeration systems* GPG 178 (London: Department of Environment, Transport and Regions) (1997)

14   *Ice storage systems* CIBSE Technical Memoranda TM18 (London: Chartered Institution of Building Services Engineers) (1994)

15   CFCs, HCFCs *and halons: Professional and practical guidance on substances which deplete the ozone layer* CIBSE Guidance Note GN1 (London: Chartered Institution of Building Services Engineers) (1993)

16   CFCs *in buildings* Digest 358 (Garston: Building Research Establishment)

17   *Minimising refrigerant emissions from air conditioning systems in buildings* IP1/94 (Garston: Building Research Establishment) (1994)

18   *Phase-out of* CFCs *and* HCFCs: *options for owners and operators of air conditioning systems* IP14/95 (Garston: Building Research Establishment) (1995)

19   *The safety and environmental requirements of new refrigerants* IP16/95 (Garston: Building Research Establishment) (1995)

20   *Energy efficient design and operation of refrigeration compressors* GPG 59 (London: Department of Environment, Transport and Regions) (1993)

21   *Heat rejection systems — some methods and their operating costs* TA 1/93 (Bracknell: Building Services Research and Information Association) (1993)

22   *Minimising the risk of Legionnaires' disease* CIBSE Technical Memoranda TM13 (London: Chartered Institution of Building Services Engineers) (1991)

23   Smith J and Webb B *A Fair* COP *Building Services Journal* (September 1993)

24   Smith J and Webb B A comparison of the CO_2 emission rates from gas fired and electrically driven chillers *CIBSE National Conference 1995* (London: Chartered Institution of Building Services Engineers) (1995)

25   Tozer R M and James R W *Chiller operating comparison, absorption and centrifugal* Research Memorandum 140 (London: School of Engineering, South Bank University) (1993)

26   Tozer R M, James R W Theory and application of absorption refrigeration systems *Institute of Refrigeration Proceedings* (1995)

27   *Selection and application of heat pumps* CIBSE Technical Memoranda TM11 (London: Chartered Institution of Building Services Engineers) (1985)

28   *Design guidance for heat pump systems* CIBSE Technical Memoranda TM15 (London: Chartered Institution of Building Services Engineers) (1988)

29   *Variable flow control* GIR 41 (London: Department of Environment, Transport and Regions) (1996)

30   *Automatic controls* CIBSE Applications Manual AM1 (London: Chartered Institution of Building Services Engineers) (1985)

31   Calder K Optimising the control of chillers *Building Services Journal* (May 1995)

Bibliography

HVAC *Applications* ASHRAE Handbook (Atlanta, GA: American Society of Heating, Refrigeration and Air Conditioning Engineers) (1995)

Refrigeration ASHRAE Handbook (Atlanta, GA: American Society of Heating, Refrigeration and Air Conditioning Engineers) (1998)

Refrigeration systems CIBSE Commissioning Code R (London: Chartered Institution of Buildings Services Engineers) (1991)

Wall G Optimisation of refrigeration machinery *Int. Journal of Refrigeration* 14[(6)] 336–340 (1991)

Eto J H and de Almeida A Saving electricity in commercial buildings with adjustable speed drives *IEEE Trans. on Ind. Applications* 24[(3)] (1988)

Addy M Cooling it *Energy Manager* pages 25–26 (July/August 1988)

Mills M Variable speed drives *Refrigeration, Air Conditioning and Heat Recovery* pages 19–20 (February 1987) (See also Parts 2, 3 and 4 in March, April and May issues)

Cooper P J Cutting refrigeration energy costs in supermarkets *Refrigeration, Air Conditioning and Heat Recovery* pages 44–48 (February 1987)

Refrigeration design for part-load operation *Building Services Journal* (June 1995)

Tassou S A, Marquand C J and Wilson D R The effects of capacity modulation on the performance of vapour compression heat pump systems *Int. Symp. on the Industrial Application of Heat Pumps Coventry* Paper E3 187-196 (Cranfield: BHRA Fluid Engineering) (1982)

Air infiltration and natural ventilation CIBSE Guide A4 (London: Chartered Institution of Building Services Engineers) (1986)

Dossat R J *Principles of refrigeration* (Chichester: John Wiley and Sons)

Martin P L and Oughton D R *Faber and Kell: Heating and air-conditioning of buildings* 7th edn (Oxford: Butterworth Heinemann) (1989)

Thermal storage: environmental benefits CIBSE Research Report RR6 (London: Chartered Institution of Building Services Engineers) (1998)

8 Lighting design

This section sets out some of the main issues in designing energy efficient lighting systems in line with the principles at the front of this Guide. Energy issues related to lighting maintenance are considered in 8.1.2 and section 17. For further detail on lighting issues, reference should be made to the CIBSE *Code for interior lighting*[1] (referred to as the *Code*), DETR Fuel efficiency Booklet No 12[2], Thermie Maxibrochures: *Energy Efficient Lighting In Buildings*[3] and *Energy Efficient Lighting In Commercial Buildings*[4].

8.0 General

Energy efficient lighting should:

— maximise natural daylight

— avoid unnecessarily high illuminance

— incorporate the most efficient luminaires, control gear and lamps

— include effective lighting controls.

Lighting is often the single largest item of electrical consumption and cost in buildings. For example, lighting can account for over 40% of electricity costs in naturally ventilated offices. Good lighting design can reduce these running costs and can also reduce internal heat gains, thus affecting the need for air conditioning. Attention to fabric detail at the sketch design stage to ensure the integration of daylighting is particularly important in achieving this (see section 4 and 8.5).

8.1 Design objectives

An approach to good lighting design is shown in Figure 8.1; the process is covered in detail in the *Code*[1]. Designers should specify the adopted design criteria in order that clients may fully understand what they are likely to get from the system.

The energy efficiency actions to consider in achieving the design objectives are:

— Identify the visual tasks and locations where they will be performed and consider the type of lit environment that is required for the space (see 8.1.5).

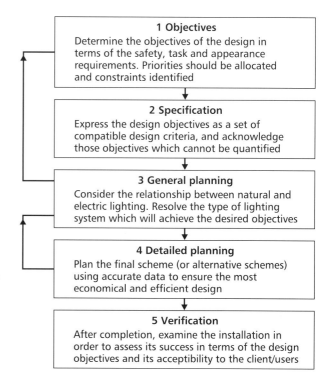

Figure 8.1 Lighting design flow diagram (adapted from CIBSE *Code for interior lighting*[1])

— Select the design maintained illuminance and limiting glare index required for the tasks, or interior, in accordance with the *Code*[1], noting any special requirements (see 8.1.1).

— Consider the amount of daylight that may be used to minimise running costs (see section 4).

— Select the preferred type of lighting system, i.e. general, localised or local (see 8.1.3 and Figure 8.2).

— Select the most appropriate controls to ensure that lighting is reduced or switched off when not required (see 8.5 and Figure 8.5).

— Select the most efficient lamp, ballast and luminaire that also meet the optical and control requirements (see 8.2, 8.3, 8.4, and Figures 8.3 and 8.4).

— Consider the most energy effective maintenance programme for adoption throughout the life of the installation (see 8.1.2).

— Calculate the installed power density per 100 lux and check that it comes within the recommended range (see Table 8.2 and 8.1.4).

8.1.1 Required lighting levels

The *Code*[1] provides an extensive list of illuminances for various areas and tasks. Using this, it is the responsibility of designers to determine the correct task illuminance for each project.

Design of the visual environment is more than simply illuminating the task. Room surface reflectance and the illuminance received on the walls and ceiling affect the efficiency of an installation, as well as the visual comfort and satisfaction of occupants (see 8.1.5). In general, the lighter and more reflective the finishes, the less light is required to achieve a given illuminance level. Figure 2.1 in the *Code*[1] provides recommended ranges of reflectance and illuminance ratios for general lighting in commercial interiors.

8.1.2 Design maintained illuminance

The *Code* gives recommendations in terms of design maintained illuminance. This is defined as 'the average illuminance over the reference surface at the time maintenance must be carried out by replacing lamps and/or cleaning the equipment and room surfaces'.

Table 8.1 provides some examples of standard maintained illuminance for various 'typical' tasks or interiors, a more detailed list is provided in the *Code*[1]. Identifying the task correctly is a key part of the design process and will help minimise installed load and running costs. The *Code* contains a flowchart which is intended to help designers to determine the correct design maintained illuminance if it differs from the value for the typical conditions assumed in the main lighting schedule. This is achieved by adjusting the standard value according to the size, contrast, duration and importance of the task.

Maintained illuminance takes into account luminaire, lamp and room surface depreciation due to soiling, as well as the loss of lamp light output over the lamp's life. The maintenance factor (the ratio of initial illuminance to the maintained illuminance) will be affected by:

— the choice of lamp: the lumen depreciation and mortality rate will determine the economic lamp life (see Table 8.3)

Table 8.1 Recommended maintained illuminance for various activities/interiors

Standard maintained illuminance (lux)	Representative activities/interiors
50	Cable tunnels, indoor storage tanks, walkways
100	Corridors, changing rooms, bulk stores, auditoria
150	Loading bays, medical stores, plant rooms
200	Foyers and entrances, monitoring automatic processes, casting concrete, turbine halls, dining rooms
300	Libraries, sports and assembly halls, teaching spaces, lecture theatres, packing
500	General offices, engine assembly, painting and spraying, kitchens, laboratories, retail shops
750	Drawing offices, ceramic decoration, meat inspection, chain stores
1000	General inspection, electronic assembly, gauge and tool rooms, retouching paintwork, cabinet making, supermarkets
1500	Fine work and inspection, hand tailoring, precision assembly
2000	Assembly of minute mechanisms, finished fabric inspection

— the choice of luminaire: the accumulation of dirt and dust will be dependent on the environment, the cleaning cycle and the design of the luminaire

— room surfaces: the frequency of cleaning will affect the reflected component of light.

Regular planned maintenance of a lighting installation can reduce the installed lighting load due to the higher maintenance factor for the design illuminance calculation. Avoid specifying long periods between maintenance since it can result in excessive depreciation which, in turn, can lead to higher connected loads and higher initial illuminance than can be justified. For this reason, half steps in the design maintained illuminance flow chart have been introduced into the *Code*. The use of these half steps is covered in the explanatory notes on the flow chart and in the section dealing with the calculation of the maintenance factor[1].

Once the design solution has been established, it should be checked against the installed power density (per 100 lux) targets for maintained illuminance. This is to ensure that the maintenance regime has not resulted in over-design by keeping the installation within the target ranges; examples are shown in Table 8.2.

More recent benchmarks for office lighting[5] indicate that a lighting load of less than 12 W/m^2 of treated floor area can be regarded as good practice, based on a level of 350–400 lux at an efficiency of 3 W/m^2 per 100 lux. For 500 lux, or an uplighting installation of 300–350 lux, 15 W/m^2 of treated floor area may be required.

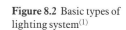

Figure 8.2 Basic types of lighting system[1]

A general lighting system employs a regular array of luminaires to provide a uniform illuminance across the working plane.

A localised lighting system uses luminaires located adjacent to the work stations to provide the required task illuminance. The necessary ambient illuminance in the surrounding areas is provided by additional luminaires if required.

A local lighting system employs a general lighting scheme to provide the ambient illuminance for the main area with additional luminaires, located at the workstations, to provide the necessary task illuminance.

8.1.3 Types of lighting system

There are three types of electric lighting system as shown in Figure 8.2, and these are distinguished by the balance between task and building, or ambient, illuminance.

Local or localised task lighting schemes normally consume less energy than general lighting systems, but care must be taken to co-ordinate the lighting layout with task positions and orientation. On the other hand, control systems that integrate daylight with ceiling mounted general lighting (see 8.5) can achieve lower energy consumption.

With both local and localised systems, the average illuminance over non-task and circulation areas should not be less than one third of the illuminance over the task areas.

The problem of variation of illuminance over the working plane is covered by two measures:

— Uniformity: the ratio of the minimum illuminance to the average illuminance over the specified task areas (i.e. the task and the immediate surround) for a local or localised lighting system or the core area[1] of the working plane for a general lighting installation. This should not be less than 0.8.

— Diversity: the ratio of the minimum to the maximum illuminance over the core area of the working plane of a room when task lighting is used. This should not be less than 0.2. In this case, of course, a uniformity of 0.8 must be achieved over the specified task areas.

8.1.4 Installed lighting loads

Table 8.2 is taken from Table 2.2 of the *Code* and shows the ranges of installed power density per 100 lux, for a room index of 2.5 and light source type[1]. These apply to general lighting installations using a regular array of luminaires.

A range of installed power density per 100 lux, rather than a single value, is necessary because the maintained illuminance will range from 150 to 750 lux depending upon the application. This will affect the choice of lamp wattage which, in turn, affects the circuit luminous efficacy, see Figures 8.3 and 8.4. The influence of different lamp types on the installed power density can be seen from the different ranges in Table 8.4. The most efficient equipment should be used, compatible with the lighting design criteria for the space.

8.1.5 Visual comfort and satisfaction

If visual performance is impaired by poor lighting, poor controls or glare[6], the system is not effective. In these circumstances, low energy consumption is being achieved at the cost of reduced staff productivity. The lighting designer should, therefore, find a balance between energy efficiency and a sufficient quantity and quality of

Table 8.2 Target ranges of installed power density (per 100 lux) for general lighting

Application area and lamp type	Power density range (W/m² per 100 lux) for a room index (K) of 2.5
High bay industrial (reflectance C/W/F = 0.5/0.5/0.2 to 0.3/0.3/0.1):	
— metal halide, clear or coated	2.1 – 3.6
— high pressure mercury, coated	3.5 – 5.1
— high pressure sodium, improved colour	2.0 – 2.9
— high pressure sodium, standard colour	1.2 – 2.2
Industrial (reflectance C/W/F = 0.7/0.5/0.2 to 0.3/0.5/0.2):	
— fluorescent, triphosphor	1.9 - 3.5
— fluorescent, halophosphate	2.4 – 4.5
— metal halide, clear or coated	2.3 – 4.4
— high pressure mercury, coated	3.7 – 6.1
— high pressure sodium, improved colour	2.1 – 3.5
— high pressure sodium, standard colour	1.3 – 3.0
Commercial (reflectance C/W/F = 0.7/0.5/0.2 to 0.5/0.5/0.2):	
— fluorescent, triphosphor	2.2 – 4.2
— fluorescent, halophosphate	2.8 – 5.4
— fluorescent, compact	2.8 – 4.9
— metal halide, clear or coated	3.6 – 5.7
— high pressure mercury, coated	5.4 – 7.9
— high pressure sodium, improved colour	3.1 – 4.6
— high pressure sodium, standard colour	2.0 – 3.9

Note: C/W/F: ceiling/wall/floor reflectance

illumination to perform the visual task efficiently without experiencing discomfort or disability glare. Discomfort glare is avoided by meeting the recommended limiting glare index for the interior[1]. Disability glare is most commonly caused by the veiling reflections of windows and luminaires on visual display screens.

The *Health and Safety Regulations*[7] require that any possible disturbing glare on display screens should be prevented by co-ordinating the work space location and the electric lighting design. While calling for lighting of workspaces to be naturally lit where reasonably practicable, windows should be fitted with adjustable coverings to attenuate the daylight that falls on the workstation. CIBSE has produced guidance[8] on recent health and safety legislation which focuses on the implications for building services design and operation. CIBSE Lighting Guide LG3[9], provides further guidance on this subject.

Visual satisfaction has to do with 'pleasantness' of the visual environment. Whether the interior is lit by daylight or electric lighting, the observed brightness patterns should not be too bland or have excessive contrasts. This is covered by the recommended values of illuminance ratios, surface reflectance, limiting glare index, etc. Giving users some control of their luminous environment can also contribute to their satisfaction.

8.2   Selecting luminaires

A luminaire comprises a housing, a reflector, a lamp and shielding (either louvres, or a lens or diffusing material) and, for discharge lamps, some form of control gear. The photometric efficiency is measured in terms of its light output ratio. This is the ratio of the total light output of the luminaire to that of the lamp(s) under reference conditions.

The higher the light output ratio, for a given light distribution, the more efficient the luminaire. The distribution and other characteristics of over 70 generic types of luminaire are described in 3.3.2 of the *Code*[1].

Designers must select equipment by comparing manufacturers' published photometric data. If it is found that recommended power density targets are not met, it is probable that an inefficient luminaire has been selected.

The maintenance characteristic of a luminaire is an important consideration in arriving at the maintenance factor in the design calculation. This means that well sealed or ventilated self-cleaning designs will contribute more to lower installed loads than other luminaires with poorer maintenance characteristics.

8.3   Selecting light sources

Lamp and circuit selection is a crucial part of energy efficient design[10–12]. Information on lamp efficacies, lumen output and wattage range is given in Figures 8.3 and 8.4, while Table 8.3 provides a summary of other performance and operational characteristics of the major groups of lamp types. These data are for comparison purposes only and should not be used for lighting design. Lamp manufacturers should be consulted for information on specific lamps.

The factors involved in lamp selection are:

—   luminous efficacy (lumen output/watts input)

—   rating (consumption watts)

—   mortality (rated life of the lamp)

—   lumen maintenance (lumen depreciation over life)

Table 8.3 Characteristics of principal lamp types

Lamp type	Colour temperature (K)	Colour rendering group†	Average life to 50% survival‡ (hours × 10³)	Hours to 70% lumen maintenance‡ (hours × 10³)	Control gear/ability to dim	Start/re-start time (minutes)
Filament:						
— GLS and reflector	2700 (approx.)	1A	1	—	No/Yes	Prompt/prompt
— tungsten halogen (mains voltage)	3000 (approx.)	1A	2	—	No/Yes	Prompt/prompt
— tungsten halogen (low voltage)	3000 (approx.)	1A	4	—	Transformer/Yes, with suitable equipment	Prompt/prompt
Fluorescent:						
— linear MCF	2700–6500	1A–3	6–12 (26 mm diam., multi-triphosphor)	15–30 (26 mm-diam., multi triphosphor)	Yes/Yes, with suitable circuit	Prompt/prompt
			5–15 (HF operation)	15–30 (HF operation)		
			5–10 (38 mm diam., halophosphate)	12–24 (halophosphate)		
				10–24 (38mm diam., halophosphate)		
— compact	2700–6500	1B	8-10	10–14 (dependent on wattage)	Yes/Yes with suitable circuit above 13W	Prompt/prompt
— induction QL	3000–4000	1B	60 (to 80% survival)	60	Yes/No	Prompt/prompt
— low pressure sodium (SOX, SOX-E)	—	—	11.5–23	15–30	Yes/No (not for full range dimming	8–15/10 (re-start prompt up to 55W)
— high pressure sodium (HPS, HPS-DL, W-HPS)	2000–3000	1B–4	15–30 (Plus)	16.5–31 (Plus)	Yes/No (not for full range dimming	1.5–6/>1 (3 for 1000 W)
			14–28 (Deluxe) 6 ('White')	14–28 (Deluxe) 6 ('White' for >90%)		
			Dependent on colour quality			
— high pressure mercury (HPMV)	3300–4000	3	14–28 (fluorescent)	14–28 (fluorescent)	Yes/No (not for full range dimming)	2–5/4–7
			6–12 (blended)	6.5–13 (blended)		
— metal halide (MBI-F, MBT-F)	3000–6000	1A–2	5.6–13 (fluorescent)	6–12 (fluorescent)	Yes/No (not for full range dimming)	1–2/5–15
			6.5–13 (clear tubular)	6.5–13 (clear tubular)		

† The 5 colour rendering groups are: 1A and 1B — 'Good', 2 — 'Moderate', 3 — 'of little significance' and 4 — 'of no importance'.

‡The range of values represents measurements in controlled test conditions, e.g. voltage, ambient temperature, switching cycle and circuit parameters. Practical values would tend to be in the lower limits of the ranges.

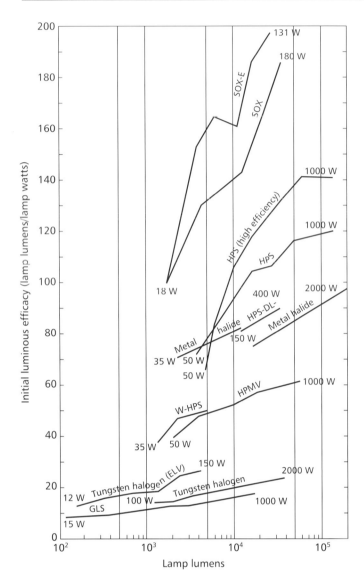

Figure 8.3 Initial luminous efficacies of various types of lamp[1]

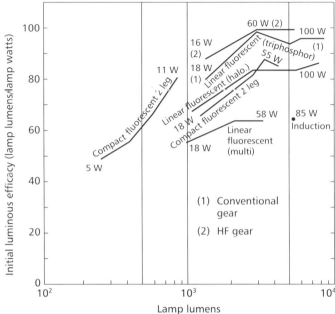

Figure 8.4 Initial luminous efficacies of fluorescent lamps[1]

above 10,000 lm tend to be used for heavy industrial and exterior lighting.

Where controllability is important, lamps that can be switched on and off or dimmed easily should be chosen[11]. Fluorescent lamps are the most energy efficient available that meet these criteria. Sodium and mercury discharge lamps have longer run-up and re-strike up times and are generally inappropriate for use with automatic controls, other than simple time controls for the beginning and end of the working day.

8.3.1   Minimum efficacy of lamps

Building Regulations[13,14] require that at least 95% of the installed lighting capacity in circuit Watts, excluding display lighting and emergency escape lighting, should be lamps of the types listed in Table 8.4.

The requirements of *Building Regulations*[13,14] can also be met if the installed lighting capacity comprises lamps with an average initial efficacy of not less than 50 lumens per circuit watt. This is a minimum statutory requirement. Modern design practice[1] suggests that, for most commercial office installations, a target of 65 lm/W should be achieved.

8.3.2   Tungsten filament lamps

Where it is essential to use tungsten lamps for reasons of colour rendering or light control, e.g. lighting for display and special effects, low voltage tungsten halogen sources should be used in preference to the equivalent mains voltage general lighting service (GLS) or PAR reflector lamps since the former have the highest efficacy and longest life for lamps of this type. The advantages and disadvantages of the two types of tungsten lamp are shown in Tables 8.5 and 8.6. Where possible, GLS and tungsten-halogen lamps should be replaced with compact fluorescent lamps[15] (see also 8.3.4).

—   operating position (in some cases this may affect efficacy)

—   size (physical properties can affect optical efficiency of light control)

—   control gear type and controllability (switching or dimming)

—   colour appearance (appearance of the source in terms of 'warm' or 'cool')

—   colour rendering

—   starting, run-up and re-start times

—   minimum starting temperatures.

Within the overall design requirement, lamps with the highest efficacy, and circuits with the lowest losses, should be selected to minimise installed load and running costs.

Figures 8.3 and 8.4[1] show the relationship between initial lamp luminous efficacy (excluding gear losses) and the lamp–lumen 'package' for each lamp type. For clarity, fluorescent lamps are shown separately in Figure 8.4. The most commonly used lumen package range is from 2000 to 10,000 lm. Lamps below 2000 lm tend to be used for domestic, display and local lighting applications. Lamps

Table 8.4 High efficacy light sources, required by the *Building Regulations*

Light source	Type/ratings
High pressure sodium	All types/ratings
Metal halide	All types/ratings
Induction lighting	All types/ratings
Tubular fluorescent	All 25 mm diameter (T8) lamps provided with low-loss or high frequency control gear
Compact fluorescent	All ratings above 11 W

Table 8.5 Advantages and disadvantages of tungsten filament (GLS) lamps

Advantages	Disadvantages
Low purchase price	Low efficacy, i.e. 8 to 15 lm/W
Excellent colour rendering	Short life, usually 1000 hours
Immediate full light when switched on	High running costs
No ballast required	
Ease of dimming	
Sparkle lighting effects can be created	
Operates in any plane (universal operating position)	

Table 8.6 Advantages and disadvantages of tungsten halogen lamps

Advantages	Disadvantages
Higher efficacy than conventional tungsten filament lamps	Transformer required for low voltage lamps
Life of 2000 to 5000 hours depending on type	Operating positions of double ended types is limited to horizontal
Excellent colour rendering	Requires careful handling
Brighter, whiter light	
No ballast required	
Sparkle lighting effects can be created	
Can be dimmed	
Immediate full light output when switched on	

Table 8.7 Advantages and disadvantages of tubular fluorescent lamps

Advantages	Disadvantages
Low running cost	Excessive switching shortens life
High efficacy	Requires ballast
Up to 8% energy saving when replacing equivalent 38 mm lamps on switch-start circuits	Can be dimmed but requires special ballast and dimmer
Long life in normal use	
Minimal reduction of light output through life	
Prompt start and re-start with quick run-up to full light output	
Very good to excellent colour rendering	
Universal operating position	

8.3.3 Tubular fluorescent lamps

Fluorescent lamps have high efficacy, long life, good controllability and relatively low cost. The older argon-filled 38 mm diameter lamps are largely superseded and should only be used for replacements in starter-less circuits. The modern range of krypton-filled, 26 mm diameter, triphosphor lamps are the preferred choice for switch-start circuits, suitable electronic start circuits, and electronic high frequency ballasts. Fluorescent lamps are available in the full range of colour appearance giving colour rendering from 'good' to 'moderate'.

Because of their characteristics, fluorescent lamps are used for the majority of commercial lighting applications. Where appropriate, heat recovery should be considered by extracting air through the luminaires. This can improve the light output by maintaining the lamp at its optimum operating temperature (see section 6). The advantages and disadvantages of tubular fluorescent lamps are shown in Table 8.7.

8.3.4 Compact fluorescent lamps

Compact fluorescent lamps (CFLs) are available in various configurations, some types having integral control gear, others with a separate ballast.

CFLs provide the equivalent light output of GLS filament lamps for about 20–25% of the power. So that the lamp size and weight (of those with integral gear) can be kept to a minimum, some of these lamps operate at a low power factor. However, a wide range of luminaires designed specifically for compact fluorescent lamps is available and the extra available space usually allows the incorporation of power factor correction in these luminaires.

Before retrofitting[15] CFLs in existing GLS luminaires, it is necessary to ensure that the light distribution and light output ratio is not adversely affected and that the operating position and temperature of the lamp do not significantly reduce its efficacy.

CFLs were originally developed as energy efficient replacements for filament lamps with ratings up to about 20 W. However, the same lamp technology has been applied to higher wattages (up to 40 W) giving light outputs equivalent to some linear fluorescent lamps. The shorter twin-leg construction means that these can be housed in more compact luminaires for general and localised lighting. The advantages and disadvantages of compact fluorescent lamps are shown in Table 8.8.

8.3.5 Mercury and sodium discharge lamps

High pressure sodium (SON) and metal halide (MBI) lamps offer greater efficacies than high pressure mercury lamps (MBF). The colour rendering properties of the SON range, particularly the SON-DL lamp has increased the range of applications from industrial use to some commercial applications. The efficacy of the MBI lamp is lower than the SON lamp but comparable to that of the SON-DL lamp, with a cooler colour appearance and better colour rendering properties.

Table 8.8 Advantages and disadvantages of compact fluorescent lamps (CFLS)

Advantages	Disadvantages
Low running cost	Excessive switching shortens life
Replacement for tungsten lamps	Ballast required (but built-in on some lamps)
Five times the efficacy of equivalent tungsten lamps	Not suitable for use on standard domestic dimmer
Average life of 8000 to 10 000 hours	
Very good colour rendering	
Prompt start and re-start and quick run up to full light output	
Four pin lamps can be dimmed with suitable ballast and dimmer	
Universal operating position but light output may be reduced with some types for certain positions	

Table 8.9 Advantages and disadvantages of SON lamps

Advantages	Disadvantages
Low running cost	High purchase cost
High efficacy	Does not provide high-fidelity colour rendering
Very long life	
Universal operating position	Requires ballast
	Requires 1.5 to 6 minutes to reach full output
	Delayed restart when hot on most lamps

The increasing popularity of free-standing and wall-mounted uplighters means that these high pressure lamps are now being used in office installations, although it is advisable to check the colour rendering characteristics before fitting an entire installation. Metal halide and high pressure sodium lamps operated on standard control gear have significant run-up and re-strike times, limiting their use with lighting control systems.

The advantages and disadvantages of SON lamps are shown in Table 8.9.

8.4   Control gear (ballasts)

All discharge lamps require a ballast to start and control the lamp and, possibly, power factor correction. Matching the control gear to the lamp achieves the optimum lamp performance and circuit efficacy. Until recently, ballasts consisted of a wire-wound choke with losses representing 10–20% of the total load. Low-loss wire wound ballasts are now available which are specifically designed to be more energy efficient.

High-frequency (around 30 kHz) electronic ballasts are now available for a wide range of linear and compact fluorescent lamps[16]. These can reduce losses by more than 50% and, as the efficacy of a fluorescent tube increases at high frequency, this provides further energy savings. Additional advantages are virtually instantaneous starting, the possibility of dimming, flicker-free lighting, softer starting conditions that increase lamp life and a power factor of 0.95.

Electronic ballasts for the 70 W and 150 W (MBI) metal halide lamps are now available. These provide faster warm-up periods, instant re-strike, improved circuit efficacy and extended lamp life, but are more expensive than wire wound ballasts.

8.5   Lighting controls

Effective control of electric lighting is the key to realising the potential energy saving from daylight. The control system for the electric lighting should reduce light output when daylighting levels are adequate, and when the space is unoccupied.

Lighting controls should ensure that light is provided in the right amount, in the right place for the required time[17–20]. Figure 8.5 provides guidance on the selection and application of lighting control.

There are many factors influencing the specification of lighting controls, including:

— occupancy pattern

— available daylight

— type of lighting (i.e. can it be dimmed?)

— the desired level of control sophistication

— capital costs and the potential for saving.

Even with efficient lamps and luminaires, the energy used for lighting can be wasted in various ways[17]. For example, users cannot be relied upon to turn lighting off when they leave an area, or when daylighting has increased. Exhortation can be helpful in the short term, but the ideal solution is to provide manual 'on' switching and some form of automatic 'off' switching. Energy is also wasted where a large area of lighting is controlled by a small numbers of switches, or where the switches are not located in convenient positions.

The choice of the number of control zones is a balance between cost and energy saving. The more zones of electric lighting, the better the match between lighting and demand. Zones should start at the perimeter and work away from the windows, corresponding to the reduction in daylight factor (see section 4). It is generally cost-effective to have zones from 1.5–3.0 m deep since this coincides with the minimum module for one person.

The five basic methods of lighting control that can be used separately or in combination are:

— localised manual switching

— time control

— reset control

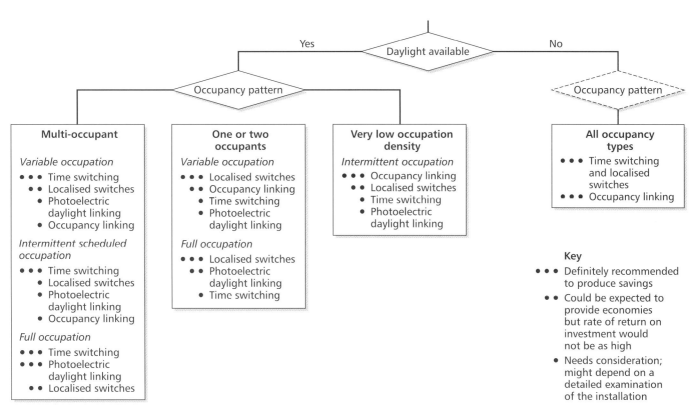

Figure 8.5 Decision chart for the selection of a lighting control strategy[3] (reproduced from Thermie Maxibrochure *Energy efficient lighting in buildings*. Crown copyright (1993))

— occupancy control

— photoelectric and dimming.

8.5.1 Requirements of *Building Regulations*

The 1995 *Building Regulations*[13,14] require the following:

— Where practicable, the aim of lighting controls should be to encourage the maximum use of daylight and to avoid unnecessary lighting during times when spaces are unoccupied.

— Local switches should be provided in easily accessible positions within each working area or at boundaries between working areas and general circulation routes. Local switches could include:

    (*a*) switches that are operated by the deliberate action of the occupants either manually or by remote control (manual switches include rocker switches, press buttons and pull-cords; remote control switches include infra-red, acoustic or ultra-sonic transmitters and telephone handset controllers)

    (*b*) automatic switching systems, including controls which switch the lighting off when they sense the absence of occupants.

One means of satisfying these requirements is to provide local switching, as shown in Figure 8.6. The distance from any switch to the furthest luminaire it controls is generally not more than eight metres or three times the height above floor level of the light fitting if this is greater.

8.5.2 Localised manual controls

Switching arrangements should permit individual rows of luminaires parallel to window walls to be controlled separately. Switches should be as near as possible to the luminaires that they control. One simple method that has been used effectively is a pull cord switch adjacent to each luminaire.

Localised switching is important where the electric lighting only needs to be on in part of a large space, either because the other parts are unoccupied or because daylight is adequate. Controls that allow for these variances can produce significant energy savings compared with single switch lighting. In general, the area controlled by a particular switch should have a similar daylight level in all parts, related to the occupancy pattern. For example, in an office where individual occupants may be absent, it should cover the space of a single occupant or small working group; in a factory, it could be related to a particular production line or process.

8.5.3 Time switch controls

If the occupation of a building ceases at a fixed time each working day, it may be worth installing a time switch for the lighting, although arrangements will need to be made

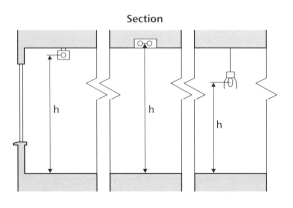

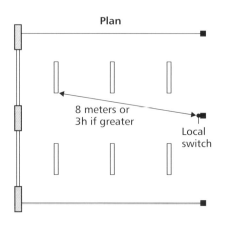

Figure 8.6 Location of local switch controls as required by the *Building Regulations*[13] (Crown copyright; reproduced from Building Regulations *Approved Document L* with the permission of the Controller of Her Majesty's Stationery Office)

for security lighting. Individuals working late should be able to override the controls in their zone (see 8.5.4), and an extension timer should be used to avoid lights being left on. The building cleaning routine may also need special arrangements. Sequential control of lighting may be appropriate when a cleaning gang moves from floor to floor. However, arrangements must be made to ensure that no one has to enter an unlit space, or be in a space where all lighting is out of their control.

The introduction of time controls and/or photoelectric controls is particularly important in external lighting to minimise energy consumption. Simple time switches are highly cost-effective but only allow fixed 'on' and 'off' times. Photoelectric controls can ensure that external lighting is only on when it is dark.

8.5.4   Reset controls

Time control systems that automatically switch the whole lighting installation off at predetermined times are available. Occupants are provided with local switches, often pull cords, to 'reset' lights on if they are still required. Reset control is particularly applicable in open plan spaces where energy savings of 20–30% are possible. Maximum savings can be achieved through the careful selection of switching times. Post-cleaning, lunchtime and soon after the working day has ended are particularly advantageous times. Signals are transmitted to luminaires through mains wiring or through a dedicated low voltage wiring bus connected to receivers in each luminaire. The use of remote switching (e.g. by infra-red transmitters) to fulfil the localised override facility is also possible.

8.5.5   Occupancy controls

Occupancy detectors use infra-red, acoustic, ultrasonic or microwave sensors, to detect either movement or noise in the space. These usually switch the lighting on when occupancy is detected and off again once they have failed to detect occupancy for a set time. A time delay built into the system can help avoid excessive switching which reduces lamp life. In some cases, occupancy controls can allow manual switches to be dispensed with, thus reducing capital costs.

Lighting linked to occupancy can show considerable savings in energy usage particularly in intermittently occupied spaces. For example, lighting in warehouse aisles

can be switched in response to a detector which senses the approach of a fork-lift truck. This form of control can be applied to a wide range of lamp types as long as the run-up and re-strike characteristics are taken into account.

8.5.6   Photoelectric and dimming controls

Photoelectric daylight linking can take two forms, either simple on/off switching, or dimming. An externally mounted photocell provides very coarse control and should be applied only to the rows of luminaires closest to the windows. Photocells mounted inside the space measure the actual daylight penetration by monitoring the illumination under the first (and possibly the second) row of luminaires from the window walls. In both cases, it is important to incorporate time delays into the control system to avoid repeated rapid switching caused, for example, by fast moving clouds.

Photoelectric switching can cause sudden and noticeable changes in lighting level and can lead to occupant complaints. It is, therefore, suited to well-daylit areas and those areas where the switching frequency will be low. In order to reduce this effect, the illuminance at which the switching occurs should not be too low. Switch-off should occur when the total illuminance is around 3 to 4 times the required task illuminance and switch-on when the daylight illuminance is around 2 to 3 times the required task illuminance.

To achieve energy savings from daylighting, it is essential to integrate the control of daylight with the control of electric lighting. For example, an automatic, external, blind control system should be linked to an internal dimming lighting control system. In addition, consideration should be given to occupant override of either the blind or electric lighting control, using 'user-friendly' controls.

Tungsten lamps and most standard tubular and compact fluorescent lamps above 13 W, with suitable control gear, can be dimmed. Unlike photoelectric switching, photo-electric dimming control is relatively unobtrusive. The control system ensures that the sum of daylight and electric lighting always reaches the design level by sensing the total light in the controlled area and adjusting the output of the electric light to top-up the daylight as necessary. The energy saving potential of dimming control is greater than that of photoelectric switching. The mode of control is also more likely to be acceptable to the occupants, although initial cost is greater.

Photoelectrically controlled dimming, particularly with high frequency fluorescent electronic ballasts, can also be used to maintain the design illuminance at a constant level throughout the life of the installation. When the lamps are new and the installation is clean, the luminaires are operated at low power and this is increased automatically as lamp lumen and luminaire depreciation occurs. This can be a very effective means of saving energy as it applies to all luminaires, whereas daylight linking only achieves energy savings for the luminaires close to the windows.

High pressure discharge lamps are not generally dimmable, although there are some power saving circuits which permit the lamp to be run at reduced power and lumen output. Generally, this only applies to mercury vapour, sodium and the lower power types of metal halide lamp. Dimming is suitable for areas where light is required for security reasons or where there is infrequent occupancy. The reductions in power and light output do not have a linear relationship and lamp colour may change.

8.5.7 Lighting management systems (LMS)

LMSs can integrate the control strategies mentioned above and provide many of the advantages of building management systems (BMSs) (see section 5) by including centralised control, monitoring and alarms. LMSs can control individual luminaires, groups of luminaires or lighting zones. Space layout alterations can be made and the lighting adjusted through a computer to suit the new layout, avoiding the need for the expensive relocation of luminaires and alterations to switching arrangements. Modern LMSs also provide monitoring capabilities so that lamp performance and hours run can be logged allowing better maintenance regimes to be undertaken.

It is possible to interface a BMS and an LMS in order to provide certain control commands from the BMS to the lighting. Most BMS can carry out the function of the LMS although this is generally a more expensive approach. It is not generally cost-effective to use the BMS to provide discrete localised lighting control to individual luminaires, but rather to achieve load shedding or zone switching.

8.5.8 Selection of controls

The cost of a control system installation should be compared with the cost of a traditional hard-wire installation, and the difference related to the projected energy savings. Any control system must ensure that acceptable lighting conditions are always provided with safety, visual effectiveness and comfort taking priority over energy saving.

Automatic controls need to be selected carefully since perceived changes in lighting levels can prove distracting and an irritation to occupants. Control systems that are obtrusive are counter-productive and may even be sabotaged by the staff. Problems of this kind can often be minimised by making staff aware of the purpose behind the

control system, how it works and how they can interact with it (see section 5).

Experience in use can improve the operation of lighting control systems by gradually fine tuning settings to meet the needs of the occupants. Only the occupants can determine the absolute level at which switching should occur to suit their needs. This requires a responsive management approach to the control system.

References

1   *CIBSE Code for interior lighting* (London: Chartered Institution of Building Services Engineers) (1994)

2   *Energy management and good lighting practice* FEB 12 (London: Department of Environment, Transport and Regions) (1993))

3   *Energy efficient lighting in buildings* Thermie Maxibrochure (Building Research Energy Conservation Support Unit/OPET) (1993)

4   *Energy efficient lighting in commercial buildings* CADDET Analyses Series: 6 (Sittard: Centre for the Analysis and Dissemination of Demonstrated Energy Technologies) (1990)

5   *Energy efficiency in offices — a technical guide for owners and single tenants* ECON 19 (London: Department of Environment, Transport and Regions) (1997)

6   *Daylighting requirements for display/screen equipment* IP14/93 (Garston: Building Research Establishment) (1993)

7   *The Health and Safety (Display Screen Equipment) Regulations* 1992 (London: Stationery Office) (1992)

8   *Healthy workplaces* CIBSE Guidance Note GN2 (London: Chartered Institution of Building Services Engineers) (1993)

9   *The visual environment for display screen use* CIBSE Lighting Guide LG3 (London: Chartered Institution of Building Services Engineers) (1996)

10 *Energy efficient lighting — a guide for installers* GPG 199 (London: Department of Environment, Transport and Regions) (1996)

11 *Lamp guide* (London: Lighting Industry Federation) (1994)

12 *Energy efficiency in hotels. A guide to cost-effective lighting* GPG 189 (London: Department of Environment, Transport and Regions) (1996)

13 *The Building Regulations Part L: Conservation of fuel and power* (London: Stationery Office) (1995)

14 *Lighting requirements of Building Regulations Part L* CIBSE Guidance Note GN4 (London: Chartered Institution of Building Services Engineers) (1996)

15 *Converting to compact fluorescent lighting — a refurbishment guide* GPG 159 (London: Department of Environment, Transport and Regions) (1995)

16 *High frequency luminaires: Specification, construction, installation* Technical Statement No 21 (London: Lighting Industry Federation) (1997)

17 *People and lighting controls* IP6/96 (Garston: Building Research Establishment) (1996)

18 *Lighting controls and daylight use* Digest 272 (Garston: Building Research Establishment)

19　　　*Electric lighting controls — a guide for designers, installers and users* GPG 160 (London: Department of Environment, Transport and Regions) (1997)

20　　　*Lighting controls: an essential element of energy-efficient lighting* IP5/87 (Garston: Building Research Establishment) (1987)

Bibliography

Baker N V and Steemers K *The LT Method 2.0. An energy design tool for non-domestic buildings* (Cambridge: Cambridge Architectural Research/Building Research Energy Conservation Support Unit) (1994)

Baker N V *Energy and environment in non-domestic buildings. A technical design guide* (Cambridge: Cambridge Architectural Research/Building Research Energy Conservation Support Unit) (1995)

Slater A I Occupant use of lighting controls: a review of current practice, problems and how to avoid them *CIBSE National Conference 1995* (London: Chartered Institution of Building Services Engineers) (1995)

Rohde M F Concerted Light — day and artificial light as interaction with architecture *CIBSE National Conference 1995* (London: Chartered Institution of Building Services Engineers) (1995)

Loe D Interior lighting quality and the potential for energy saving *CIBSE National Conference 1995* (London: Chartered Institution of Building Services Engineers) (1995)

Embrechts R Energy savings and lighting: making room for individuality *CIBSE National Conference 1995* (London: Chartered Institution of Building Services Engineers) (1995)

Environmental comfort and productivity LB 79/94 (Bracknell: Building Services Research and Information Association) (1994)

Jackman P J *Specification of indoor environmental performance of buildings* TN 3/87 (Bracknell: Building Services Research and Information Association) (1987)

Lighting for offices CIBSE Lighting Guide LG7 (London: Chartered Institution of Building Services Engineers) (1993)

Office lighting for good visual task conditions Digest 256 (Garston: Building Research Establishment)

A new method for predicting energy saving from on/off photoelectric controls IP14/84 (Garston: Building Research Establishment) (1984)

Daylighting requirements for display-screen equipment IP14/93 (Garston: Building Research Establishment) (1993)

New ways of predicting discomfort glare IP24/93 (Garston: Building Research Establishment) (1993)

Managing and motivating staff to save energy GPG 84 (London: Department of Environment, Transport and Regions) (1993)

Energy management training GPG 85 (London: Department of Environment, Transport and Regions) (1993)

Littlefair P J Innovative daylighting: review of systems and evaluation methods *Lighting Research and Technology* 22(1) 1990

Hunt D R G Predicting lighting use — a method based upon observed patterns of behaviour *Lighting Research and Technology* 12(1)(1980)

Lynes J A and Littlefair P J Lighting energy savings from daylight estimation at the sketch design stage. *Lighting Research and Technology* 22(3) 1990

9 Heating and hot water design

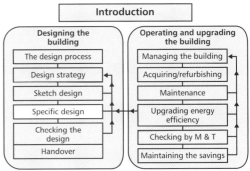

9.0 General

9.1 Primary plant

9.2 Distribution systems

9.3 Controls

This section sets out key issues in designing energy efficient heating and hot water systems, in line with the principles at the front of this Guide. In most buildings, heating and hot water account for the largest annual consumption of delivered energy and hence CO_2 emissions from heating systems are often high. For each unit of delivered energy, the most common fuels used for heating, such as gas and oil, produce lower emissions to the atmosphere than electricity. Attention to fabric detail at the sketch design stage to minimise the requirement for space heating is particularly important in reducing energy consumption (see section 4). Efforts should also be made to minimise hot water demand by incorporating low-flow alternatives such as showers and spray taps. Energy issues related to heating maintenance are covered in section 17. For further detail on heating issues, reference should be made to CIBSE Guide B[1], DETR Fuel Efficiency Booklet Nos. 3[2], 7[3], 14[4], 15[5] and 17[6], DETR General Information Reports 40[7] and 41[8].

9.0 General

Energy efficient heating should:

— incorporate the most efficient primary plant to generate heat/hot water

— ensure that heat/hot water is distributed effectively and efficiently

— include effective controls on primary plant and distribution systems to ensure that heat/hot water is only provided when and where it is needed and at the correct temperature

— be responsive to changes in climate, solar gains, occupancy, activity and internal gains.

9.1 Primary plant

The mix of primary plant can have a major influence on overall system efficiency, e.g. CHP with condensing boilers. In particular designers should:

— select fuels and tariffs that promote efficiency and minimise running costs

— segregate hot water services generation wherever possible

— consider de-centralised heating and hot water services generation plant on large sites to reduce standing losses and improve load matching

— locate plant to minimise distribution system and losses

— insulate pipework, valves etc. effectively

— provide appropriate margins but avoid oversizing

— ensure that the base load is provided by the most efficient plant.

9.1.1 Boilers

9.1.1.1 Boiler efficiency

By definition, the outside design condition is only exceeded on a certain percentage of days so that heating plant will operate for much of the time at less than full load. Designers should therefore consider boiler efficiency across the whole range of likely loads, not just at the design condition.

Quoted instantaneous boiler efficiencies are not generally representative of practical situations in buildings. Seasonal (or annual) efficiencies, as shown in Table 9.1[9], provide a measure of true operation, averaged over a season or a year, based on the total useful heat output versus the total energy input over the period in question. This takes into account the low efficiency of some boilers at part load (see Figure 9.1[9]). In practice, seasonal efficiency is not easy to measure but can be estimated using methods shown in CIBSE Applications Manual AM3[9].

Table 9.1 Typical seasonal efficiencies

System	Seasonal efficiency (%)
Condensing boilers:	
— underfloor or warm water system	90
— standard size radiators, variable temperature circuit (weather compensation)	87
— standard fixed temperature emitters (83/72°C flow/return)†	85
Non-condensing boilers:	
— modern high efficiency non-condensing boilers	80 82
— good modern boiler design closely matched to demand	75
— typical good existing boiler	70
— typical existing oversized boiler, (atmospheric cast-iron sectional)	45–65

† Not permitted by current *Building Regulations*

High efficiency boilers

High efficiency boilers have now become the minimum standard for new and replacement installations after 1997[10] having some or all of the following characteristics:

— Low water content and/or low thermal mass.

— Improved heat exchangers and insulation.

— A packaged modular arrangement.

— They are more efficient, offering a 10% improvement in efficiency in comparison with traditional boilers across the range of loads.

— They are sometimes more expensive than traditional boilers, typically 10–20%.

— Higher part load efficiencies make them particularly suitable for applications with a wide range of loads.

Monitored annual fuel consumption often shows a 5–10% saving, with much of the saving realised by the 'lead' boiler. Multiple or modular arrangements require good sequence control (see 9.3.2).

Condensing boilers

Condensing boilers are generally gas fired, although oil fired versions are available. Condensing boilers:

— use an additional heat exchanger to extract extra heat by condensing water vapour from the products of combustion

— operate at a minimum efficiency of around 85%, even when not condensing

— can achieve efficiencies in the range 85–95% and efficiency can sometimes be higher at part load than at full load (see Figure 9.1)

— are more expensive than traditional boilers, typically by 30–50%

— should normally be the first choice, at least for 'lead' gas boilers

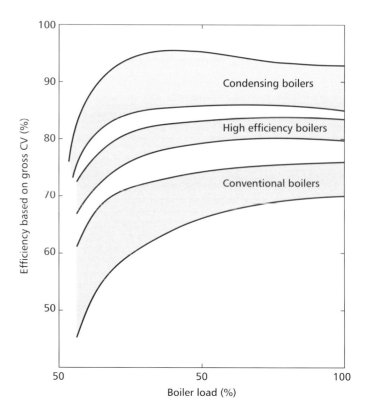

Figure 9.1 Typical seasonal LTHW boiler efficiencies at part load[9]

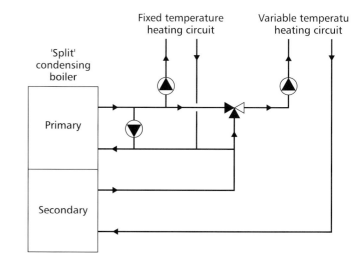

Figure 9.2 Typical condensing boiler circuit (adapted from DETR Good Practice Guide 16[11]. Crown copyright (1990))

— provide energy savings of 10–20% with paybacks of 2–5 years[11,12].

Lower return water temperatures lead to more condensation, resulting in higher efficiencies. There are a number of hydraulic arrangements and controls that can promote these lower temperatures[7,9], weather compensation being the most common and conventional method, as shown in Figure 9.2.

The operation of a condensing boiler with weather compensation is shown in Figure 9.3. The boiler moves into the condensing mode (and higher efficiencies) in the milder parts of the season when return water temperatures are lower, giving seasonal efficiencies of around 87–88%.

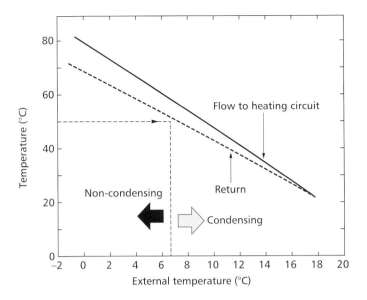

Figure 9.3 Weather compensation and condensing boilers[11] (reproduced from DETR Good Practice Guide 16. Crown copyright (1990))

Table 9.2 Boiler plant oversizing limits

Building	Boiler plant yardstick (heating load) (W/m²)
Offices and industrial buildings	90
Retail, health care and education establishments	110

Table 9.3 Advantages and disadvantages of centralised heating

Advantages	Disadvantages
Capital cost per unit output falls with increased capacity of central plant	Capital cost of distribution systems is high
Convenient for some institutions.	Space requirements of central plant and distribution systems are significant, particularly ductwork
Central plant tends to be better engineered, operating at higher efficiencies, (where load factors are high) and more durable	As the load factor falls the total system efficiency falls as distribution losses become more significant
Some systems will naturally require central plant, e.g. heavy oil and coal burning plant	
Flexibility in the choice of fuel	
Better utilisation of CHP etc.	

Table 9.4 Advantages and disadvantages of de-centralised heating

Advantages	Disadvantages
Low capital cost, savings made on minimising the use of air and water distribution systems	Equipment tends to be less robust with shorter operational life
Zoning of the systems can be matchedmore easily to occupancy patterns	Flueing arrangements can be more difficult
Maintenance less specialised	Fuel needs to be supplied throughout the site
Can be readily altered and extended	
Energy performance in buildings with diverse patterns of use is usually better	
Plant failure only effects the area served	

9.1.1.2 Plant sizing

Careful consideration should be given to the size and number of boilers to be installed as oversizing heating plant will generally reduce seasonal efficiency and increase capital cost unnecessarily.

Boiler plant is sized for mid-winter requirements, giving it considerable over capacity for the rest of the year. Heating plant is often oversized due to excessive design margins and this exacerbates the part-load efficiency problem. Heating design loads for the purpose of sizing HVAC systems should be determined in accordance with the procedures detailed in the CIBSE Guides.

BSRIA Guidance Note 12/97[13] covers the oversizing of heating plant and indicates that heating plant capacities larger than those shown in Table 9.2 are likely to be oversized.

9.1.1.3 Centralised versus decentralised systems

The argument for the selection of centralised or de-centralised services is complex (see Tables 9.3 and 9.4). For example, if a building is multi-tenanted with diverse periods of occupancy, the use of decentralised services could match the type of operation better than a centralised arrangement. However, for a building having a large energy demand with a high load factor, the use of centralised plant working at high efficiencies and possibly using dual fuel facilities, may provide a better solution.

The argument for decentralised heating often hinges on the price and availability of fuels, the space available for plant and distribution pipework, the losses in a centralised system and the size of the loads involved.

9.1.2 Hot water plant

Hot water plant should always be sized correctly thus minimising capital and running costs[1].

Reducing temperatures saves energy and the risk of scalding, but should not be achieved at the expense of safety. To avoid legionella[14], hot water should be stored at 60(±2.5)°C.

Primary and secondary distribution losses should always be minimised as part of an energy efficient design. Hot water circulation loops should be compact and well insulated, while dead legs should be kept to a minimum size and length. The length of pipe between an outlet and a storage vessel, or a secondary flow and return system, should not exceed the lengths given in Table 9.5.

Hot water systems should be equipped with effective, automatic temperature controls (see 9.3.8).

The four main types of hot water system are:

— central calorifiers, supplied by the main heating boilers

Table 9.5 Maximum lengths of pipe to outlet

Nominal bore of pipe (mm)	Maximum length (m)
Up to 20	12
21 to 25	7
Over 25	3

— central self-contained gas or electric

— local storage, gas or electric

— local point of use, usually electric.

9.1.2.1 Central calorifier systems

Where hot water loads are high and distribution systems compact, a well controlled central boiler/calorifier plant can operate reasonably economically. However, where hot water loads are not substantial, particularly in summer, separate heating and hot water systems will be more energy efficient.

Combination boilers can also provide an energy efficient approach to both heating and hot water in small (domestic sized) centralised systems. Hot water is heated almost instantaneously on demand, although interaction between the heating and hot water may occur where winter demand is high.

9.1.2.2 Central self-contained systems

Self-contained central hot water systems are normally much more efficient than systems combined with the main heating. This is because standing losses are lower and the poor part-load efficiencies characteristic of boilers sized for the full heating duty are avoided during summer operation. Relatively high efficiency storage water heaters are commonly used and condensing versions offer a further high efficiency option.

Electric immersion heating is generally only economic where there is adequate capacity for off-peak storage. Suitable tariffs must be available, and the system well controlled to minimise daytime top-ups. This method can be used during summer, with heat generation via the main boilers in winter. Although highly efficient in terms of delivered energy, with comparable running costs to storage water heaters, the primary energy consumption and CO_2 emissions are relatively high.

9.1.2.3 Local storage systems

Small de-centralised gas fired storage water heaters close to the point of use can significantly improve efficiency since standing and distribution losses are greatly reduced, particularly for larger buildings. Problems associated with minimising the risk of legionella are also normally reduced with localised systems. Capital and maintenance costs can be higher, but this is normally more than offset by the increased efficiency and other advantages. This option can also be useful for catering and sports facilities with high peak demand.

Local electric storage systems are usually designed to take advantage of off-peak electricity tariffs, and can be located

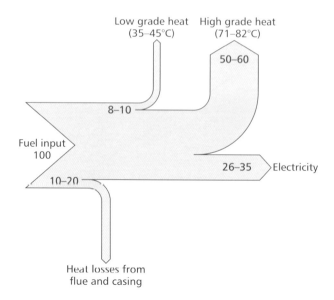

Figure 9.4 Energy balance of a typical reciprocating CHP unit[16] (reproduced from DETR Good Practice Guide 1. Crown copyright (1993))

close to the point of demand. The disadvantages are as described for central electric storage systems in 9.1.2.2.

9.1.2.4 Point of use water heaters

Monitored projects suggest that local instantaneous point of use water heating is extremely economical where hot water demand is low, e.g. for offices without catering facilities. Capital cost and delivered energy consumption is generally low. Water softening may be desirable to prevent units scaling up, but this can cause premature failure.

9.1.3 Combined heat and power (CHP)

CHP has a wide range of applications in buildings[15,16]. Small scale CHP plant are packaged units with an electrical output not exceeding 1 MW electrical (MWe) and usually less than 500 kWe. Small scale units are most commonly retrofitted to existing installations although CHP can prove to be even more beneficial in new buildings. CHP should always be considered alongside other high efficiency boiler plant when evaluating boiler replacement, new designs or refurbishment schemes.

CHP installations can run on natural gas, bio-gas or diesel (gas oil). They have a similar reliability to conventional boilers and availability factors of over 95% are common. The energy balance of a typical CHP unit is shown in Figure 9.4.

The high efficiencies achieved are much greater than conventional power stations, thus reducing the amount of primary energy required to satisfy a given heat and electrical load. Site energy cost can be reduced significantly using CHP. The primary energy consumed on a site will increase due to CHP but overall energy consumption and CO_2 emissions will decrease[17].

In general, to achieve a simple payback of 4 to 5 years, a CHP unit must operate for 4500 hours per year or about 12–14 hours/day; 6000 hours per year for a simple payback of 3

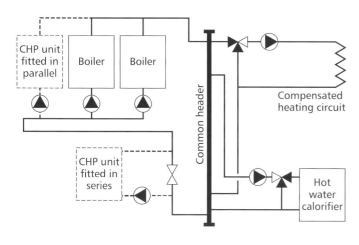

Figure 9.5 Alternative ways of connecting CHP into conventional heating plant[15] (reproduced from DETR Good Practice Guide 176. Crown copyright (1996))

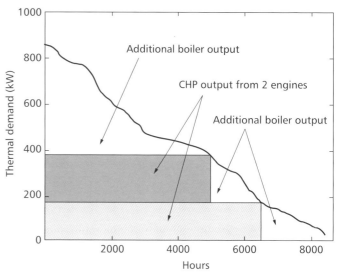

Figure 9.6 Load duration curves and CHP sizing[16] (reproduced from DETR Good Practice Guide 1. Crown copyright (1993))

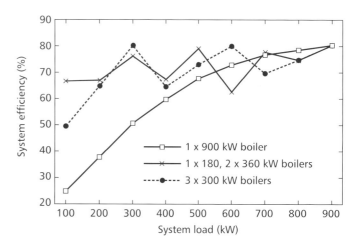

Figure 9.7 Effect of multiple boilers on overall efficiency

years. Usually, these shorter paybacks can only be achieved where there is a significant demand for heating and hot water, e.g. in hospitals, hotels or swimming pools. However, CHP can be used to provide the heat source for absorption chillers to supply cooling and standby generation capacity.

CHP plant should always operate as the lead boiler to maximise savings. The electricity generated is best utilised on site, although it is also possible to export electricity back to the electricity companies. This is often uneconomic since the 'sell back' tariffs are usually at low rates.

A CHP unit can be connected into an existing heating system in two ways, as shown in Figure 9.5:

— in series as a by-pass in a suitable return to the boilers (generally used in new installations

— in parallel with the boilers (usually for retrofit installations).

Economic viability is heavily dependent on the demand for heat and the price of electricity and gas. Detailed energy demand profiles for both heat and electricity are fundamental to accurately sizing CHP and hence its ultimate viability[16].

Figure 9.6 shows an example load duration curve of a system with two engines, one of 180 kW running for about 6500 hours per annum and a second of 200 kW running for about 5000 hours. The remaining thermal load should be met by the conventional boiler plant. Designers can use this technique to optimise the number and size of CHP units alongside the top-up boilers required.

CHP requires more maintenance than conventional boiler plant. This represents a significant running cost which must be taken into account in the feasibility study.

For small scale units, overall maintenance costs generally lie in the range of 0.5 to 1.0 p/(kW h) of electricity generated, typically 0.7 p/(kW h). Very large CHP systems can have maintenance costs below 0.5 p/(kW h).

Percentage availability and reliability are key factors that represent the success of the maintenance regime. These need careful estimation when assessing feasibility and daily monitoring during operation.

9.1.4 Multiple boiler arrangements

Multiple boiler arrangements match the demand for heat more closely and hence improve energy efficiency. These may comprise an integrated package of modules or independent boilers, including CHP. As the load increases, individual modules are progressively switched on. Since each boiler performs close to its individual design duty, efficiency is maintained. The overall plant can therefore provide a much improved part load efficiency characteristic, as shown in Figure 9.7. Careful sequence control is fundamental to this approach (see 9.3).

Within practical limits, and where the dilution effect of parallel connected boilers is not significant, the greater the number of stages of sequence control, the better the control and efficiency (due to greater use of on-line boilers). It is normally preferable to use a greater number of smaller boilers to provide more stages of control, than create more

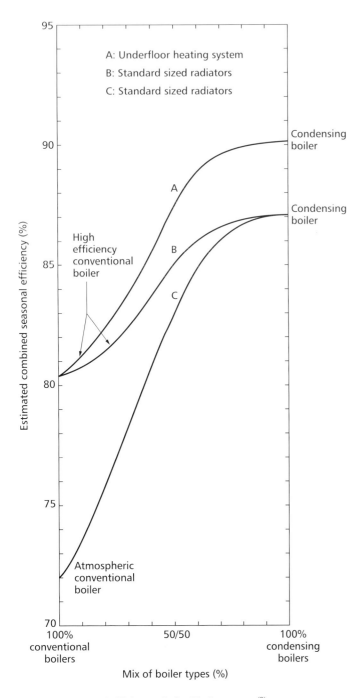

Figure 9.8 Seasonal efficiency of mixed boiler systems[9]

Table 9.6 Minimum coefficients of performance for heat pumps in heating cycle

Heating capacity (kW)	COP
Up to 20	2.2
21 to 60	2.4
61 to 120	2.5
Over 120	2.6

optimises capital cost while still keeping overall plant efficiency high[12].

Figure 9.8[9] provides a means of estimating the overall seasonal efficiency when combining condensing and high efficiency boiler plant. Moving from left to right increases the proportion that is condensing and hence there is a rise in overall efficiency. Whilst there is only a relatively small drop in overall efficiency in moving from 100% to two thirds condensing, this will reduce significantly the capital cost of the plant. It is common to find that 50–75% condensing often provides the shortest payback periods.

Condensing and high efficiency boilers can also be combined with CHP plant, as shown in Figure 9.9. The most efficient plant should take the base load, i.e. the CHP plant in the first case and the condensing boilers in the second. However, the most cost-effective solution often involves some CHP modulating capacity and/or heat dumping capacity (see the dotted line in Figure 9.9). A full option appraisal should consider all the available possibilities and gradually focus on the most efficient, economic and practical combination[18,19].

9.1.5   Heat pumps

Heat pumps can produce high coefficients of performance (COP) when operating at low temperature differentials, as shown in Figure 9.10. Heat pumps have found wide use in applications where low grade heat is available, e.g. where low grade process heating is being dumped, or for ventilation extract heat recovery such as in swimming pools and supermarkets.

When used to provide heating only, the COP of heat pumps does not usually compensate for the increased financial and environmental cost of using electricity. Where the need for cooling has been established, e.g. in retail outlets, reversible heat pumps can be an effective way of providing both cooling and heating.

The coefficients of performance for heat pumps in the heating cycle should not generally be less than shown in Table 9.6.

More detailed advice on the application and design of heat pump systems is provided in CIBSE Technical Memoranda TM11[20] and TM15[21].

9.1.6   Electric heating

Panel radiators, natural draught and fanned electric convectors are available with outputs up to 5 kW. Electric heating systems:

stages by switching combinations of different sized boilers. Different sized boilers are often used where one acts as the summer boiler for hot water services. However, complete segregation of hot water services is normally more efficient. Different sized boilers also require much more complex sequence control systems when being controlled from return water temperature, and they could have different response times when controlled from flow temperature. Whilst these problems can be overcome by careful engineering and commissioning, boiler sequence control systems are normally best kept to simple principles for long term efficient operation. Identical boilers also reduce potential maintenance and spares problems.

Other than for low temperature systems, it is not usually economic to specify all the boilers in a multiple arrangement as condensing. Specifying the lead boiler(s) as condensing, with high efficiency boiler(s) to top-up,

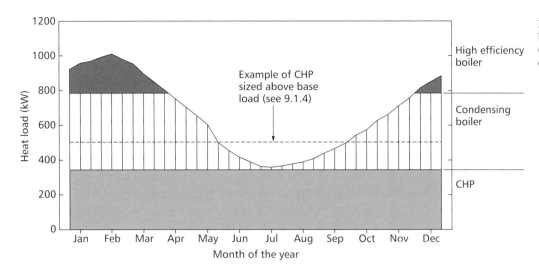

Figure 9.9 Combining CHP and boiler plant (adapted from DETR Good Practice Guide 176[15]). Crown copyright (1996))

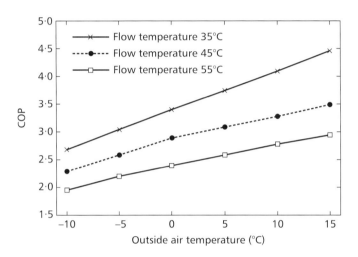

Figure 9.10 Effect of temperature range on heat pump performance

— are generally inexpensive to install

— can reduce space requirements

— require little or no maintenance

— provide very quick response to controls

— are highly efficient but can have high CO_2 emissions

— are suitable for intermittently heated areas.

Owing to the high unit cost of electricity, high levels of insulation and good central/local control are essential for the efficient use of electric heating. Simple, effective systems can give heating energy consumption in the range 40–60 (kW h)/m² per year[22].

Electric storage heaters can take advantage of low electricity costs at night. They also have a low capital cost, are easy to install and maintenance free. However, their main disadvantages are the limited charging capacity and the difficulty of controlling output. This lack of control can give rise to comfort problems and higher than necessary energy consumption.

9.2 Distribution systems

The characteristics of distribution circuits for space heating systems can have a significant effect on thermal performance and energy consumption. The main sources of inefficiency are:

— incorrectly sized distribution systems resulting in high pump and fan energy consumption (the position of plant rooms, and the consequent length of pipework will influence both the capital and running cost of the distribution system)

— unwanted heat losses from the pipework or ductwork (*BS 5422*[23] details the minimum standards of insulation required for heating pipework)

— wasteful operation at part loads.

Table 9.7 shows typical utilisation efficiencies of various systems. Multiplying these by the seasonal boiler efficiency provides an overall system efficiency.

As heating demands reduce due to improved standards of insulation and air tightness, the relative importance of distribution losses increases. More detailed information on the sizing of emitters and the design of individual heating systems is provided in CIBSE Guide B[1].

Different types of emitter have different output characteristics in terms of the split between convective and radiant heat. Where there is a high ventilation rate, the use of a radiant heating system results in lower energy consumption. Fully radiant systems heat occupants directly without heating the air to full comfort temperatures.

Where convection is the predominant form of heat in tall spaces, care must be taken to avoid vertical temperature stratification. Increased temperatures at high level also increase heat losses through the roof in atria or warehouse/factory buildings.

Table 9.7 Typical distribution system utilisation efficiencies

Type of distribution system	Utilisation efficiency, η_s
Intermittent:	
— automatic centrally-fired radiator or convector systems	0.97
— automatic centrally-fired warm air ventilation systems	0.93
— fan assisted electric off-peak heaters	0.90
— direct electric (non-storage) floor and ceiling systems	0.95
— district heating/warm air systems	0.90
Continuous:	
— automatic centrally fired radiator or convector systems	1.00
— automatic centrally fired warm air ventilation systems	1.00
— electric storage radiator systems	0.75
— direct electric floor and ceiling systems	0.95
— district heating/radiator systems	1.00
Water heating:	
— gas circulator/storage cylinder	0.80
— gas or oil fired boiler/storage cylinder	0.80
— off-peak electric storage with cylinder and immersion heater	0.80
— local instantaneous electric water heaters	1.00
— instantaneous gas heaters	0.95
— district heating with local calorifiers	0.80
— district heating with central calorifier and distribution	0.75

9.2.1 Wet systems

9.2.1.1 Radiators

Radiators have a convective component of between 50% and 70% and provide a positive room air temperature gradient. They are cheap and easily controlled with a reasonably quick response.

9.2.1.2 Natural convectors

Natural convectors have a radiant/convective split of 20/80 and tend to produce a more pronounced vertical temperature gradient that can result in inefficient energy use. They are best used in well insulated rooms with low air change rates.

9.2.1.3 Fan convectors

Fan convectors, like natural convectors, are suitable for well insulated rooms with low air change rates. Fan convectors:

— provide good temperature control and the possibility of using a fan-only operating mode in summer

— respond rapidly to control

— can have a variable speed and, hence, a variable output

— require compensated circuits with a high minimum flow temperature and should be separated from circuits serving other types of emitter

— require additional wiring for fan interlock with time control.

The minimum flow temperature for circuits serving fan convectors should not be below 50–55°C to prevent cold draughts. Disadvantages include higher capital costs,

higher maintenance requirements, the need to have an electrical supply to every unit and an increased electrical requirement due to the fans.

9.2.1.4 Underfloor heating

Underfloor heating usually consists of a low temperature warm water distribution system set into the floor slab giving a slow response that is more suited to areas of continuous occupation. However, the system does have some built-in self-regulation; as the room warms up, the temperature difference between the floor and the room air decreases, reducing the heat output. Generally, operating at 45/35°C, these systems provide an ideal opportunity to use condensing boilers as seasonal efficiencies of over 90% can be achieved due to the low return water temperature. The selection of heating zones and their control will have a considerable impact on comfort and energy. There is a high thermal inertia with underfloor heating and less opportunity to respond to local heat gains.

9.2.1.5 Radiant panels

Radiant panels can be supplied with medium or high temperature hot water, or steam, and can have a radiant component of up to 65%. They are suitable for use in large spaces with high airchange rates such as factories or warehouses.

9.2.2 Warm air systems

The three main types of warm air systems are direct gas fired units; indirect gas or oil-fired units and indirect units fitted with water or steam coils. Operation can be with either air recirculation to maintain space temperature, or with a full fresh air supply to provide the minimum fresh air requirement. Direct gas fired unit heaters have additional fresh air requirements for combustion.

Warm air systems:

— have a quick response to control but can promote stratification

— often require significant lengths of ductwork and, therefore, fan power can add to overall energy consumption

— are generally more difficult to control in zones, requiring air dampers and room thermostats.

Direct gas fired unit heaters should preferably have modulating burners controlled in relation to the discharge temperature and room temperature. Also available are gas fired condensing unit heaters that operate in the condensing mode constantly.

9.2.3 Radiant systems

These are typically used in large volume buildings that have high air change rates, such as factories, warehouses and garages. Radiant systems:

— are more efficient because they only heat the occupants and building fabric and do not generally raise the temperature of the internal air to full comfort levels

Table 9.8 Selection of heating controls

Plant	Control function
Heating systems:	
— up to 30 kW	Timeswitch; resolution better than 15 minutes, spring reserve/battery back-up
— 30 to 100 kW	Optimum start/stop recommended
— over 100 kW	Optimum start/stop required by current building regulations
Single boilers	Packaged controls to HSE PM5[24]
Multiple boilers	Packaged controls to HSE PM5[24] plus boiler sequence control
Compensated circuits:	
— temperature	Compensator control required by current Building Regulations. Separate circuits where solar gain, occupancy patterns, building structure or emitter characteristics vary. Resets where appropriate for space temperature, solar gain, wind influence.
— flow	Variable flow control of pumps recommended
Radiators and other emitters	Individual control via TRVs or more advanced controls
Intermittently occupied areas	Occupancy sensing controls with appropriate default values dependent upon system response
Randomly occupied zones and buildings	Push-button timed period user operation

— generally provide a rapid response, requiring less heat up time at the beginning of the day.

Significant energy savings compared with convective systems are therefore possible. Types of radiant heater include gas fired tube heaters, plaque heaters and electric quartz-halogen units.

The radiant effect is only maintained when heater surfaces are above a certain temperature, hence two stage switching which operates above and below the critical temperature gives closer control than simple on/off switching.

Temperature control is required for each heater and time control for the overall system. Black-bulb radiant heat sensors should be used to achieve good temperature control of radiant heating systems. The sensors must be located in positions that representative of the radiant effect of the panels being controlled.

The height of radiant heaters is particularly important as overheating can occur if they are positioned too low. Locating them too high can result in comfort problems and increased energy consumption due to the heaters often being left on continuously.

Where areas have different temperature requirements, they should be zoned accordingly. This necessitates the use of a sensor and controller plus a time switch for each zone. In general, the more zones the better the control, although large zones are acceptable in areas requiring low heat levels.

Electric quartz heaters use a quartz lamp to provide a high intensity radiant effect. Due to their high capital and running cost they are mainly used for spot heating in intermittently occupied areas. They have very rapid response times and can therefore be used in conjunction with occupancy sensors or local run-back timers to control heat output.

9.3 Controls

Good control of primary heating/hot water plant and distribution systems is a vital part in achieving low energy consumption. The key requirement is to provide heat/hot water only when and where it is needed, and at the right temperature, whilst minimising boiler cycling. Table 9.8 provides useful guidance for selecting heating controls.

Section 5 covers overall control strategies and more detailed guidance is available in CIBSE Applications Manual AM1[25]. DETR General Information Report 40[7] also provides a series of application sheets explaining the operation of controls for particular systems. DETR Good Practice Guide 132[26] sets out minimum standards of control for small commercial buildings. Domestic heating controls are covered in DETR Good Practice Guide 143[27].

9.3.1 Circuit design

The successful operation of controls depends heavily on good circuit design. A constant, or near constant, water flow is normally required for modern boilers. A variable flow is created by the action of manual and automatic valves etc. Therefore, for most applications, the use of a separately pumped secondary circuit which is 'decoupled' from the primary circuit by a common header or buffer vessel, is recommended (see Figure 9.13). This avoids any interaction between circuits, enables the return temperature for the primary circuit to represent the load on the system and permits return temperature sequence control of multiple boilers.

Small, single boiler applications are often provided with a single pumped circuit. This can cause problems due to reduced flow through the boiler. A differential pressure by-pass can be provided to maintain a minimum boiler flow, although these are expensive and require careful setting up and maintenance to maintain an adequate boiler flow. A more satisfactory arrangement is shown in Figure 9.11. In this arrangement the primary and secondary circuits are

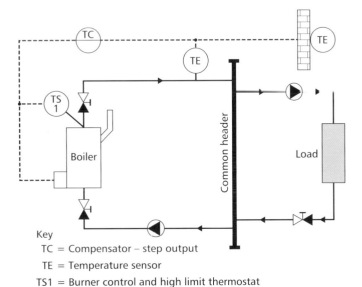

Key

TC = Compensator – step output

TE = Temperature sensor

TS1 = Burner control and high limit thermostat

Figure 9.11 Directly compensated single boiler system plant[7] (reproduced from DETR General Information Report 40. Crown copyright (1996))

separately pumped but, since the boiler is directly compensated, no compensated valve is necessary.

9.3.2   Boiler controls

Effective control of boilers is a significant factor in achieving good energy efficiency. Inadequate or incorrect application of boiler control can add 15–30% to fuel consumption. The following points should be noted:

—   The control of multiple boilers is often poor.

—   The reduced standing losses and improved part load efficiency of modern well insulated, low water content boilers normally allows very simple hydraulic arrangements to be used for multiple boilers.

—   Simple layouts do not require the use of individual boiler pumps, or automatic isolation valves, which are the cause of many problems when associated with the control of multiple boilers.

—   Boiler controls must be considered at an early stage in the design. Adding controls after plant layouts are designed can often result in uncontrollable systems.

9.3.2.1   Avoiding boiler dry cycling

Preventing excessive boiler cycling saves energy. Small (domestic) boilers should have their operation interlocked with the main heating and hot water thermostats. Interlocking in this way ensures that the boiler and pump only operate when there is a demand for heat.

Boiler anti-cycling controls

Stand alone boiler anti-cycling controls that delay boiler firing to reduce unnecessary cycling by increasing the 'off' time of the boiler are available. These devices provide little or no improvement to boiler efficiency compared with good, standard controls[26,27].

Demand-based boiler control and system inhibit

Standing losses and excessive part load operation can be reduced where boilers and associated primary pumps are only enabled when there is a demand. This can significantly reduce energy consumption where boilers and systems have high standing losses. However, response times must be adequate to meet demand, particularly where the boilers serve hot water services systems. For modern high efficiency, low standing-loss, boilers the benefit is reduced but still worthwhile.

Sophisticated strategies can be developed with advanced control systems and some lower cost systems are now available with demand-based control of central plant dependent upon zonal demand.

Combined optimisers and compensators can also incorporate functions for system inhibition or daytime optimisation, which stop the complete system operating. These can be very successful for small buildings but can cause problems in larger buildings due to response times. Demand-based control strategies should be used for larger buildings.

9.3.2.2   Boiler sequence control

Controlling multiple boilers in sequence:

—   matches the number of boilers firing to suit the load

—   minimises the number of boilers firing, thus, maximising overall efficiency

—   avoids short cycling of burner operation and, therefore, enhances energy efficient and stable operation

—   is normally carried out with respect to boiler circuit return temperature, although flow temperature can be used.

Return temperature sequence control cannot be used where the flow varies as a result of individual boiler pumps or automatic isolation valves. Flow temperature sequence control can have problems due to interaction with boiler thermostats and flow temperature dilution on parallel connected boilers, unless thermostats are set with an adequate margin. Individual boiler thermostats must be set in accordance with HSE Guidance Note PM5[24]. Therefore, systems must have an adequate head of water or be pressurised to permit boiler thermostat settings higher than 82°C.

Common primary pumps are recommended to provide a constant flow in the boiler primary circuit and through individual boilers. Constant primary circuit flow permits proportional sequence control in relation to return temperature and provides a simple energy efficient solution which can be easily maintained over the life of the plant (see Figure 9.13).

Where boilers have individual pumps, or automatic isolation valves are used, the primary circuit flow normally varies and the return temperature is not representative of the load on the system. Therefore, return temperature sequence control cannot be used.

Where boilers do not have separate primary and secondary heating circuits, the minimum flow due to compensated control is unlikely to be sufficient for the minimum turn down of the boiler(s) and hence boiler control is lost. This is due to the closing of the two port TRVs and/or local emitter isolation valves for space temperature control. To give near constant flow through the boiler(s), a by-pass can be installed and controlled in relation to differential pressure. At periods of low heat load, this will circulate the flow back to the boiler and reduce potential savings for integral condensing boilers. A 'split' condensing boiler used with the secondary heat exchanger in the variable flow return will maximise the seasonal efficiency of this system.

The problems can be avoided by using a more energy efficient system, in which the primary boiler circuit is separately pumped and connected to the secondary circuit via a common header. In this way, a variable flow compensated secondary circuit can also be used with variable speed drives for energy efficient operation.

Flow temperature sequence control should be set so that there is a margin between the boiler thermostats and the sequence control setting to prevent interaction. The margin must allow for boiler control thermostat switching differential and the dilution effect of flow through off-line boilers. The margin is normally to at least 8°C and can be significantly higher. Therefore, to provide a normal LTHW flow temperature of 82°C, systems must have an adequate head or be pressurised and the boiler thermostats set correspondingly higher. The margin is significantly reduced where modulating burners are used.

Sequence control related to outside air temperature can provide stable sequence control. However, it is totally open loop control and does not respond to actual system load. It should only be used, therefore, where other methods are not possible.

Sequence selection can be manual or automatic, based on time or usage with more sophisticated control systems. Condensing boilers should always operate first and modular boilers with a common combustion chamber normally require a fixed sequence of operation.

9.3.2.3 Burner controls

Single-stage, two-stage and modulating burners are available. Two-stage burners provide improved part load efficiency compared with single-stage burners. However, the high fire of a two-stage burner must be at a lower temperature than low fire when controlled from boiler outlet temperature. This creates a wide variation in flow temperature. For multiple boilers, the high fire can be incorporated into the sequence control, provided the boiler outlet thermostat control limits the outlet temperature in both low and high fire.

Modulating burners provide the most efficient part load operation and offer the opportunity for oxygen trim control to optimise the air/fuel ratio. Oxygen trim control can provide savings from 2% for a well maintained boiler, up to 5% for older boilers with hysteresis in linkages, etc.

9.3.2.4 Directly compensated boilers

Direct compensation of boilers is normally of little benefit with modern high efficiency boilers due to their low standing losses and the need for separately pumped secondary circuits (see 9.3).

Direct compensation of boilers supplying hot water services often causes problems. Either insufficient heat is available for hot water when flow temperatures are reduced or the compensation is overridden when hot water is required, resulting in overheating of the space.

Direct compensation of multiple boiler sequence control reduces problems caused by thermostat interaction and flow temperature dilution compared with constant temperature, flow temperature sequence control. However, it can be difficult to set up and maintain compared with return temperature sequence control of constant temperature boiler systems. Therefore, constant temperature boiler circuits with compensated secondary circuits are normally preferred.

Condensing boilers with integral heat exchangers that are not used in warm water applications must be directly compensated to facilitate condensing operation. Separately pumped secondary circuits should also be used (see 9.3.1 and Figure 9.11).

9.3.2.5 Reducing boiler standing losses

Significant energy savings can be achieved by minimising the standing losses associated with boilers. Standing losses are typically 0.75% of rated output for recent designs (but can be as low as 0.2% for high efficiency and condensing boilers) and 7% of rated output for older boiler designs with higher water content.

Ideally, standing losses should be less than 10% of total consumption. The *Boiler (Efficiency) Regulations*[10] stipulate minimum levels for full and part load efficiency from January 1998. This will also reduce standing losses for new boilers.

Hot water loads are a very small proportion of heating loads in many buildings. Therefore, even where boilers with low standing losses are used, considerable energy savings can be made by segregating heating and hot water systems so that heating boilers are not run for long periods at low loads during summer.

Boilers with forced, or induced, draught fans should have the fans interlocked with burner operation to minimise standing losses. Large boilers should have air inlet or flue dampers interlocked with burner operation to prevent standing losses from natural draughts.

Automatic boiler isolation valves can be used in multiple boiler installations to isolate the flow through off-line boilers and reduce losses from individual boilers. However, this adds to the complexity of multiple boiler systems and often leads to control problems. Using boilers with low standing losses alleviates the need to isolate flows through off-line boilers. Isolation of flow through off-line boilers is rarely effective and the additional cost of automatic isolation valves is pointless when they leak between ports or are set to part-open.

When boiler output is not required, boilers and primary circuits should be inhibited to minimise boiler and pipework standing losses, as well as pump energy. Inhibition should occur when compensator valves are on full re-circulation and time delays are required to prevent rapid cycling. The complete heating system should shut down when outside temperatures are high.

It is difficult to achieve satisfactory standing losses with large high water content boilers. Effective automatic isolation is normally complex and losses from associated distribution systems are often high. Distributed systems with smaller boilers located nearer the loads reduce distribution losses and, with well designed control and monitoring systems such as BMS, can often be operated more efficiently.

9.3.3 Time controls

Time controls should be provided to automatically control the number and duration of operating periods, with provision for day omissions, in accordance with section 5 and the *Building Regulations*[28].

9.3.3.1 Fixed time controls

A timeswitch provides a simple, robust and easily understood means of saving energy and should have a resolution of 15 minutes or less for effective operation.

Run-back timers are useful where occupancy is particularly unpredictable, requiring extensions to the normal heating period. They are particularly useful in offices and shops where evening work is sometimes carried out, and in function rooms where occupancy is unpredictable.

9.3.3.2 Optimum start/stop control

Optimum start controls are weather dependent timeswitches that vary the start up time in the morning to achieve the building temperature by the required time. Heat up times are reduced during milder weather, thus saving 5–10% of heating energy[26]. Figure 9.12 shows the operation of optimum start controls and the potential energy savings compared with a timeswitch. Optimum start controls can be relatively simple using a single internal sensor and a linear delay of start-up. However, sophisticated self-learning units with an external sensor are available. These can also provide optimum stop facilities to turn the boiler off early at the end of the day in milder weather.

The greatest energy savings from optimum start control are likely to be gained in buildings of lightweight construction and with heating systems of low thermal capacity. Heavyweight buildings are less influenced by external fluctuations and are likely to require smaller variations in required start-up times. Similarly, heating systems with a slow response require a longer preheat time and are, therefore, likely to realise reduced savings with optimum start control.

The thermal inertia of the building and its heating system should be considered when determining heating plant termination times. Boiler operation can be terminated early and the thermal mass of the plant relied upon if some

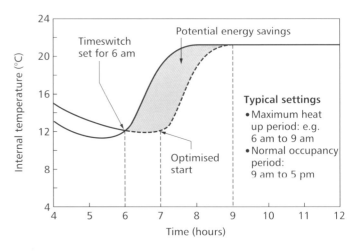

Figure 9.12 Example of the operation of optimum start control plant[26] (reproduced from DETR Good Practice Guide 132. Crown copyright (1997))

degradation of inside temperature is acceptable towards the end of the occupied period.

9.3.4 Temperature controls

Distribution systems should be compensated in accordance with the current *Building Regulations*[20]. This reduces system losses and provides basic space temperature control, although it will not react to internal gains etc. Multiple compensated circuits are ideal for zoning a building because not only can different occupancy patterns be incorporated but also circuit temperature reset can respond to solar gain, typical space temperatures, etc. Where different emitters are used, or parts of the building are better insulated, the compensator schedule can be set to reflect the differing zonal temperature requirements.

Good control of space temperature is required for energy efficient operation. Control of space temperature can often be achieved at low cost using TRVs. Reducing the room temperature by 1°C can reduce the fuel use by around 10%.

9.3.4.1 Weather compensation

The flow temperature of compensated circuits reduces as ambient temperature increases (see Figure 9.3). This provides basic control of space temperature and reduces distribution system losses. The compensator slope is normally linear, often with a maximum and minimum flow temperature. In milder weather, the system operates at lower temperatures thus saving energy. Compensators with non-linear slopes are also available to match heat output more closely to ambient temperature.

The most common version requires a three-port motorised valve to control water temperature, although direct boiler compensation is also possible. Weather compensation can provide low return water temperatures in milder weather causing condensing boilers to operate at higher efficiencies.

The controls should be installed so that the weather compensator is overridden during the heat up period. Many units provide a high temperature limit, which shuts off the heating entirely above a set external temperature (ambient temperature shutdown). Other units provide room reset control, whereby a room sensor signals the compensator to lower (reset) the temperature when the required space temperature is reached. Compensated circuits with space temperature reset provide more effective control than temperature averaging systems for control of a large number of emitters.

Space temperature reset of compensators is often desirable to take into account local heat gains. The maximum number of reset sensors should be limited to four, with a reset of 3°C flow temperature to 1°C space temperature. This is to prevent an undue influence from space temperature which may be unrepresentative of the total area served.

Proper siting of the external sensor is key, since it must reflect the ambient weather condition. Placing it near the building exhaust or on a wall exposed to solar radiation can lead to incorrect operation. Separate compensated circuits should be provided where occupancies, building structure, solar gain or emitter characteristics vary (see section 5).

Deep plan buildings often require heating at their perimeter during the winter and mid-seasons, while the core may not require any heating at all. Where a compensated wet heating system is being used around the perimeter of a building in conjunction with an air conditioning system, care must be taken to ensure that there is no interaction between systems. Where the compensated circuit has a relatively small duty, primarily to prevent cold down draughts etc., space temperature control of the heating may not be required. Where the perimeter heating has a higher duty, space temperature control can be difficult due to differing reaction times for the two systems, and space temperature controls sensors need careful siting to prevent interaction between the two systems. In some circumstances, it may be possible to link the space temperature and air conditioning.

9.3.4.2 Night setback

These controls reduce or set back the temperature during a given time period and are often part of the weather compensator controls. Night setback can also be applied to space temperature control. It is best to apply night setback to both compensation and space temperature control as imbalance can result when applied to compensation only. This is particularly useful at night in continuously occupied buildings, e.g. in elderly persons' homes. Night setback provides an alternative to simply switching the heating off at night, allowing a minimum temperature to be maintained during the night and thus providing energy savings compared with continuous operation. However, generally it is more economical to switch the heating off at night with a low limit to bring it back on.

9.3.5 Zone controls

Heating is often required at different times, temperatures and areas of a building. A successful control system will satisfy these different requirements on a zone by zone basis. A zone may be regarded as a part of the building the heating system of which is capable of independent control, in terms of time, temperature, or both.

Space temperature control is required by the current *Building Regulations*[28] for each part of the system designed to be separately controlled, by thermostats, TRVs, etc. Individual emitters should have separate control wherever possible for energy efficient operation and to comply with the *Building Regulations*[28]. However, emitters should not have local control where sensors are located for space temperature reset of compensators.

Zone control can be implemented by:

— thermostatic radiator valves (TRVs)

— motorised valves and room thermostats.

9.3.5.1 Thermostatic radiator valves (TRVs)

Thermostatic radiator valves provide a low cost method of local temperature control of individual emitters, particularly where there are high incidental gains. TRVs are normally two port and should be used in association with variable speed pumps to provide good control (see 9.3.7). Correct direction of flow through the TRV is essential, this may require the TRV to be fitted to the radiator return connection, rather than the flow.

Lockable tamper-proof heads are also recommended. These can either be completely locked on one setting, or provide a minimum level of control for the adjacent occupants.

9.3.5.2 Motorised valves and room thermostats

Motorised valves and room thermostats can be used to provide temperature and/or time control of a zone. This method is probably best used in areas with a small group of emitters, say totalling over 5 kW. Sensing locations are better than TRVs and a wider range of emitters can be controlled. Reset of space temperature for unoccupied periods can also be more easily achieved.

Further energy savings can be achieved by installing time control in zones using 2-port motorised valves, room thermostat and time control independent from the main heating time control. Programmable room thermostats are a convenient way of achieving this as they combine the roles of timeswitch and electronic room thermostat, e.g. by varying the room temperature at different times of the day in an elderly persons' day centre.

Larger zones should be weather compensated, particularly where a boiler supplies a number of buildings to allow for solar gains on different facades. Multiple secondary circuits should normally be connected in parallel across the header so that each one has the full heat source available to it (see Figure 9.13). This system is relatively simple and allows good control to be achieved. More sophisticated space temperature control systems are also available including occupancy sensing[3].

9.3.6 Temperature sensor location

Correct installation of sensors is key to the efficient and effective operation of control systems. Poor siting can result in excessive energy consumption.

Room thermostats and sensors must be positioned:

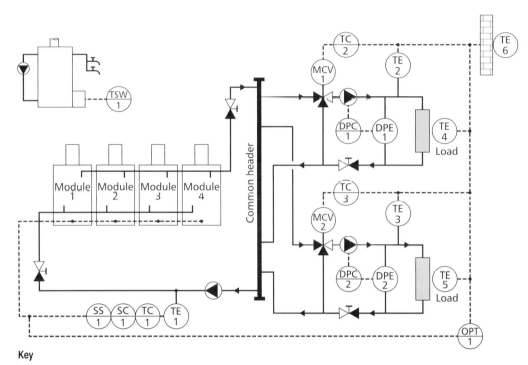

Figure 9.13 Pumped primary circuit with multiple secondary circuits plant[7] (reproduced from DETR General Information Report 40. Crown copyright (1996))

Key

TE1 = boiler return water temperature sensor	TC2 = zone 1 compensator
TE2 = zone 1 compensated flow temperature sensor	TC3 = zone 2 compensator
TE3 = zone 2 compensated flow temperature sensor	SC1 = boiler sequence control step controller
TE4 = zone 1 space temperature sensor	SS1 = boiler sequence selector switch
TE5 = zone 2 space temperature sensor	MCV1 = zone 1 compensator valve
TE6 = outside temperature sensor	MCV2 = zone 2 compensator valve
TSW1 = HWS timeswitch	DPE1 = zone 1 differential pressure sensor
OPT1 = heating optimiser	DPE2 = zone 2 differential pressure sensor
TC1 = boiler sequence proportional	DPC1 = zone 1 differential pressure controller
temperature controller	DPC2 = zone 2 differential pressure controller

—   about 1.5 m (5 feet) above floor level

—   out of direct sunlight

—   away from draughts

—   away from sources of heat

—   not in a partitioned office, if it also serves others.

Internal sensors for optimum start control should always be located in the coldest part of the building to signal how much heat is still stored in the building.

External sensors also need careful siting:

—   on a north or north-west wall, out of the sun

—   in a position which is representative of the zone being controlled

—   away from heat sources such as openable windows, extract ducts and chimney stacks.

9.3.7   Variable flow control

Most heating systems are constant volume and use the same amount of energy for pumping power throughout the year regardless of the load on the system. Heating systems normally only require maximum flow during the boost period, which is a small percentage of total heating time. Variable speed pumps can respond to the reduced demand and decrease the flow of the pumps so that they match the load on the system[8].

Considerable pumping energy savings and improved space temperature control can be achieved by controlling the speed of distribution system pumps to respond to system demand (see section 10). Pump speed is normally controlled in relation to system differential pressure using two port valves, or TRVs, throttling the flow through individual emitters. Pumps are now available with in-built variable speed drives, which provide rapid payback of the additional capital cost.

Typically between 25 and 50% of annual pumping energy consumption can be saved by using variable flow heating systems. This is commonly achieved using two port control valves and a differential pressure controller on a by-pass. The pump is then controlled using a variable speed drive to maintain a constant differential pressure. Capital costs and commissioning is also reduced as coil by-pass pipework and regulating valves can be eliminated[8].

9.3.8   Hot water controls

Hot water generators and calorifiers should have time and temperature control in accordance with *Building Regulations*[28]. The controls should be capable of holding the water temperature to within ±3°C of the set point temperature. The controls should also include a time switch to turn off the heating source and any circulating pumps (both primary and secondary) during periods when hot water will not be needed[7].

Segregation of hot water generation from heating systems is recommended (see 9.1.2). Where possible, hot water should be generated locally to minimise distribution losses.

To avoid legionella[14], hot water should be stored at $60°(\pm 2.5)°C$. Stored hot water should be raised to $70°C$ and allowed to cool to safe levels prior to occupancy. Systems should also be designed for a minimum return water temperature above $50°C$.

References

1   Installation and equipment data CIBSE Guide B (London: Chartered Institution of Building Services Engineers) (1986)

2   Economic use of fired space heaters for industry and commerce FEB 3 (London: Department of Environment, Transport and Regions) (1993)

3   Degree days Fuel Efficiency Booklet No. 7 (London: Department of Environment, Transport and Regions) (1993)

4   Economic use of oil-fired boiler plant Fuel Efficiency Booklet No.14 (London: Department of Environment, Transport and Regions) (1993)

5   Economic use of gas-fired boiler plant Fuel Efficiency Booklet No. 15 (London: Department of Environment, Transport and Regions) (1993)

6   Economic use of coal-fired boiler plant Fuel Efficiency Booklet No. 17 (London: Department of Environment, Transport and Regions) (1993)

7   Heating systems and their control GIR 40 (London: Department of Environment, Transport and Regions) (1996)

8   Variable flow control GIR 41 (London: Department of Environment, Transport and Regions) (1996)

9   Condensing boilers CIBSE Applications Manual AM3 (London: Chartered Institution of Building Services Engineers) (1989)

10   The Boiler (Efficiency) Regulations 1993 Statutory Instrument SI 1993/3083 (London: Stationery Office)

11   Guide for installers of condensing boilers in commercial buildings GPG 16 (London: Department of Environment, Transport and Regions) (1990)

12   Condensing boilers. Part 1 — an introduction to more efficient boiler houses in the 90s TA 1/90 (Bracknell: Building Services Research and Information Association) (1990)

13   Oversized heating plant Guidance Note GN 12/97 (Bracknell: Building Services Research and Information Association) (1997)

14   Minimising the risk of Legionnaires' disease CIBSE Technical Memoranda TM13 (London: Chartered Institution of Building Services Engineers) (1991)

15   Small scale combined heat and power for buildings GPG 176 (London: Department of Environment, Transport and Regions) (1996)

16   Guidance notes for the implementation of small-scale packaged combined heat and power GPG 1 (London: Department of Environment, Transport and Regions) (1993)

17   An environmental guide to small-scale combined heat and power GPG 115 (London: Department of Environment, Transport and Regions) (1994)

18   Heating system option appraisal - an engineer's guide for existing buildings GPG 187 (London: Department of Environment, Transport and Regions) (1996)

19   Heating system option appraisal — a manager's guide GPG 182 (London: Department of Environment, Transport and Regions) (1996)

20   Selection and application of heat pumps CIBSE Technical Memoranda TM11 (London: Chartered Institution of Building Services Engineers) (1985)

21   Design guidance for heat pump systems CIBSE Technical Memoranda TM15 (London: Chartered Institution of Building Services Engineers) (1988)

22   Energy efficiency in offices. BRE Low Energy Office GPCS 62 (London: Department of Environment, Transport and Regions) (1993)

23   BS 5422: 1990: Method for specifying thermal insulating materials on pipes, ductwork and equipment (in the temperature range $-40°C$ to $+700°C$) (London: British Standards Institution) (1990)

24   Automatically controlled steam and hot water boilers Guidance Note PM5 (London: Health And Safety Executive)

25   Automatic controls CIBSE Applications Manual AM1 (London: Chartered Institution of Building Services Engineers) (1985)

26   Heating controls in small, commercial and multi-residential buildings GPG 132 (London: Department of Environment, Transport and Regions) (1997)

27   Upgrading controls in domestic wet central heating systems — a guide for installers GPG 143 (London: Department of Environment, Transport and Regions) (1994)

28   The Building Regulations Part L: Conservation of Fuel and Power (London: Stationery Office) (1995)

Bibliography

Martin P L and Oughton D R Faber and Kell: Heating and air-conditioning of buildings 7th edn (Oxford: Butterworth Heinemann) (1989)

Energy efficiency in offices. Review of twelve office case studies GIL 11 (London: Department of Environment, Transport and Regions) (1994)

Introduction to small scale combined heat and power GPG 3 (London: Department of Environment, Transport and Regions) (1990)

Introduction to large scale combined heat and power GPG 43 (London: Department of Environment, Transport and Regions) (1992)

The application of combined heat and power in the Health Service GPG 60 (London: Department of Environment, Transport and Regions) (1992)

Private and standby generation of electricity CIBSE Applications Manual AM8 (London: Chartered Institution of Building Services Engineers) (1992).

Small scale cogeneration CADDET Analyses Series: 1 (Sittard: Centre for the Analysis and Dissemination of Demonstrated Energy Technologies) (1989).

Contract energy management CIBSE Applications Manual AM6 (London: Chartered Institution of Building Services Engineers) (1991)

Brown R Radiant heating AG 3/96 (Bracknell: Building Services Research and Information Association) (1996)

Energy efficiency in schools: potential benefits of boiler replacement GPCS 73 (London: Department of Environment, Transport and Regions) (1996)

HVAC Applications ASHRAE Handbook (Atlanta, GA: American Society of Heating, Refrigeration and Air Conditioning Engineers) (1995)

Levermore G J Building energy management systems. The basics DLP 1 (Bracknell: Building Services Research and Information Association) (1988)

Levermore G J Control with a building energy management system DLP 2 (Bracknell: Building Services Research and Information Association) (1988)

Holmes M J How boiler selection and controls affect annual energy consumption AG 1/78 (Bracknell: Building Services Research and Information Association) (1978)

10.0 Motors and transportation

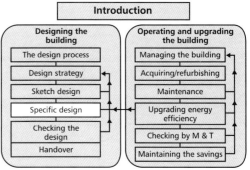

This section sets out key issues in designing systems to minimise the energy consumption of motors and drives, in line with the principles at the front of this Guide. It covers minimising the motor load, sizing and selecting motors, motor drives and controlling the motor load, including that of variable speed drives (VSDs). The operation and maintenance of motors and drives is covered in section 17 and the upgrading motor driven systems to improve energy efficiency in section 18. Further details on the energy efficient use of motors and drives can be found in DETR Good Practice Guide 2[1], Fuel Efficiency Booklet 9[2] and General Information Report 41[3]. The factors relating to the internal heat gains from electric motors are detailed in CIBSE Guide A7[4].

10.0 General

The motor load should always be minimised by good system design prior to motor selection. Effective system regulation and control are also essential for efficient operation.

Electric motors and drives can account for a significant part of the energy demand in buildings. A modestly sized 11 kW induction motor costing £300 to buy can build up a running cost of over £8,000 in an intermittently occupied building with seasonal system operation over ten years, and up to £30,000 with continuous operation.

The following are key issues for electric motors and drives:

— Higher-efficiency motors should always be considered as they often have no additional capital cost and they offer efficiency and economic benefits in virtually all situations.

— Motors should be sized correctly to avoid the greater losses when part loaded.

— Use direct drives rather than belt drives where practical.

— Where belt drives are used, consider modern flat, synchronous, or ribbed belt drives rather than traditional V-belts, to reduce drive losses.

— Systems should be carefully designed to minimise pressure loss and hence reduce energy consumption.

— Efficient system regulation by matching fan and pump characteristics to the system (normally via speed change) can provide significant energy savings compared with increased system resistance.

Typically, 20% energy saving for a 10% flow regulation and 40% saving for a 20% regulation can be expected.

— Variable flow control can provide significant opportunities for energy saving. Building services are sized for peak loads and spend most of their time operating well below full output. Typically, only 20% of full volume energy is required to move air and water at 50% of maximum volume.

— The use of VSDs should always be considered for efficient system regulation and variable flow control.

10.1 Minimising the motor load

Considerable energy savings can be achieved by good system design to minimise the motor load. Accurate calculations of system resistance are essential for effective fan and pump selection. Due to fundamental relationships, a small increase in duct and pipe size can significantly reduce system losses and thus a greater reduction in the power required.

10.1.1 Ventilation systems

Energy can be wasted by:

— unnecessary bends

— reduced duct size

— excessive duct length

—   poor inlet and outlet conditions

—   accumulation of dirt.

Poor fan performance, and hence inefficient operation, can be caused by poor inlet and outlet conditions, often referred to as 'installation effects'. Measures to reduce installation effects at the fan inlet and outlet include the following

Fan inlet:

—   Ensure that air enters axial fans without spin by improved inlet design or a splitter.

—   Include turning vanes where there is a duct bend close to fan inlet.

—   Include a transition piece where the duct size reduces.

—   Ensure flexible connections are correctly fitted without offset or slack.

—   Where fans are installed in plenum chambers, ensure the fan inlet is a minimum of one diameter from plenum wall with no obstructions.

Fan outlet:

—   Ensure a minimum of two diameters straight duct.

—   Where bends are close to the outlet, ensure that they radius bends with splitters are used.

—   Preferably, axial and propeller fans should be fitted with guide vanes to provide energy recovery. Where guide vanes are not fitted, air swirl will significantly increase system resistance. This can be corrected by a carefully designed cross-piece.

Additional guidance on efficient fan and ventilation system design can be found in various HEVAC publications[5–8].

10.1.2   Hydraulic systems

Energy can be wasted by:

—   unnecessary bends

—   reduced pipe size

—   excessive pipe lengths.

On large sites, distributed generation of heating and hot water will reduce pumping power requirements as well as thermal losses.

10.2   Motor sizing and selection

There is scope for saving capital and running costs through better sizing of electric motors. Motors are often rated well above the power levels at which they operate. For example, the basic duty may require a delivered power of 7.5 kW. Designers may specify a 10% margin and the project engineer responsible for the system may apply a further 10% contingency, resulting in a specification of 9.1 kW. As 9.1 kW is not a standard rating, an 11 kW motor is selected. The installed motor, therefore, operates at two thirds or less of its rated output.

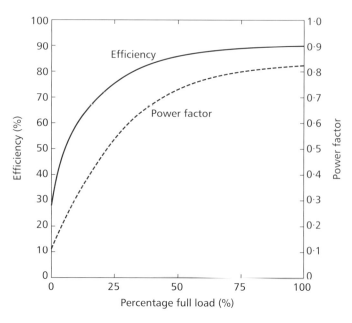

Figure 10.1 Standard induction motor efficiency and power factor (adapted from DETR Fuel efficiency booklet No. 9[2]. Crown copyright (1993))

Modern motors are designed for maximum efficiency at 75% full load, although between 50 and 100% load there is minimal variation in efficiency. Significant reductions in efficiency occur at 25% or less of full load, and it is at this level that serious consideration should be given to fitting a reduced-rating 'higher-efficiency' motor with a lower capital cost.

Figure 10.1 shows how the efficiency of standard motors falls rapidly at low load. At low loading, power factor falls off even more rapidly than efficiency. Smaller motors also reduce the cost of associated cabling and switchgear.

Therefore over-sizing of motors increases:

—   the capital cost of the motor

—   the capital cost of matching switch gear and wiring

—   the capital cost of power factor correction equipment

—   the running cost due to lower efficiencies.

10.2.1   High efficiency motors

High efficiency motors (HEMs) are designed to minimise the inherent losses and save, on average, 3% of energy consumption compared with standard motors; they are also quieter. Many manufacturers now offer 'energy efficient' or 'high efficiency' motors as their standard product for no extra cost. Purchasing policies should reflect their availability[9].

10.2.2   Rewinding motors

The cost of rewinding a motor can be high compared with the cost of a new motor and, unless the motor is rewound to high standards, the efficiency can be reduced by between 0.5 and 2%, or more. Therefore, the decision to rewind or to replace with a new high efficiency motor should be based on lifetime costs.

10.3   Motor drives

10.3.1   Direct drives

Directly driven fans and pumps avoid the need for belt drives and therefore eliminate belt drive losses and maintenance. Belt drives have traditionally been used to enable the matching of fan and pump speeds to duty. However, this can normally be achieved more rapidly and efficiently using VSDs.

10.3.2   Belt drives

There are now a number of alternatives to the traditional V-belt which offer better efficiency and lower maintenance costs. Consideration should be given to the following where belt drives are used:

—   Modern synchronous, flat and ribbed belts are typically 5–6% more efficient than V-belts.

—   Wedge and ribbed wedge belts are normally around 2% more efficient than V-belts.

—   The efficiency of wedge and V-belts deteriorates by around 4% over the life of the belt when well maintained and a further 5–10% if poorly maintained.

—   Over-sizing or under-sizing of V- and wedge belts produces additional losses.

—   Multiple belt drives should be avoided where possible since equal tension on each belt is rarely maintained, causing inefficiency.

—   Where used, always replace belts on multiple drives with complete sets of matched belts.

—   Ensure pulleys are not misaligned.

—   Ensure belts are checked and properly tensioned at the recommended intervals.

—   Consider changing the drive type when pulleys require replacement.

10.3.3   Motor location

Where possible, motors should be located out of the air stream on air conditioning systems to avoid additional unwanted heat input, although this is reduced with HEMs.

10.4   Controlling the motor load

10.4.1   Variable speed drives

Variable speed drives (VSDs) can be used for both efficient system regulation and variable flow control.

VSDs vary motor speed through output waveforms at reduced frequencies. VSDs for fans and pumps are normally pulse width modulation inverters with variable torque characteristics. Modern VSDs are very efficient and reliable with sophisticated features for setting speeds, acceleration

rates, etc. Little, if any, allowance has to be made for de-rating motors when used with modern VSDs. VSDs also normally provide a high power factor at all loads.

Electronic variable voltage VSDs provide a far less efficient drive system than pulse width modulation inverters but are acceptable for very small (fractional kW) motors. They should be avoided on larger drives because special motors with extra cooling are required. The additional cooling requirement is an indication of an inefficient drive system.

As a rule of thumb, the capital cost of VSDs is roughly £115 per kW motor rating, excluding installation costs, see DETR Good Practice Guide 2[1]. Costs are normally higher per kW for small drives, although real costs are continuing to fall. There is an increasing number of pump and fan manufacturers who supply in-built VSDs that provide significant cost savings compared to separate VSDs. Reference should be made to DETR General Information Report 41[3] for further information on VSDs for building services applications.

10.4.2   Efficient system regulation

Fans and pumps are normally at least 15–20% over-sized due to safety factors and available pressure/flow characteristics making it necessary for them to be regulated to provide design flow rates. Fan and pump pressure/flow characteristics must be matched as closely as possible to the system characteristics to provide the design flow rate. Increasing system resistance to reduce flow rates is inherently inefficient as fan or pump absorbed power is in proportion to the pressure generated. Energy is often wasted due to insufficient care being taken with system regulation.

10.4.2.1   Traditional regulation

Traditional regulation methods match the fan or pump to the system as closely as possible, the use system regulation through increasing system resistance until the flow is reduced to the design figure. The amount of system regulation should be minimised as far as possible due to its inherent inefficiency.

In the first stage the fan or pump is matched to the system as follows:

—   For belt drives, a change of pulleys normally allows the pump or fan speed to be reduced and the duty to be matched to within 5–10% (belt drives have additional losses, see 10.3.2).

—   Smaller impellers can be used with pumps, although this will cause a slight reduction in pump efficiency.

—   Multiple speed motors have coarse adjustment of speed and will rarely permit an accurate matching of fan/pump characteristics.

—   Axial fans often permit accurate matching of characteristics by blade pitch adjustment.

Lack of time, or readily available components, should not be used as an excuse for inadequate matching the fan or pump to system.

In the second stage, the system is regulated as follows:

— System resistance is increased, by regulating valves or dampers, until the flow rate is reduced to the design flow rate.

10.4.2.2   Regulation using VSDS

VSDs can be used to match fans or pumps to the system, their additional cost often being justified purely for regulation. Regulation using VSDs offers the following advantages:

— Very rapid results are possible compared with those from traditional first stage regulation methods.

— There is no need for a second stage.

— Accurate setting of speeds and flow provides minimum energy consumption.

— Ease of resetting to match flow to actual loads is possible where system flow requirements are changed.

— Additional flexibility allows variable flow control, maximum demand control, etc.

— There are cost savings for regulating valves or dampers.

— 20 to 40% savings are possible with 10 to 20% regulation.

— They normally (but not always) operate nearer the point of maximum efficiency, compared with conventional flow regulation.

In the unlikely event of an exact match of pump/fan to system, there would be an energy penalty of up to 10% with a typical VSD. However, for most applications, VSD regulation will often dramatically reduce energy consumption and the savings can justify the cost of the VSD on grounds of regulation alone.

Figure 10.2 shows a relatively flat pressure/flow characteristic for the pump (dotted lines) and corresponding system curves (solid lines). The intersection point A is the operating point when the system is unregulated, giving a flow of 4.0 l/s at a pump head of 54.6 kPa. If the desired flow rate were 3.6 l/s, the system would normally be regulated via a regulating valve to alter the system curve. The operating point would then be at B, giving 3.6 l/s at 59.2 kPa. If a VSD is used to reduce the pump speed and hence reduce the pump characteristic, rather than increase the system resistance, the operating point will be at C, giving 3.6 l/s at only 43.8 kPa.

For a 10% reduction in flow, the energy used is as follows.

Energy at point A is:

$$E_A = \frac{\text{flow} \times \text{pump head}}{\text{pump efficiency}}$$

$$= \frac{(4 \times 54.6)}{0.8} = 273 \text{ W}$$

Energy at point B is:

$$E_B = \frac{(3.6 \times 59.2)}{0.8} = 266 \text{ W}$$

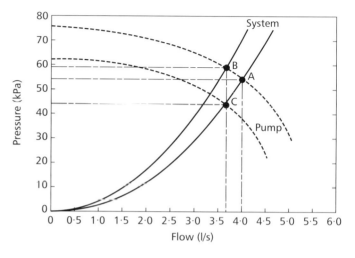

Figure 10.2 The effect of 10% regulation of a pump[3] (reproduced from DETR General Information Report 41. Crown copyright (1996))

Energy at point C is:

$$E_C = \frac{\text{flow} \times \text{pump head}}{\text{pump efficiency} \times \text{VSD efficiency}}$$

$$= \frac{(3.6 \times 43.8)}{(0.78 \times 0.92)} = 214 \text{ W}$$

Hence:

$$\text{Energy saved (\%)} = [(E_B - E_C)/E_B] \times 100$$

$$= 19.5\%$$

The following points should be noted:

— Nearly 20% of the energy is saved by using a VSD for 10% flow regulation.

— For general guidance, unless the pump or fan curves are exceptionally flat, it is safe to assume around 20% saving for 10% flow regulation and 40% for 20% flow regulation using a VSD compared with a regulating valve.

— In many instances, these savings make the use of VSDs viable purely for regulation.

— Similar savings can be achieved through speed matching by pulley changes where belt drives are used (although the belts will consume additional energy), or impeller changes, etc. However, in practice, time and the availability of components often preclude optimising the fan or pump characteristic.

For further information on regulation using VSDs, reference should be made to DETR General Information Report 41[3].

10.4.3   Variable flow control

Building services are generally sized for peak loads and spend most of their operating life at part load. Power absorbed by fans and pumps is proportional to the speed (volume) cubed and, typically, less than 20% of full volume input energy is required at 50% flow. The significant potential energy savings of variable flow control are illustrated in Figure 10.3.

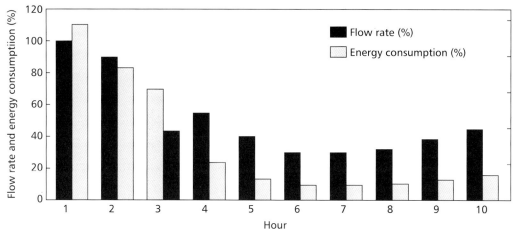

Hour	1	2	3	4	5	6	7	8	9	10	Average
Flow rate (%)	100	90	70	55	40	30	30	32	38	45	53·0
Energy consumption (%)	110·0	82·9	42·3	23·6	13·4	9·7	9·7	10·3	12·5	16·1	33·1
Energy saving (%)	−10·0	17·1	57·7	76·4	86·6	90·3	90·3	89·7	87·5	83·9	66·9

Figure 10.3 Heating pump energy savings[3] (reproduced from DETR General Information Report 41. Crown copyright (1996))

Figure 10.3 illustrates the savings for a heating pump in a typical office on an average heating system day. It shows that:

— full flow is only required during boost

— the average flow rate is 53%.

— the average energy saving is 66.9%.

Effective variable flow control requires a well designed system, with controllability considered from very early stages. Methods of controlling variable flows in building services are discussed in some detail in DETR General Information Report 41[3]. Types of fans and pumps and design details are contained in CIBSE Guide B16[10] for pumps and B3[11] for fans.

10.4.3.1 Mechanical variable flow control methods

Variable pitch axial fans provide a very efficient method of variable flow control and, unlike variable speed fans, can maintain high static pressures at low volumes. However, care must be taken with the selection of variable pitch axial fans to avoid stall problems. Complex hub mechanisms and actuation systems can also cause problems.

Other methods of mechanical variable flow control are very inefficient compared with VSDs and variable pitch axial fans. However, dampers used in association with VSDs and variable pitch axial fans, such as VAV terminal units, provide an efficient system.

Where mechanical variable flow methods result in variable motor loads the power factor will also vary, making automatic power factor correction desirable.

Reference should be made to DETR General Information Report 41[3] for further information on mechanical variable flow control methods.

10.4.3.2 Ventilation and air conditioning systems

Variable air volume (VAV) systems are suitable for buildings where there is predominantly a cooling load throughout the year, such as deep plan office buildings, where they can be an energy efficient form of air conditioning. VAV systems are complex compared with other forms of air conditioning and considerable care has to be taken in system design and control. In particular, sensor locations must be carefully considered.

There are a number of opportunities for variable flow control with other ventilation and air conditioning systems, such as air quality control and heating/cooling demand control. These systems normally have limited flow reduction due to factors such as cold air dumping. However, due to the 'cube law' relationship between flow and absorbed power, significant energy savings are also possible.

Fans for dry air coolers and air-cooled condensers are normally controlled in stages by multiple fans and/or multiple speed motors. The control and energy efficiency of cooling towers is normally improved by variable speed control of the fans (via VSDs) rather than on/off control or staged control by multiple speed motors.

Reference should be made to DETR General Information Report 41[3] for further information on variable flow control of ventilation and air conditioning systems.

10.4.3.3 Variable flow heating and chilled water systems

Variable flow can be applied to most heating and chilled water distribution systems, see Figure 10.4, with significant pumping energy savings. Care must be taken in system design to ensure design water flow rates through boilers and chillers, and constant flow primary pumps with secondary circuits served via a buffer vessel (or common header), are normally required.

Capital cost savings can be made by using two-port valves instead of three-port valves for applications such as air conditioning. By-pass pipework and regulating valves are also eliminated. Many heating systems use two-port TRVs for emitter control so that there will be no system capital cost savings, although effective variable flow control will permit TRVs to operate effectively and provide further energy savings.

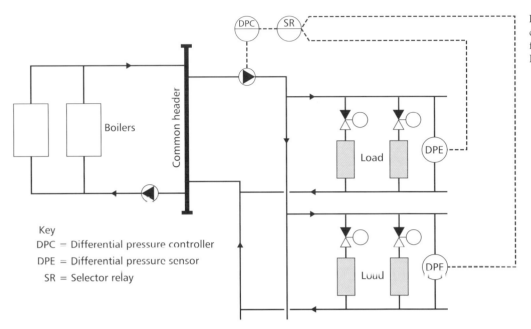

Figure 10.4 Variable flow heating or chilled water system[3] (reproduced from DETR General Information Report 41. Crown copyright (1996))

Key
DPC = Differential pressure controller
DPE = Differential pressure sensor
SR = Selector relay

Pumps should be controlled in relation to system differential pressure to maintain a near constant differential pressure across the loads and control valves. Systems must be designed for relatively low pressure loss to minimise variation in differential pressure at different loads. Control valves should be sized against loads with some allowance for variation in system differential pressure. TRVs should be sized for a nominal pressure drop. Care should be taken not to compromise efficient operation by using differential pressure control valves, which are unnecessary for most single building applications.

Pumps are now available with in-built VSDs and differential pressure control. These include control strategies that reduce pump differential pressure at low loads, allowing differential pressure control similar to that above. These pumps significantly reduce the cost of variable flow heating and chilled water systems.

Reference should be made to DETR General Information Report 41[3] for further information on variable flow heating and chilled water systems.

10.4.4   Additional control methods

Additional control methods that can be used to reduce motor energy consumption and associated costs are described in 10.4.4.1 to 10.4.4.4.

10.4.4.1   Demand based control

Energy consumption is minimised where plant only runs when required. Demand based control will only run central plant when there is a demand from the zones served. Pump, fan, boiler and chiller energy, plus distribution system thermal losses, can all be reduced.

Care must be taken to ensure that response times are adequate if central plant and distribution systems are allowed to start and stop according to zone demand. Logical strategies (often incorporating time delays and minimum operating times) must be developed to permit safe and reliable operation in all circumstances. Additional control functions such as optimum stop/start, which then demand central plant operation, will be required at each zone.

Demand based control strategies are available with a number of modern control systems and these can provide additional economy of operation at minimal, or zero, cost. However, where fixed strategies are built into controllers, care must be taken to ensure that they are suitable for the application.

10.4.4.2   Duty cycling

Duty cycling switches off plant for a percentage of the normal operating time and is normally on a fixed cyclical basis, such as 15 minutes in an hour. This can disturb building occupants and cause problems such as additional belt wear due to more frequent starting.

Duty cycling is an indication of over-sized systems and should not be necessary for well designed and controlled plant. Where services are over-sized it is normally much better to reduce fan or pump output by efficient system regulation, such as by using a VSD. This will give far greater gains than duty cycling due to the cube relationship between flow and absorbed power.

Duty cycling can make savings, but should normally be regarded as a stop-gap measure prior to the implementation of more satisfactory and energy efficient methods.

10.4.4.3   Maximum demand control

Reducing the maximum electrical demand of a building can reduce supply costs with many tariffs. Maximum demand control limits the maximum load and hence eliminates charges imposed for exceeding the agreed supply limit. Effective control can offer the opportunity for lower limits with the consequent reduction in supply costs.

The use of maximum demand control has often been limited because building users are reluctant to allow any item of plant to be switched off. Where VSDs are used, maximum demand control can be used effectively as the cube law relationship between flow and absorbed power permits significant power reductions for a small reduction in flow.

Plant with a high energy consumption such as chillers can also have the number of stages limited at times of maximum demand, rather than be turned off. Care must be taken to ensure that safe and reliable operating strategies are devised.

10.4.4.4 Energy optimisers

Factors relating to the possible use of energy optimisers are complex and reference should be made to DETR Good Practice Guide 2[1].

10.5 Building transportation systems

This section sets out some important issues in designing energy efficient transportation systems for buildings, in line with the principles at the front of this Guide. Lifts and escalators can be significant energy consumers in some buildings, depending on the layout and use of the building. Where possible, designers should minimise transportation requirements through good building layout during the sketch design stage (see section 4).

Energy consumption can also be minimised through good design, selection and control of transportation equipment at the detailed design stage. Although increased energy efficiency can often involve higher initial capital cost, this can be recovered through energy savings and, therefore, each application warrants a full cost analysis. Detailed design of transportation systems are covered CIBSE Guide D[12].

10.5.1 Lifts

The following issues should be taken into account when designing energy efficient lifts:

— Where possible, group lifts together to allow group controls to minimise journeys and, hence, reduce energy consumption.

— Where possible, locate stairs before lifts. If passengers pass a staircase on the way to the lift, the demand for the lift may be less.

— Select the lift control strategy to match the likely traffic patterns with the minimum number of journeys and hence minimise energy consumption.

— Select lift speeds that are appropriate to the task, e.g. slower speeds for goods lifts.

— Select an energy efficient motor to drive the lift.

— Consider recovering heat from lift motor rooms if the lifts are used intensely. Typically, a 20 kW lift motor can produce 7 kW of heat in the machine room (see CIBSE Guide D Table 9.1[12]).

Lifts require about the same installed power as escalators but operate intermittently. Therefore, with respect to energy use, lifts are preferred. There may be a break-even point for buildings of about five storeys, below which escalators are more economical to run. However, escalators occupy greater floor area.

Energy consumption of lifts is affected by:

— speed of movement

— car size

— travel distance

— duty cycle (i.e. starts per hour, average run distance, load variation, direction when loaded, idle time etc.)

— method of drive and speed control

— system losses (e.g. machinery inefficiencies, controller power consumption).

To take proper account of these factors requires specialist knowledge applied to specific applications. However, for comparative purposes, estimates have been made of the

Table 10.1 Lift energy consumption

Type of drive	Load (kg)	Speed (m/s)	Number of starts per hour	Energy consumption (kW h)
Hydraulic	630	0.63	69	6.7
Geared, 2-speed AC	630	0.63	100	9.8
Geared, variable voltage AC	630	1.0	125	15.9
	800	1.6	155	31.9
Geared, variable voltage, variable frequency	630	1.0	150	7.8
	800	1.6	180	24.3
	1000	1.0	150	12.1
Gearless direct drive DC	1250	2.5	165	25.0
	1600	4.0	150	55.0
Gearless motor generator DC	1250	2.5	165	38.0
	1600	4.0	150	75.0

Table 10.2 Escalator energy consumption

Direction of motion	Rise (m)	Incline (degrees)	Speed (m/s)	Energy saving control	Energy consumption (kW h)
Up	6	30	0.5	No	35.2
	6	30	0.5	Yes	30.1
Down	6	30	0.5	No	27.7
	6	30	0.5	Yes	20.7

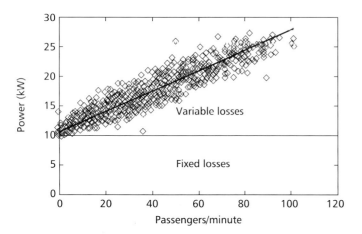

Figure 10.5 Fixed and variable losses for an up-escalator[13]

electrical consumption over a 10 hour period for a typical duty cycle. The estimates are shown in Table 10.1 and serve as an indication of lift energy consumption for comparison with other energy uses.

10.5.2   Escalators and conveyors

Escalators, conveyors and travelling walk-ways operate constantly and require constant speed, but widely varying torque. Their motors run at the same speed whether they are fully or partially loaded. Factors affecting escalator energy consumption are:

—   rise

—   mechanical design

—   number of passengers

—   walking factor[13].

Consumption can be broken down into fixed and variable losses, as indicated in Figure 10.5. Variable losses for a down-escalator will have a negative gradient. Variable losses account for only 20% of consumption in general.

The motors driving these loads often use a power factor controller. Variable speed drives that reduce speed when traffic is light can also provide control for these loads, but at a higher cost. Other options include 'delta' to 'star' switching of motors and systems that switch 'off' when traffic is zero. High efficiency motors and 'soft start' are now in common use on passenger conveyors, escalators and baggage handling systems.

Table 10.2 gives the example energy consumption for some typical operation of an escalator over a 10 hour period. In these examples, it can be seen that the energy saving controls would achieve a 15% to 25% reduction in consumption. Whilst these are typical, each application

should be fully analysed by experts to determine the energy and cost-effectiveness of alternative systems.

References

1   *Guidance notes for reducing energy consumption of electric motors and drives* Good Practice Guide 2 (London: Department of Environment, Transport and Regions)

2   *Economic use of electricity in industry* Fuel Efficiency Booklet No. 9 (London: Department of Environment, Transport and Regions) (1993)

3   *Variable flow control* General Information Report 41 (London: Department of Environment, Transport and Regions) (1996)

4   *Internal heat gains* CIBSE Guide A7 (London: Chartered Institution of Building Services Engineers) (1986)

5   *Air handling units* HEVAC Guide To Good Practice (Marlow: HEVAC Association)

6   *Fan application guide* (Marlow: Fan Manufacturers Association/HEVAC Association)

7   *Fan and ductwork installation guide* (Marlow: Fan Manufacturers Association/HEVAC Association)

8   *Fan noise and vibration* (Marlow: Fan Manufacturers Association/ HEVAC Association)

9   *Purchasing policy for higher efficiency motors* GPCS 222 (London: Department of Environment, Transport and Regions) (1994)

10   *Miscellaneous equipment* CIBSE Guide B16 (London: Chartered Institution of Building Services Engineers) (1986)

11   *Ventilation and air conditioning* CIBSE Guide B2/3 (London: Chartered Institution of Building Services Engineers) (1986)

12   *Transportation systems in buildings* CIBSE Guide D (London: Chartered Institution of Building Services Engineers) (1993)

13   Al-Sharif L Lift and escalator energy consumption *CIBSE National Conference 1996* (London: Chartered Institution of Building Services Engineers) (1996)

Bibliography

Variable speed drive on a boiler fan GPCS 35 (London: Department of Environment, Transport and Regions)

Two-speed motors on ventilation fans GPCS 219 (London: Department of Environment, Transport and Regions) (1994)

Variable speed drives on secondary refrigeration pumps GPCS 124 (London: Department of Environment, Transport and Regions) (1992)

Variable speed drives on cooling water pumps GPCS 89 (London: Department of Environment, Transport and Regions) (1992)

Variable speed drives on water pumps GPCS 88 (London: Department of Environment, Transport and Regions)

High efficiency motors on fans and pumps GPCS 162 (London: Department of Environment, Transport and Regions) (1993)

Higher efficiency motors on HEVAC plant GPCS 266 (London: Department of Environment, Transport and Regions) (1997)

Variable speed drive on a cooling tower induced draught fan GPCS 270 (London: Department of Environment, Transport and Regions) (1995)

Higher efficiency induction motors FPP 50 (London: Department of Environment, Transport and Regions) (1996)

Permanent star running of a lightly loaded motor GPCS 267 (London: Department of Environment, Transport and Regions) (1996)

Thorpe S *Specifier's handbooks No 2: wheelchair stairlifts and platforms lifts* CS2 (Garston: Building Research Establishment)

Lifts LB 2/96 (Bracknell: Building Services Research and Information Association) (1996)

11 General electrical power

11.0	General
11.1	Installed power loads
11.2	Diversity of use
11.3	Energy consumption
11.4	Heat gains and air conditioning

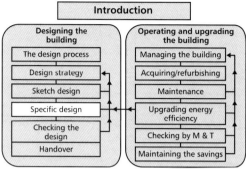

This section sets out some of the key issues in the energy efficient design of small power systems in buildings, in line with the principles at the front of this Guide. It discusses installed power loads and the impact that office equipment, particularly information technology (IT), has on the ultimate design and energy consumption of the building services. Purchasing policies for office equipment are discussed in section 14 and upgrading systems for energy efficiency in section 19.

11.0 General

Small power loads form a significant part of the total energy use in buildings. Currently, office equipment accounts for more than 20% of the energy used in a typical office[1]. With equipment levels doubling every few years, this is likely to become increasingly important. However, small power use is often over estimated at the design stage, and this has led to oversized or unnecessary air conditioning and consequent energy wastage.

11.1 Installed power loads

The actual energy used by office and other equipment is often far less than design calculations predict[2–4]. A report[5] based on measurements in six buildings indicates that allowances of 15 W/m² are more than adequate for all but the most intensive users. Recent figures[1] indicate that

less than 10 W/m² of treated floor area in a naturally ventilated office and less than 15 W/m² in a prestige air conditioned office can be regarded as good practice. Typical average operational power demands are shown in Figure 11.1. Most units are in the areas of heaviest shading. The power consumed by most items of office equipment is often considerably less than that stated on equipment nameplates, as shown in Figure 11.2.

Average power consumption can vary between similar items of equipment, even from the same manufacturer[4]. It is advisable, therefore, to obtain energy consumption data on specific equipment. However, not all manufacturers provide representative data. Some may only provide maximum power demand values rather than representative average loads.

Most modern office equipment has a standby or 'sleep' mode whereby power consumption is considerably less than that for normal operation. These standby levels should

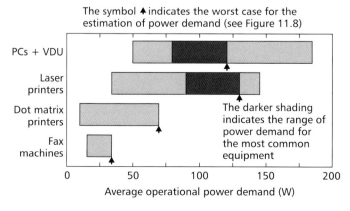

Figure 11.1 Average operational power demand for ranges of office equipment (adapted from DETR GPG 118[3]. Crown copyright (1997))

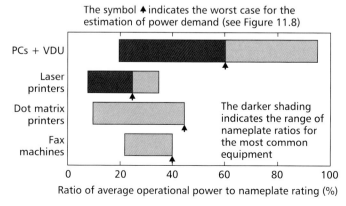

Figure 11.2 Ratio of average operational power demand to nameplate ratings (adapted from DETR GPG 118[3]. Crown copyright (1997))

Table 11.1 Typical levels of energy used by office equipment

Item	Peak rating (W)	Average power consumption (W)	Stand-by energy consumption obtainable (W)	Typical recovery time
PCs and monitor	300	120	30–45	Almost immediate
Personal computers	100	40	20–30	Almost immediate
Monitors	200	80	10–15	Almost immediate
Laser printers	1000	90–130	20–30	30 seconds
Photocopiers	1600	120–1000	30–250	30 seconds
Fax machines	130	30–40	10	Almost immediate
Vending machines	3000	350–700	300	Can be almost immediate

be taken into account in determining true installed power loads. Typical levels of standby power consumption are shown in Table 11.1.

11.2   Diversity of use

Diversity of use is an important variable in predicting installed electrical loads and energy consumption. The actual use of equipment depends heavily upon the individual's job function and routines. The degree to which computers are used by staff in various branches of commerce is shown in Figure 11.3.

The average operating time for a computer and, hence, the average power demand, can be assessed using Figure 11.3. This is based on the percentage operating time for intermittent users and allowing for the time that staff are absent from the office.

The number of computers in operation within each user group will also vary from hour to hour and day to day. For example, if 100 computers are in operation for an average of 20% of the time, it is probable that up to 30% of them could be in use simultaneously. To determine the likely maximum power demand, a usage diversity factor has to be applied to the average percentages to determine the likely maximum

number of computers in use at any one time. Usage diversity factors for groups of computers are shown in Figure 11.4 and the typical daily use of office equipment in Table 11.2.

Sites with high power demands per unit floor area (W/m²) tend to be relatively densely populated e.g. 8 m² per person, therefore the power demand per person may be more representative. Surveys indicate that for most general purpose office buildings, the power demand of general IT equipment is within the range 5–30 W/m² or 100–200 W/person[2]. Less than this is possible where organisations operate successful energy efficiency policies. However, for intensive users, the load can increase to as much as 50 W/m².

In modular offices, there is less opportunity to apply a diversity factor since the distribution of heat gains is more concentrated. The heat gain allowance for an individual room may be much higher than the average load for the floor area as a whole.

The average power demand of variable load machines, such as vending machines and photocopiers, is closely related to the amount of work done by them. Most vending machines only have a small standing load with only nominal local heat gains. Figure 11.5 shows typical average power

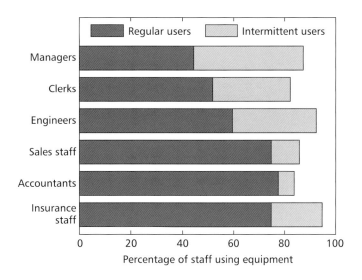

Figure 11.3 Percentage of staff using PCs[3] (reproduced from DETR Good Practice Guide 118. Crown copyright (1997))

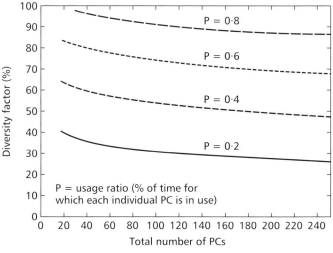

Figure 11.4 Usage diversity factors for groups of PCs[4] (reproduced from BSRIA Technical Note TN 8/92 by permission of the Building Services Research and Information Association)

Table 11.2 Typical daily use of office equipment

Equipment	Time per day for which equipment is in use
Personal computers	4 hours
Printers	1–2 hours
Photocopiers	1–2 hours
Fax machines	20–30 minutes
Vending machines	8–10 hours

Table 11.3 Minimum staff numbers per machine

Machine	Persons per machine
PCs	1
Laser printers	3
Photocopiers	20
Fax machines	20
Modems	20

demands relative to the number of hot drinks supplied per 8 hour working day.

The power demand of photocopiers while printing is approximately 80% of the nameplate rating, and while idling is approximately 20%.

Typically, photocopiers are in use for around 10% of the time in general offices and 40% in typing pools. However, large print runs can lead to the time spent printing to increase to as much as 80% in print rooms. Based on this assumption, Figure 11.6 indicates average power demand values.

Machines such as laser printers, photocopiers and fax machines are usually shared between a number of users. Table 11.3 indicates the minimum likely staff numbers per machine for larger offices.

If the highest consumption machines are chosen from Figure 11.1 and the worst case numbers are assumed from Table 11.3, then for self-contained offices of around 50 persons the load could in theory reach 300 W/person.

Localised 'hot spots', where the heat gain is much higher than the average power demand across the floor, should be identified and taken into account in the design. For example, offices with less than 10 staff will still require access to photocopiers, printers and fax machines, as well as individual computer terminals. Locating all these facilities in the same area could result in a power demand between 30 and 40 W/m².

Figure 11.7 indicates worst case power demands per person for offices of different staff numbers. The values are based on the worst case individual machine loads and worst case numbers of persons sharing. The steps indicated in Figure 11.8 will assist in estimating the office power demands.

Designers will need to acquire information about the future office functions and the numbers and types of equipment. If the office is a speculative new development, designers may

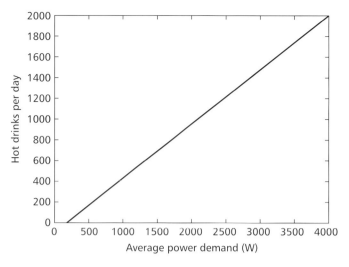

Figure 11.5 Average power demands for vending machines[4] (reproduced from BSRIA Technical Note TN 8/92 by permission of the Building Services Research and Information Association)

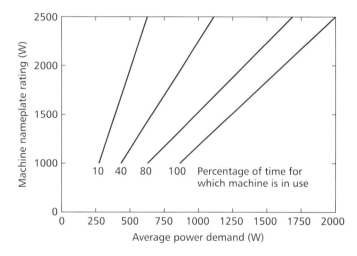

Figure 11.6 Average power demands for photocopiers[4] (reproduced from BSRIA Technical Note TN 8/92 by permission of the Building Services Research and Information Association)

have little information on which to base estimates. In these situations, a design estimate for equipment power demands and numbers of machines can be made based on Figure 11.1 and Table 11.3, with further additions to allow for 'hot spot' areas and future trends.

11.3   Energy consumption

Personal computers (PCs) and associated monitors typically account for two-thirds of energy used by office equipment. Often left on all day, they are used for only a few hours. A typical PC (including monitor) left on for 24 hours each day can use 1000 (kW h) of energy per year. Turning it off at night, holidays and weekends can reduce energy costs by 75%. Half to two thirds of the energy is consumed by the monitor. Screen savers primarily prolong screen life, but can reduce consumption by 10–20% as an interim measure.

Automatic standby and switch-off modes should be implemented wherever possible to reduce energy consumption and therefore heat gains by a further 60% or more.

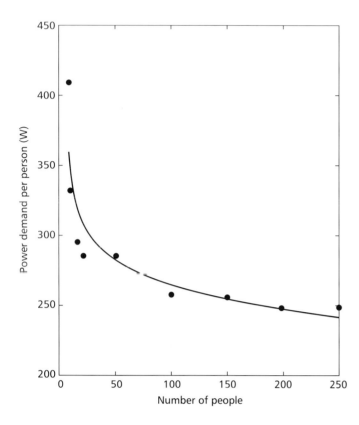

Figure 11.7 Worst case power demands per person for self-contained offices[2] (reproduced from DETR Energy Consumption Guide 35. Crown copyright (1993))

The annual energy consumption for laser printers can be reduced from 1000 (kW h) per year for 24 hour operation to just 250 (kW h) per year if their operation is restricted to 8 hours per day, 5 days per week and turned off at night.

Half of the annual 2000 (kW h) energy consumption for a typical photocopier can be the result of having to ensure that the unit is ready when required. Therefore, good stand-by modes are essential.

Recent statistics[1] indicate that an annual energy consumption for office equipment less than 12 (kW h)/m² of treated floor area in a naturally ventilated office and less than 23 (kW h)/m² per year in a prestige air conditioned office can be regarded as good practice.

Overall office equipment consumption will probably continue to rise, the dominant factor being the ever increasing use of IT equipment. However, advances in technology will probably result in a gradual reduction in equipment loads.

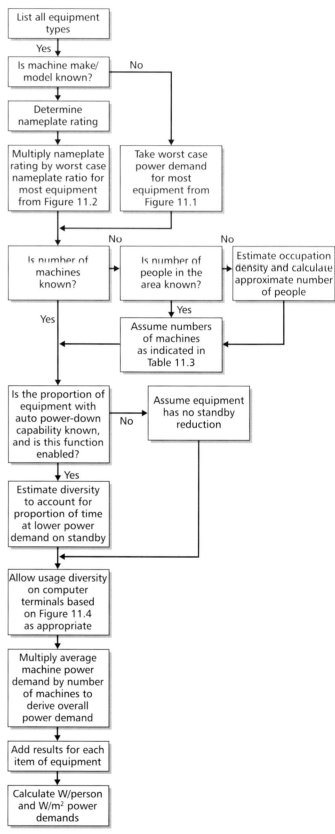

Figure 11.8 Decision guide for estimation of likely power demands (adapted from DETR Good Practice Guide 118[3]. Crown copyright (1997))

11.4 Heat gains and air conditioning

In air conditioned offices, it can take 50% more energy to remove the heat that the equipment generates than that used to run the equipment itself. Therefore, it is important to obtain an accurate estimate of the heat gains from office equipment and not rely on the nameplate ratings given by manufacturers.

Oversized cooling plant and air conditioning affects the selected air handling plant and ductwork sizes, as well as chillers and chilled water pipework. Apart from the initial cost penalty, over estimating will reduce the operating efficiency of cooling installations and can affect comfort

Table 11.4 Average heat emissions from equipment

Item	Worst case power demand (W)	Worst case nameplate ratio (%)
Personal computers with VDU	187 (116)	70 (46)
Mini/mainframe computer workstations	160	60
Laser printers	150 (98)	20 (15)
Dot matrix printers:		
— nameplate rating 100–120W	54	45
— nameplate rating 120–220W	67	31
Plotters:		
— B/W A4-A0 electrostatic	300	60
— colour A4-A0 electrostatic	850	75
— colour A4 thermal	400	51
— colour A0 thermal	750	56
Pen plotter	200	43
Fax machine	38	25
Electronic typewriters	38	40
Modems	20	—
Punching machines	110	44
Microfiche viewers	150	50
Overhead projector	300	99
Slide projector	350	100

Note: values in brackets represent typical averages for these machines.
Nameplate ratio = (actual power demand × 100) / nameplate rating

Table 11.5 Sensible and latent heat emissions from equipment

Item	Nameplate rating (W)	In average use		
		Sensible heat gain (W)	Latent heat gain (W)	Total heat gain (W)
Kettle	1850–2200	430–500	270–315	700–815
Hot water urn	3500	800	500	1300
Hot water urn	5000	1000	700	1700
Gas hot plate	3000–5000	1300–2300	900–1600	2200–3900
Electric hot plate	1200–1800	1200–1800	—	1200–1800
Grill (300x300mm)	3000	600	1200	1800
Microwave	600–1400	600–1400	—	600–1400
Toaster:				
— two slice	2200	1500	400	1900
— four slices	3000	1800	800	2600
Dishwasher	7600	1120	2460	3580
Refrigerator	125	50	—	50
Freezer	810	320	—	320

levels[5]. Chillers will operate for large proportions of the time under part load conditions with, consequently, lower energy efficiency. Although this effect will be less marked with modular chillers and good capacity control, fans and pumps will still be over sized. Internal heat gains from small power equipment are given in CIBSE Guide A7[6] and Figure 11.1.

For VAV systems, air diffuser selections are often made with throw distances based on the estimated peak design condition. If the system operates continuously at a considerably reduced rate, there may be complaints of an apparent lack of air movement. Instead, the supply air temperature can be increased so that more air can be supplied without over cooling although there will be a significant increase in fan energy consumption.

Table 11.4 shows the worst case power demands for office equipment in normal use based on a sample of machines tested[4]. It should be noted that the values in the table are not usually the same as the manufacturers nameplate ratings. Typical variations identified, as the 'nameplate ratio', are also shown in Table 11.4.

In new-build or refurbishment, consideration should be given to clustering shared equipment to avoid full air conditioning, or to minimise its effect on the overall air conditioning system. Localised air conditioning can be sized to meet the specific loads within a zone and appropriate zone controls can be installed.

Catering equipment, such as hot water boilers, kettles, refrigerators and particularly vending machines, can also contribute significantly to the heat gains. Table 11.5 indicates sensible and latent heat emissions from miscellaneous electrical cooking appliances under normal use. The values shown in the table incorporate diversities of up to 50% to allow for intermittent use and the effects of thermostatic controls.

References

1   *Energy efficiency in offices — a technical guide for owners and single tenants* ECON 19 (London: Department of Environment, Transport and Regions) (1997)

2   *Energy efficiency in offices — small power loads* ECON 35 (London: Department of Environment, Transport and Regions) (1993)

3   *Managing energy use. Minimising running costs of office equipment and related air-conditioning* GPG 118 (London: Department of Environment, Transport and Regions) (1997)

4   Hejab M and Parsloe C *Small power loads* TN 8/92 (Bracknell: Building Services Research and Information Association) (1992)

5   LoPinto, Fairfield and Eaves *An assessment of small power loads for commercial buildings* (London: Stanhope Properties PLC) (April 1993)

6   *Internal heat gains* CIBSE Guide A7 (London: Chartered Institution of Building Services Engineers)

Bibliography

Parloe C and Hejab M *Power demands due to portable office equipment* Report No 633 10/1 (Bracknell: Building Services Research and Information Association) (1992)

Fundamentals ASHRAE Handbook (Atlanta, GA: American Society of Heating, Refrigeration and Air Conditioning Engineers) (1997)

Information technology and buildings CIBSE Applications Manual AM7 (London: Chartered Institution of Building Services Engineers) (1992)

Norford L, Rabl A, Harris J and Roturier J *Electronic Office Equipment. The Impact of Market Trends and Technology on End-Use Demand for Electricity: Efficient End- use and New Generation Technologies and their Planning Implications* Eds. Johansson T, Bodlund B and Williams R H (Lund University Press) (1989).

Leary J and Herridge S *General power in offices, the implications for HVAC design* (London: Electricity Association)

12 Checking the design

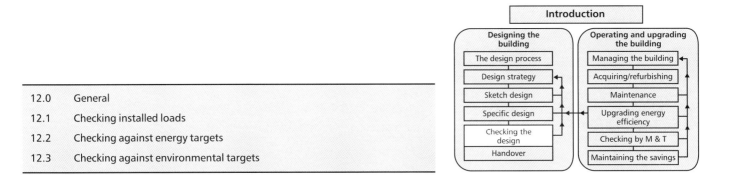

12.0   General

12.1   Checking installed loads

12.2   Checking against energy targets

12.3   Checking against environmental targets

This section sets out how and when the design should be checked for energy efficiency, in line with the principles at the front of this Guide. The design team must spend time checking that energy efficiency objectives and briefing requirements have not been compromised.

12.0   General

The early checks on the overall conceptual design philosophy are covered in section 2. However, both qualitative and quantitative checks should be carried out at various stages throughout the design process to ensure that it meets the energy targets set at the briefing stage. Time for ongoing checks must be included in the plan of work and the design reviewed if it does not meet the targets. There is a range of indicators that contribute to understanding the performance of a building, as shown in Figure 12.1[1].

Checks against benchmarks or yardsticks should cover:

—   overall energy consumption $((kWh)/m^2)$ of each fuel, and overall CO_2 emissions

—   installed loads (W/m^2) of each major service, e.g. lighting, pumps, fans etc.

—   end-use energy consumption $((kWh)/m^2)$ of each major service

—   efficiency indicators, such as specific fan power and lighting $(W/m^2$ per 100 lux).

In the early stages of design these checks can be quick comparisons between rough estimates and simple rules of thumb. The checks should become increasingly detailed as the design progresses. They might involve manual methods for estimating energy consumption through to sophisticated computer simulation techniques for option appraisal. However, the assumptions, accuracy and reliability of the data should always be presented alongside any estimated consumption[1].

The targets set at the briefing stage should be simple to interpret and apply. They should also allow an element of design flexibility. For example, it may be appropriate to allow one target to drift in favour of another if that allows a more integrated energy efficient design overall. In general, total 'delivered' energy should not be used when rating overall building energy efficiency. Electricity and fossil fuel should be considered separately, and converted to CO_2 or primary energy if one single indicator is required[2].

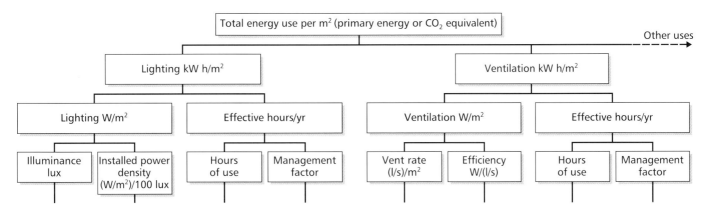

Figure 12.1 Building performance indices[1]

The principal 'integration' of the building and its services takes place in the very early stages of design. The team needs to confirm that its original design intent and energy philosophy still underpins the developing design and that energy efficiency features have not been discarded. Specifically, this should include a check on the likely interactions between the building services, and on the controls necessary to optimise energy consumption (see 5.1).

In cases where a building is composed of several parts having significantly different environmental conditions or patterns of occupancy, separate targets should be established for comparison with the corresponding demand calculations. Targets are usually based on energy use per unit floor area. Care should be taken to use the correct measurement of floor area when comparing buildings[3]. Definitions are:

—   gross area: total building area measured inside external walls

—   treated area: gross area less plant rooms and other areas (e.g. stores) not directly heated or cooled

—   net area: gross area less common areas and ancillary spaces (the letting agent's 'lettable' floor area).

In general, treated area is to be preferred, although many of the available benchmarks are based on gross floor area.

12.1   Checking installed loads

Rules of thumb for installed loads that are based on gross floor area are shown in Table 12.1[4]. In the absence of confirmed data, these figures can be used as rough indicators, but are likely to be considerably higher than those for modern, low energy designs. Although these are not strict limits, they can be used to highlight significant over-design which could lead to high energy consumption. It is anticipated that these figures will gradually be reduced over time due to improvements in design and the data available. DETR General Information Report 31[5] provides some specific installed load data for seven low energy offices.

Table 12.1 Thermal and electrical installed loads[4] (reproduced from BSRIA Rules of thumb TN17/95 by permission of the Building Services Research and Infomation Association)

Load	Type of building (or load)	Load (W/m²)
Heating load	General buildings	90
	Offices	70
	Industrial	80
	Educational	100
	Retail	110
	Residential	60
Infiltration heating load		7.5
Total cooling load	General office	125 (or 1 kW/occupant)
	Interior zones (more than 7 m from windows)	75
	Perimeter zones: — 65% glazing — 60% glazing	180 W/m² 120 W/m²
	Typical buildings: — retail — banks — restaurants — hotels — computer suites	140 W/m² 160 W/m² 220 W/m² 150 – 300 W/m² 400 W/m²
Solar heat gains	Windows with internal blinds: — south facing, June – September — east-west facing, June – September	150 (per m² of glass) 250 (per m² of glass)
Other heat gains	Metabolic	20 W/m²
	Lighting	10 – 25 W/m²
	Office machinery	20 – 40 W/m²
Electrical load	Lighting	20 W/m² (2.5 W/m² per 100 lux)
	Small power	20 – 40 W/m²
	Air conditioning	60 W/m²
	Passenger lifts	10 W/m²
	Computer rooms	270 W/m² (net area)

12.2 Checking against energy targets

12.2.1 Estimating energy consumption

Energy consumption may be crudely estimated using installed loads, estimated hours run and simple diversity factors. The results can be useful in providing an early order of magnitude indication of the likelihood that targets will, or will not be met.

As the design progresses, more sophisticated tools will be required to improve the accuracy of estimates. Manual methods include:

— Calculations based on CIBSE Guide[6].

— CIBSE Building Energy Code[7] for heated and naturally ventilated buildings provides a monthly average method and is ideal for preliminary assessments at an early design stage. A primary objective of the code is to compare early design options so that a suitable energy efficient scheme can be selected for development.

— CIBSE Building Energy Code[8] for air conditioned buildings (in preparation) is based on a calculation of mean monthly loads and demands. In common with the code for heated and naturally ventilated buildings, it is intended for comparing design options, not for forecasting the future demand of a building.

— The ASHRAE Bin Method[9].

— The LT method[10] can be used to review optimum building shapes and glazing specifications to maximise passive potential and assess the need for cooling etc. This is an example of a refined manual technique for predicting annual energy consumption and optimising solar gains, daylighting etc. The technique is based on the results of detailed simulations of a large number of design options which are presented on a set of charts. The applicability of the LT method depends upon the match between the user's intention and the simplifying assumptions, e.g. fixed values for such things as opaque fabric U-values, room height, ventilation rate, internal gains, occupancy pattern, etc. An element of good design is assumed in that automatic lighting and blind controls are incorporated. Potential users may find these restrictions too severe.

— An energy performance index method under development by BRE[11].

12.2.1.1 Dynamic building simulation

Dynamic models can provide hour by hour simulations based on average climatic data for predicting energy consumption and, in particular, for investigating the consequences of design modifications. Software can simulate the characteristics of one or more of factors such as heat, light, mass (air and moisture) and can be used to assess alternative design options to help develop the design throughout the project. More detail is available in CIBSE Applications Manual AM11[12].

Important issues that must be addressed when using a dynamic model include the following[13]:

— suitability for the required purpose

— method of use

— data requirements

— data validation

— method of checking requirements

— training.

Suitability relates to the level of detail the model requires. For example, models that need a full geometrical description of the building, may not be suitable for use at early stages in the design. Detail used to represent the plant and controls also varies. In general, dynamic plant simulation is not used, but it may sometimes be essential, e.g. with underfloor heating and thermal storage systems.

12.2.2 Comparing against good practice benchmarks

Good practice benchmarks based on the energy performance of existing buildings are listed in Table 12.2[2,3,14–23] and more recent data is presented by Jones[24]. Roughly 25% of existing buildings have an energy consumption less than these benchmarks. New designs, with improved windows, controls, insulation etc. should have a target energy consumption very much less than the good practice benchmarks. DETR General Information Report 31[5] presents a number of energy efficiency design case studies and these could be used as targets. Where several design options that meet the targets are being considered, the cost-effectiveness of each approach should dictate the final choice.

It is anticipated that these benchmarks will change as data and design is improved. However, currently they provide a useful upper limit.

Comparisons at a more detailed level are valuable in identifying where the design needs further attention. An example is shown in Figure 12.2[3]. Further examples of energy breakdowns are shown in CIBSE Applications Manual AM5[25] although these are for typical existing buildings, not new designs.

The greater the depth in which comparisons can be made, the more likely that a robust and efficient design will be achieved.

Energy from renewable sources (e.g. wind-powered generator) can be used to offset the demand for fossil fuels and electricity and hence improve on the target. On sites including CHP, a single overall CO_2 or primary energy benchmark and estimate should be developed, as indicated in section 12.3.

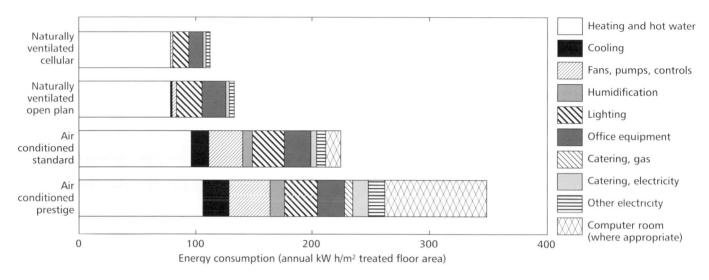

Figure 12.2 Good practice energy consumption benchmarks for particular services in offices (adapted from DETR ECON 19[(3)]. Crown copyright (1997))

Table 12.2 Good practice benchmarks

Building type	Good practice benchmark energy consumption ((kW h)/m² treated floor area) per year	
	Electricity	Fossil fuel
Offices:		
— naturally ventilated, cellular	33	79
— naturally ventilated, open plan	54	79
— air conditioned, standard	128	97
— air conditioned, prestige	234	114
Industrial:		
— general manufacturing	50	125
— factory office	55	100
— light manufacturing	31	90
— storage and distribution	20	80
Retail:		
— 'DIY' stores	130	150
— non-food stores	200	80
— department stores	240	150
— small food shops	400	80
— supermarkets	670	160
Hotels:		
— small	80	240
— holiday	80	260
— luxury	90	300
Schools:		
— primary or middle	20	126
— secondary	24	136
Sports and recreation:		
— without swimming pool	75	215
— with swimming pool	150	360
— swimming pool only	165 (550)†	775 (2950)†
Nursing and residential homes	44	247
Further and higher education:		
— teaching spaces	75	185
— residential areas	85	240
Hospitals:		
— teaching and specialist	86	339
— acute and maternity	78	422
— cottage	55	443
— long stay	48	401

† per m² of pool surface area

12.3 Checking against environmental targets

The energy consumption benchmarks ((kW h)/m²) shown in Table 12.2 can be converted into CO_2 emissions (kg/m²) by multiplying by the conversion factors shown in Table 12.3. The emissions can then be summed to provide a single target for a particular building against which estimates of future CO_2 emissions can be compared. Primary energy may also be used as a common basis to develop a single target/estimate.

The *Building Research Establishment Environmental Assessment Method*[(7)] (BREEAM) provides a methodology for assessing various environmental factors for new and existing buildings, and includes CO_2 emissions as an environmental indicator of energy use. The method has been developed for specific building sectors[(26–30)].

The environmental issues covered are grouped under three main headings:

— *Global issues*: covering global warming, acid rain and depletion of a limited natural resource.

— *Local issues*: e.g. water conservation, Legionnaires' disease and transport.

— *Indoor issues*: including lighting and air quality.

The assessment of existing buildings is in two parts. The first relates to the building fabric and services, and the second to the operation and management of the building.

Table 12.3 CO_2 performance index calculation

Fuel source	CO_2 conversion factor (kg/(kW h))
Gas	0.20
Oil	0.29
Coal	0.34
Electricity★	0.52

★ based on 1997 figures and may change due to the progressive depletion of fossil fuels or the growth in the use of non-depleting resources, see 4.3

Depending on the amount of credits obtained under each heading, a certificate is awarded expressed as a single rating of 'fair', 'good', 'very good' or 'excellent'.

References

1   Field J, Soper J, Jones P G, Bordass W, Grigg P Energy performance of occupied non domestic buildings: Assessment by analysing end-use energy consumptions *Building Services Engineering Research and Technology* **18**[(1)] (1997)

2   *Introduction to energy efficiency in buildings* Booklets EEB 1–13 (Garston: Building Research Energy Conservation Support) (London: Department of Environment, Transport and Regions) (1994)

3   *Energy efficiency in offices — a technical guide for owners and single tenants* ECON 19 (Garston: Building Research Energy Conservation Support) (London: Department of Environment, Transport and Regions) (1997)

4   Pavey N *Rules of thumb* TN17/95 (Bracknell: Building Services Research and Information Association) (1995)

5   *Avoiding or minimising the use of air-conditioning — a research report from the EnREI Programme* GIR 31 (London: Department of Environment, Transport and Regions) (1995)

6   *Design data* CIBSE Guide A (London: Chartered Institution of Building Services Engineers) (1986)

7   *Calculation of energy demands and targets for the design of new buildings and services* CIBSE Building Energy Code Part 2 (a) Heated and naturally ventilated buildings (London: Chartered Institution of Building Services Engineers) (1981)

8   *Air conditioned buildings* CIBSE Building Energy Code 2 (London: Chartered Institution of Building Services Engineers) (in preparation)

9   *Fundamentals* ASHRAE Handbook (Atlanta, GA: American Society of Heating, Refrigeration and Air Conditioning Engineers) (1997)

10   Baker N V and Steemers K *The LT Method 2.0. An energy design tool for non-domestic buildings* (Cambridge Architectural Research/Building Research and Energy Conservation Support Unit) (1994)

11   Grigg P F, Moss S A and Birtles A B Assessing non domestic building design using an energy performance index method *CIBSE National Conference 1997* (London: Chartered Institution of Building Services Engineers) (1997)

12   *Building Energy and environmental modelling* CIBSE Applications Manual AM11 (London: Chartered Institution of Building Services Engineers) (1998)

13   Computer modelling as a design tool for predicting building performance *Building Services Engineering Research and Technology* **16**(4) B41–54 (1995)

14   *Energy efficiency in hotels — a guide for owners and managers* ECON 36 (London: Department of Environment, Transport and Regions) (1993)

15   *Saving energy in schools — the headteacher's and governor's guide to energy efficiency* ECON 15 (London: Department of Environment, Transport and Regions) (1991)

16   *Saving energy in schools — the school energy manager's guide to energy efficiency* ECON 16 (London: Department of Environment, Transport and Regions) (1991)

17   *Energy efficiency in public houses. Guidance on the benefits of energy efficiency in public houses for the brewer, licensee and customer* ECON 13 (London: Department of Environment, Transport and Regions) (1992)

18   *Energy efficiency in industrial buildings and sites* ECON 18 (London: Department of Environment, Transport and Regions) (1993)

19   *Energy efficiency in sports and recreation buildings — a guide for owners and energy managers* ECON 51 (London: Department of Environment, Transport and Regions) (1996)

20   *Energy consumption guide for nursing and residential homes* ECON 57 (London: Department of Environment, Transport and Regions) (1996)

21   *Energy efficiency in further and higher education — cost effective low energy buildings* ECON 54 (London: Department of Environment, Transport and Regions) (1997)

22   *Introduction to energy efficiency. Health care buildings* EEB 4 (London: Department of Environment, Transport and Regions) (1997)

23   *Energy efficiency action pack — for retail premises* GPG 190 (London: Department of Environment, Transport and Regions) (1996)

24   Jones P G and Cheshire D Bulk data for benchmarking non-domestic building energy consumption *CIBSE National Conference 1996* (London: Chartered Institution of Building Services Engineers) (1996)

25   *Energy audits and surveys* CIBSE Applications Manual AM5 (London: Chartered Institution of Building Services Engineers) (1991)

26   *BREEAM/New Offices. Version 1/93. An environmental assessment for new offices* BR234 (Garston: Building Research Establishment) (1993)

27   *BREEAM Version 2/91. An environmental assessment for new superstores and supermarkets* BR207 (Garston: Building Research Establishment) (1991)

28   *Environmental standard: Homes for a greener world* BR 278 (Garston: Building Research Establishment) (1995)

29   *BREEAM/Existing offices. Version 4/93. An environmental assessment for existing office buildings* BRE240 (Garston: Building Research Establishment) (1993)

30   *BREEAM/New Industrial Units. Version 5/93. An environmental assessment for new industrial, warehousing and non-food retail units* BRE252 (Garston: Building Research Establishment) (1993)

Bibliography

Parsloe C J *Over-engineering in building services — an international comparison of design and installation methods* TR 21/95 (Bracknell: Building Services Research and Information Association) (1995)

Parsloe C *Design for maintainability* AG 11/92 (Bracknell: Building Services Research and Information Association) (1992)

Pavey N *Rules of thumb* TN 17/95 (Bracknell: Building Services Research and Information Association) (1995)

Halliday S P *Environmental code of practice for buildings and their services* ENCOP (Bracknell: Building Services Research and Information Association) (1994)

Halliday S *Building services and environmental issues — the background* IR 1 (Bracknell: Building Services Research and Information Association) (1992)

Fishwick P J and Alamdari F *Performance testing of buildings* TN 5/95 (Bracknell: Building Services Research and Information Association) (1995)

Saving energy in the NHS Audit Commission Occasional Paper No 2 (London: Audit Commission) (1991)

Energy efficiency in offices — small power loads ECON 35 (London: Department of Environment, Transport and Regions) (1993)

13 Commissioning, handover and feedback

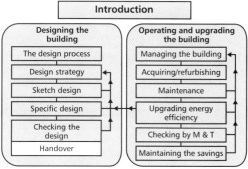

This section reviews the energy issues that arise when commissioning and handing over new or refurbished buildings, along with feedback mechanisms to improve future energy efficient designs (see the principles at the front of this Guide). It should be read in conjunction with sections 2 and 12. Further information on commissioning and handover can be found in the CIBSE Commissioning Codes[1–5].

13.0 General

Good installation, commissioning, documentation and handover are essential in achieving energy efficiency. Lack of attention to these issues has resulted in greater requirements for pre- and post-occupancy performance checks.

The period immediately after completing construction can be a make-or-break situation for future energy efficiency. It is during this period that the robustness of the design is tested, the plant checked and set into operation and steps taken to ensure that building managers understand how the building and its services are meant to work.

Often, designers and contractors are under pressure to meet deadlines and clients are preoccupied with preparations for fitting-out and occupation. This situation can lead to inadequate checks and problem solving with poor handover procedures and, in consequence, high energy consumption in the future. In some cases, it can lead to a building being out of control for the remainder of its life. Careful preparation and management is essential to ensure that energy objectives are retained, since many energy problems can be traced back to poor commissioning and handover.

13.1 On-site checks

The following checks need special attention:

— Check the integrity of the building envelope including the continuity of insulation and air/vapour barriers.

— Check air tightness, especially in buildings assembled dry from components; checks of detailing and specification, as well as pressure tests may be desirable.

— Check any ductwork for air tightness and proper insulation, since excessive leakage will make it difficult to balance the HVAC system, resulting in excessive energy consumption. Most importantly, the controls wiring/software should be checked carefully to ensure that systems can actually be commissioned and balanced correctly.

— Check lighting equipment to ensure that fixtures are installed in the proper places. A lighting strategy that mixes high efficiency and regular fittings can be confusing to installers.

13.2 The commissioning process

Successful commissioning of a system should ensure safe and reliable operation in accordance with manufacturers' instructions and design intentions. It should seek to identify and resolve operational faults while maximising plant efficiency and working life. The commissioning process acts as a checking procedure to ensure that:

— the installed equipment is as designed

— the building and its services operate correctly and safely

— equipment is adjusted, balanced and fine tuned to optimise flow rates, temperatures etc.

— any design faults or over specification are highlighted

— systems are clean.

Designers need to address the issue of 'commissionability' of building services early on, and the client should be encouraged to participate in this exercise. It is essential to allow adequate time and a suitable budget for commissioning by competent personnel. If this completion stage is squeezed, poor operation and high energy consumption is likely. CIBSE Commissioning Codes[1–5] should be followed and BSRIA commissioning guidance[6–10] consulted.

13.3 Handover

At handover, the client should be given:

— full documentation on the commissioning of the building services including a comparison with the original specifications to ensure compliance with the design intent and a check on the control of all systems under operating conditions

— operating and maintenance manuals for the building operator.

The design team should provide a brief overview of:

— the overall design and control strategy and the building services operation

— how to operate the plant efficiently in relation to seasonal changes, out of hours use, start-up and shut down

— the issues that management need to pass on to the building occupants, including the way to operate controls, window, shading etc.

A provision should be included in the contract for the contractor and designer to carry out familiarisation and training sessions for operators and managers. If the client intends to outsource all or part of the maintenance work, this should be arranged well in advance of the training to ensure attendance by the maintenance contractor.

13.4 Documenting the building

Appropriate contractual provision must be made for suitable operating and maintenance (O&M) manuals and drawings.

Information requirements should be carefully planned by the design team with a structured approach to handover. BSRIA Technical Note TN15/95[11] provides recommended contents for O&M manuals alongside legislation relevant to operating and maintaining building services. The *Construction (Design and Management) Regulations 1994*[12] require the inclusion of a health and safety file.

Typically, the operating element of O&M information is limited to plant room procedures. With the advent of low energy solutions, it is increasingly important that broader issues are included, in particular the overall design intent and how the building occupants are expected to control their environment.

Some contract allowances may cover the cost of providing only rudimentary O&M information. This may be sufficient for relatively small projects incorporating basic services but, for more complex installations, the building operator should be involved throughout the project to establish a maintenance brief and specific operating/ maintenance procedures.

Responsibility should be allocated for producing the manuals and record drawings. This could be a specialist author, which can be advantageous when producing comprehensive O&M information. Timescales need to be set for production and a system introduced to record and explain changes to the services that often occur during installation. Designers should also set up a procedure for checking the O&M manual at specific points during the project.

Detailed guidance on specifying and procuring O&M manuals is provided in the BSRIA Application Guide AG1/87[13] which includes a model specification and details of contractual arrangements.

13.5 The feedback process

Few buildings achieve maximum energy performance immediately. Complex buildings often require a troubleshooting phase and clients should be made aware of this at an early stage. Troubleshooting represents an early part of the feedback process and may involve problems associated with unexpectedly high energy consumption.

The integration of natural ventilation and daylighting with the services creates a greater need for post-occupancy performance monitoring. Details may need fine-tuning, design intentions should be discussed with occupants and management. Actual occupancy patterns may have changed since the system was designed resulting in a need for some rethinking. Continuous feedback and fine-tuning is essential within the first year of building operation. All seasonal modes of operation will have occurred and problems should have been identified.

Later in the life of the building, the original design brief should become the benchmark for post-occupancy surveys, which objectively explore whether or not the brief has been met. The information gained may then be fed into new building briefs, thereby closing the quality improvement loop. Guidelines should be developed on the frequency and detail of post-occupancy monitoring such as energy and water targets, internal comfort conditions, unsatisfactory internal air quality and lighting levels. This process should also include occupant feedback by questionnaire[14].

References

1   *Air distribution systems* CIBSE Commissioning Code A (London: Chartered Institution of Building Services Engineers) (1971)

2   *Boiler plant* CIBSE Commissioning Code B (London: Chartered Institution of Building Services Engineers) (1975)

3   *Automatic controls* CIBSE Commissioning Code C (London: Chartered Institution of Building Services Engineers) (1973)

4   *Refrigeration systems* CIBSE Commissioning Code R (London: Chartered Institution of Building Services Engineers) (1991)

5   *Water distribution systems* CIBSE Commissioning Code W (London: Chartered Institution of Building Services Engineers) (1994)

6   Loyd S *Commissioning building services* LB 110/87 (Bracknell: Building Services Research and Information Association) (1987)

7   Parsloe C *The commissioning of water systems in buildings* AG 2/89.1 (Bracknell: Building Services Research and Information Association) (1992)

8   Parsloe C *The commissioning of air systems in buildings* AG 3/89 (Bracknell: Building Services Research and Information Association) (1989)

9   *Commissioning of VAV systems in buildings* AG 1/91 (Bracknell: Building Services Research and Information Association) (1991)

10   Wild L J *Commissioning HVAC systems — division of responsibilities* TM 1/88 (Bracknell: Building Services Research and Information Association) (1988)

11   de Saules T *Handover information for building services* TN 15/95 (Bracknell: Building Services Research and Information Association) (1995)

12   *The Construction (Design and Management) Regulations 1994* (London: Stationery Office) (1994)

13   Armstrong J H *Operating and maintenance manuals for building services installations* AG 1/87 (Bracknell: Building Services Research and Information Association) (1987)

14   Bordass W and Bunn R *et al*. PROBE: Some lessons learned from the first eight buildings *CIBSE National Conference 1997* (London: Chartered Institution of Building Services Engineers) (1997)

Bibliography

Parsloe C *Pre-commission cleaning of water systems* AG 8/91 (Bracknell: Building Services Research and Information Association) (1991)

Parsloe C J *European commissioning procedures* TN 1/90 (Bracknell: Building Services Research and Information Association) (1990)

Condensing boilers CIBSE Applications Manual AM3 (London: Chartered Institution of Building Services Engineers) (1989)

Energy audits and surveys CIBSE Applications Manual AM5 (London: Chartered Institution of Building Services Engineers) (1991)

Heating systems and their control GIR 40 (London: Department of Environment, Transport and Regions) (1996)

Variable flow control GIR 41 (London: Department of Environment, Transport and Regions) (1996)

Low M and Bradshaw J H Future trends in the commissioning of heating and cooling systems *CIBSE National Conference 1995* (London: Chartered Institution of Building Services Engineers) (1995)

Halliday S P *Environmental code of practice for buildings and their services* ENCOP (Bracknell: Building Services Research and Information Association) (1994)

Part B   Operating and upgrading the building

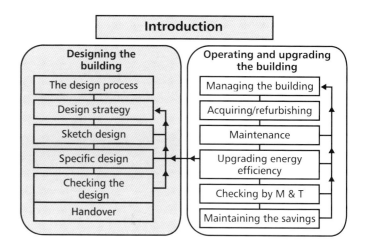

14 Managing the building

This section outlines the issues to be taken into account when operating, maintaining and managing existing buildings in an energy efficient manner, in line with the principles at the front of this Guide. It provides an overview of the main policy issues underpinning the energy efficient management[1-3] of existing buildings, and is primarily aimed at the facilities manager or building operator.

14.0   General

The energy used by a building is broadly determined by the building fabric, the building services and the management of the building. The influence of management on energy consumption is commonly underestimated[1]. Although improvements may be made to the fabric and services, the management of the building often has the biggest impact on the day-to-day energy consumption. It is common to find well-designed buildings operating badly due to poor management. Conversely, poorly designed buildings can be optimised to a great extent through good management practices[4].

Even where all the technical measures have been fully considered and implemented, there is often considerable scope for improved energy efficiency by adopting changes in the management, operation and maintenance of the building. The key to energy efficient management of existing buildings is to:

—   gain a sound understanding of how the building is meant to work, both at a strategic and detailed level

—   set out a clear energy management policy alongside a clear maintenance policy for the building and the building services, and implement these policies rigorously

—   put into place organisational structures to ensure that responsibilities are clear, regular reporting/feedback is appropriate and the necessary resources are made available

—   encourage occupants to use the building correctly and motivate them to reduce energy consumption

—   set energy targets and continually monitor performance in order to keep consumption under control (see section 20).

The energy management matrix shown in Figure 14.1 can be used to review the current state of energy management and to identify areas for improvement.

14.1   Understanding the building

The key to understanding an existing building is to:

—   gain a strategic overview of the design intent

—   ensure that the building is well documented

—   identify the current status of the building

—   identify and address problem areas.

Problems experienced in operating buildings are often due to misunderstandings about how the building design was originally intended to work. Designers intentions are not always fully communicated to the building operator and, sometimes, designers have not necessarily appreciated the operational requirements. This can happen when the client is not the ultimate occupant of the building, or when occupants or operational staff change.

14.1.1   Gaining an overview

The engineer managing specific items of plant often finds it difficult to form a strategic overview of the building and, in particular, an overview of the design intent. It is essential, therefore, to establish how the building is intended to be used and how this relates to the overall heating, lighting, ventilation and control strategies. This strategic understanding is important in providing a framework within which the building can be operated efficiently.

Level	Energy Policy	Organising	Motivation	Information Systems	Marketing	Investment
4	Energy policy, action plan and regular review have commitment of top management as part of an environmental strategy	Energy management fully integrated into management structure. Clear delegation of responsibility for energy consumption	Formal and informal channels of communication regularly exploited by energy manager and energy staff at all levels	Comprehensive system sets targets, monitors consumption, identifies faults, quantifies savings and provides budget tracking	Marketing the value of energy efficiency and the performance of energy management both within the organisation and outside it	Positive discrimination in favour of 'green' schemes with detailed investment appraisal of all new-build and refurbishment opportunities
3	Formal energy policy but no active commitment from top management	Energy manager accountable to energy committee representing all users, chaired by a member of the managing board	Energy committee used as main channel together with direct contact with major users	M&T reports for individual premises based on sub-metering, but savings not reported effectively to users	Programme of staff awareness and regular publicity campaigns	Same payback criteria employed as for all other investment
2	Unadopted energy policy set by energy manager or senior department manager	Energy manager in post, reporting to adhoc committee, but line management and authority are unclear	Contact with major users through adhoc committee chaired by senior departmental manager	Monitioring and targeting reports based on supply meter data. Energy unit has adhoc involvement in budget setting	Some adhoc staff awareness training	Investment using short-term payback criteria only
1	An unwritten set of guidelines	Energy management the part-time responsibility of someone with only limited authority or influence	Informal contacts between engineer and a few users	Cost reporting based on invoice data. Engineer compiles reports for internal use within technical department	Informal contacts used to promote energy efficiency	Only low cost measures taken
0	No explicit policy	No energy management or any formal delegation of responsibility for energy consumption	No contact with users	No information system. No accounting for energy consumption	No promotion of energy efficiency	No investment in increasing energy efficiency in premises

Figure 14.1 Energy management matrix[3] (reproduced from DETR General Information Report 12. Crown copyright (1993))

The key to gaining an overview of the building is to establish:

— occupancy levels, including cleaners, late working etc.

— a breakdown of the building into areas with different uses

— the gross and treated floor area and a breakdown of this in relation to use

— the key items of plant, what they supply and which areas they serve

— the means of heating/cooling, the areas served and how these systems are controlled

— how the building is ventilated (see section 6) and how ventilation is controlled

— the types of lighting, the areas they serve and how these should be controlled, particularly in relation to available daylight

— the means of managing, maintaining and monitoring the operation of the building.

The above can be gained using a combination of operation and maintenance (O&M) manuals, drawings, surveys and inspection. The most important aspect is to establish the design intent, alongside what is actually happening in the building. Comparing the two can help to identify energy inefficiency.

14.1.2 Documentation

Good documentation is necessary to support the efficient operation of the building. This is usually in the form of O&M manuals (see section 13), architectural and building services drawings, plant details, manufacturers' information and commissioning records, together with a detailed maintenance schedule.

Energy-efficient buildings are inherently designed within tighter parameters, the result being that they tend to be particularly sensitive to changes in use or layout. Therefore, the documentation should also provide a convenient means of logging changes that are made to the building. This also helps avoid changes that may contradict the original design intent since these can have major consequences for energy use and comfort.

A written explanation of the occupants' involvement in the operation of the building should be provided for distribution to staff. This should give guidance on practical matters such as:

— use of windows for ventilation

— use of local heating controls

— use of lighting/shading to maximise the use of daylight.

A written explanation of the overall design intent may also be helpful, e.g. the ventilation strategy, as this could deter occupants from adopting bad practices such as placing books on top of fan convectors.

14.1.3 Identifying the current status

Identifying the current status and operation of the building compared with the design intent will help building managers understand the building better, particularly when they are new to a building. Initially, this can be achieved through overall performance indicators, such as £/m² for energy[5] and maintenance. The approach should gradually become more detailed, establishing performance indicators for specific services etc., as shown in section 12, Figure 12.1[6]. A qualitative measurement of the building can also be established through detailed assessments by:

— floor area surveys

— energy audits and surveys (see section 18)

— an analysis of monitoring and targeting (M&T) data (see section 20)

— condition surveys of fabric and plant

— reviewing maintenance contracts and practices (see sections 16 and 17)

— occupant surveys, to establish comfort and satisfaction levels

— monitoring plant operation and energy consumption.

14.1.4 Problem areas

Problems should be investigated promptly and the root causes sought. Many energy problems develop from poor interaction between fabric, services and occupants. Conflict can prevent the building operating in a coherent manner. For example, partitions may prevent natural cross ventilation and cause heating/lighting sensors to become separated from their respective zones.

Building services controls are often the key to solving energy and comfort problems. Poor controls can result in under or over provision and conflict between services, e.g. simultaneous heating and cooling. Improving the function, location and set points of controls can help to avoid such problems.

14.2 Energy policy

14.2.1 General

Adopting an appropriate and realistic energy policy delivers increased and sustainable performance improvements and provides a clear sense of direction. Any new policy should review current practices and provide a good starting point to an energy campaign[7].

Figure 14.2[8] shows a framework for developing an energy policy. The process will educate the decision-makers and secure financial approval for investment. For most organisations, a policy document will comprise a few pages. It should be reviewed annually. It is important that the energy manager gains the support and agreement of all his colleagues, particularly senior management, at each review.

An energy policy will:

— establish senior management commitment to energy efficiency

— improve the overall approach to energy management

— help to keep the main objectives in full view

— maximise the use of resources, both in time and money

— provide goals against which to monitor

— provide a clear direction for the energy team

— give senior management a way forward.

The long-term policy document is likely to cover five years, but would almost certainly be supported by other documents providing more detail on a shorter time scale. One such supporting document might be an annual action plan[2] showing specific energy saving projects with target dates and costs, together with the staff charged with the actions.

The energy policy should ideally be developed in conjunction with the maintenance policy (see section 16).

Energy management and policy should be reviewed regularly[1]. Using a management matrix[2,3,9–11] to help draw an 'organisational profile' of the current position will highlight strengths and weaknesses in policy, communication, investment, information, planning and audit. Senior management should also complete the matrix from their own perspective in order to secure their commitment and identify any differences between their view and that of the energy manager.

14.2.2   Energy policy checklist

The following checklist[8] provides a starting point for energy management. It is by no means exhaustive and needs to be tailored to suit the organisation. However, this skeleton checklist poses some of the key questions that need to be addressed in formulating a policy document.

(a)   *Overall objectives*:
  — Energy saving or cost cutting.
  — Attempt to save on all sites?
  — Attempt to save on all fuels?
  — Attempt to conserve water?
  — Overall target saving?
  — Over what time-period?

(b)   *Management reporting structures*:
  — Who is responsible overall?
  — Duties/responsibilities of the energy manager?
  — Who is accountable in each cost centre?
  — Who implements savings?
  — Management structure/lines of reporting?
  — Who needs to meet and when?
  — Lines of reporting.

(c)   *Manpower resources*:
  — Total man years invested?
  — At what levels of seniority?
  — Use of external consultants?
  — Use of contract energy management?
  — Who monitors consumption/cost?

  — Who checks the bills?

(d)   *Financial resources*:
  — Total funds to be invested?
  — Separate energy budget?
  — Capital versus maintenance?
  — Mechanism for reinvesting savings?
  — Use of contract energy management?
  — Allow reinvestment of savings?

(e)   *Financial criteria*:
  — Maximum acceptable payback period?

(f)   *Monitoring*:
  — What management information is required?
  — Use of energy statistics to raise staff awareness?
  — What needs trend logging?
  — Use of performance indicators?
  — Construct a league table of buildings to assess priorities?
  — Need for a bill checking mechanism?

(g)   *Targets*:
  — Cost or consumption?
  — Targeted percentage savings over one and five years?
  — Targets for individual cost centres?
  — Targets for individual fuels?

(h)   *Motivation*:
  — Publicity campaigns?
  — Competitions?
  — General staff training to raise awareness?
  — Staff suggestion schemes?
  — Incentive schemes?

(i)   *Training*:
  — Investigate staff development/training needs.
  — List of planned course attendance (technical and managerial).

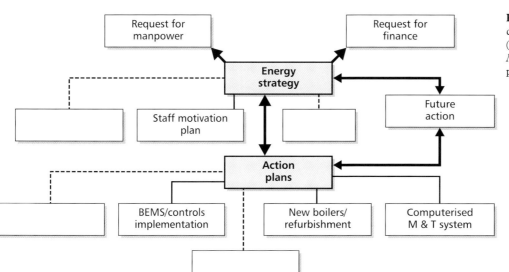

Figure 14.2 A framework for developing energy policy[8] (reproduced from *Educated Energy Management* by permission of the publisher)

(j) *Energy surveys*:
- — List of buildings targeted for surveys
- — Means of funding?
- — In-house or consultants?
- — Choice of consultant?

14.3 Management structures

The location, role, responsibility and reporting lines of staff involved in energy management are important issues for the success of the programme. It is important that energy managers and building operators understand the framework within which they can effect energy use. This may vary significantly from one organisation to another. Although energy management is sometimes seen as a technical discipline, the bulk of the work requires general management skills.

14.3.1 Responsibility and reporting

Allocating responsibility for energy is a major part of initiating a programme. Energy management needs to be an integral part of the general management structure with recognised reporting lines to senior management[3]. Someone needs to have overall responsibility for energy but all managers and staff have a role to play. In large buildings, and multi-building sites, it is often useful to nominate energy wardens for zones in order to act as the eyes and ears of the energy manager.

Larger organisations should consider setting up cost centres where line managers are responsible for their own energy costs. An energy committee with representatives from all departments may also be worthwhile.

Whatever structure is in place, it must be capable of implementing the energy policy[2,3]. This requires reporting on a regular basis; weekly, monthly, annually, to allow senior management to monitor energy costs (see section 20), identify savings made and make decisions on further investment. The energy manager will also need to identify opportunities for investment and prepare a financial case for consideration by senior management.

Where line managers are accountable for their own energy use, an effective method of feedback is necessary from the energy manager to occupants, as this can help to raise staff awareness and support for the campaign.

14.3.2 Roles and activities

All energy staff involved in the energy campaign should:
- — improve staff awareness, motivation and commitment
- — assist in collecting and analysing information
- — take informed action and review the benefits that have accrued.

Senior management should:
- — review energy policy
- — agree and enforce targets
- — agree resources and investment
- — monitor progress of the energy programme
- — provide recognition for success.

Without the commitment of senior management the programme is unlikely to succeed[2].

The energy manager should:
- — develop the energy policy
- — co-ordinate day-to-day energy management
- — collate energy consumption and cost data and develop monitoring systems
- — provide feedback and report on energy use
- — identify and evaluate opportunities to improve energy efficiency
- — prepare investment plans and implement agreed measures
- — promote energy awareness and develop staff motivation
- — gain the acceptance and support of staff at all levels
- — educate staff in energy management techniques and efficient operating practices
- — ensure adequate control and monitoring facilities are available
- — review any historical energy data, allowing for changes in building use and, hence, examine the projected energy costs for a building.

The energy manager is the focal point of the energy efficiency programme and may often require specialist support to implement the programme[2].

General staff should:
- — report energy waste
- — suggest energy saving measures.

14.3.3 Obtaining resources

Energy managers may face difficulties in justifying why their organisation should invest in energy efficiency. Organisations often give priority to investment in their core activity and will usually demand faster rates of return on investment in energy savings.

In arguing for investment in energy savings it can be helpful for energy managers to suggest ways in which cost savings from energy management could be redeployed within the organisation. These can be shown as:
- — reducing operating costs
- — increasing employee comfort and productivity
- — improving cost effectiveness and/or profits
- — enhancing the quality of service or customer care delivered
- — protecting the environment.

14.3.3.1 Financial investment

The same criteria should apply for energy investment as in other areas of business planning. Planned capital investment can produce rapid revenue savings. If current accounting practices restrict funding, new procedures should be considered. For example by:

— re-investing some of the revenue savings in energy management

— allowing a share of the energy cost savings to be used for other purposes by those who achieve the savings

— treating some energy management costs as an overhead that contributes to staff comfort and productivity

— allowing use of revenue for capital expenditure when it can be recovered by revenue savings within the accounting period.

As a guideline, the level of investment that can be justified each year in energy management is of the order of 10% of the annual expenditure on energy[3]. This figure could be exceeded in the early stages of development, when there are more opportunities for investment. A lower figure may be considered adequate in a well-developed programme until new opportunities arise.

14.3.3.2 Manpower Investment

The specific number of staff required for energy management will depend on:

— the size of the energy bills

— the extent to which the programme of energy management has been implemented

— the required reduction in energy consumption.

The number of staff involved in energy management is likely to vary over time. However, it is suggested that there should be minimum of one full-time member of staff for every million pounds of energy expenditure up to £3 million per annum[3]. Beyond this, it is advisable to have one full-time member of staff for each additional £2 million up to £10 million and, above that, there should be one for every extra £4 million. If energy costs are less than £1 million per annum, organisations should consider appointing a part-time energy manager.

14.3.4 Sub-contracting energy management

Senior management may take the view that as energy management is not a core activity, it should be sub-contracted, completely or in part. There are three main routes for sub-contracting:

— specialist consultants

— contract energy management (CEM) companies

— contract facilities management.

14.3.4.1 Specialist consultants

Should staff lack the technical knowledge or time to perform energy audits/surveys or other energy investigations, help or advice is available from specialist energy consultants[12-14] (see section 18).

14.3.4.2 Contract energy management (CEM)

Contract energy management companies offer a range of technical and financial services, some of which include the complete operation and maintenance of plant and building services. CEM companies can also provide investment in more efficient plant and will recover their investment from the saving achieved. Different types of contract are available but most incorporate improvements to energy efficiency.

Most large buildings are suitable for CEM. Small buildings with an energy bill less than say £50,000 p.a. would not normally be appropriate, except as part of a larger group. Using CEM, companies can transfer the investment risks to the contractor, who typically assumes responsibility for delivery of energy services and relevant maintenance. Figure 14.3 illustrates opportunities for introducing third-party services.

The suitability of CEM depends on:

— the availability of in-house technical expertise

— the ability to find capital projects

— the suitability of the building

— the nature and status of occupancy

— the negotiation of an acceptable contract.

If CEM is selected as the preferred option, the client should identify and implement no-cost and low-cost measures before proceeding with the contract. Such measures can be identified by the user and by the contractor carrying out an on-site energy survey (see section 18).

There are essentially three types of CEM contract. These are based on:

— variable heat charges (heat service)

— shared savings

— fixed fees.

Careful consideration is required in selecting the most suitable contract[15], and Table 14.2 summarises the main advantages and disadvantages of the three types of contract.

14.3.4.3 Contract facilities management

Contracting out overall facilities management has become increasingly popular. If facilities management is provided by an external contractor then effective liaison on energy matters should be incorporated within the contract. The contract should set out requirements for energy management, preferably in terms of a performance specification. Specifically, this should include a range of performance indicators for specific services as shown in section 12, Figure 12.1[6].

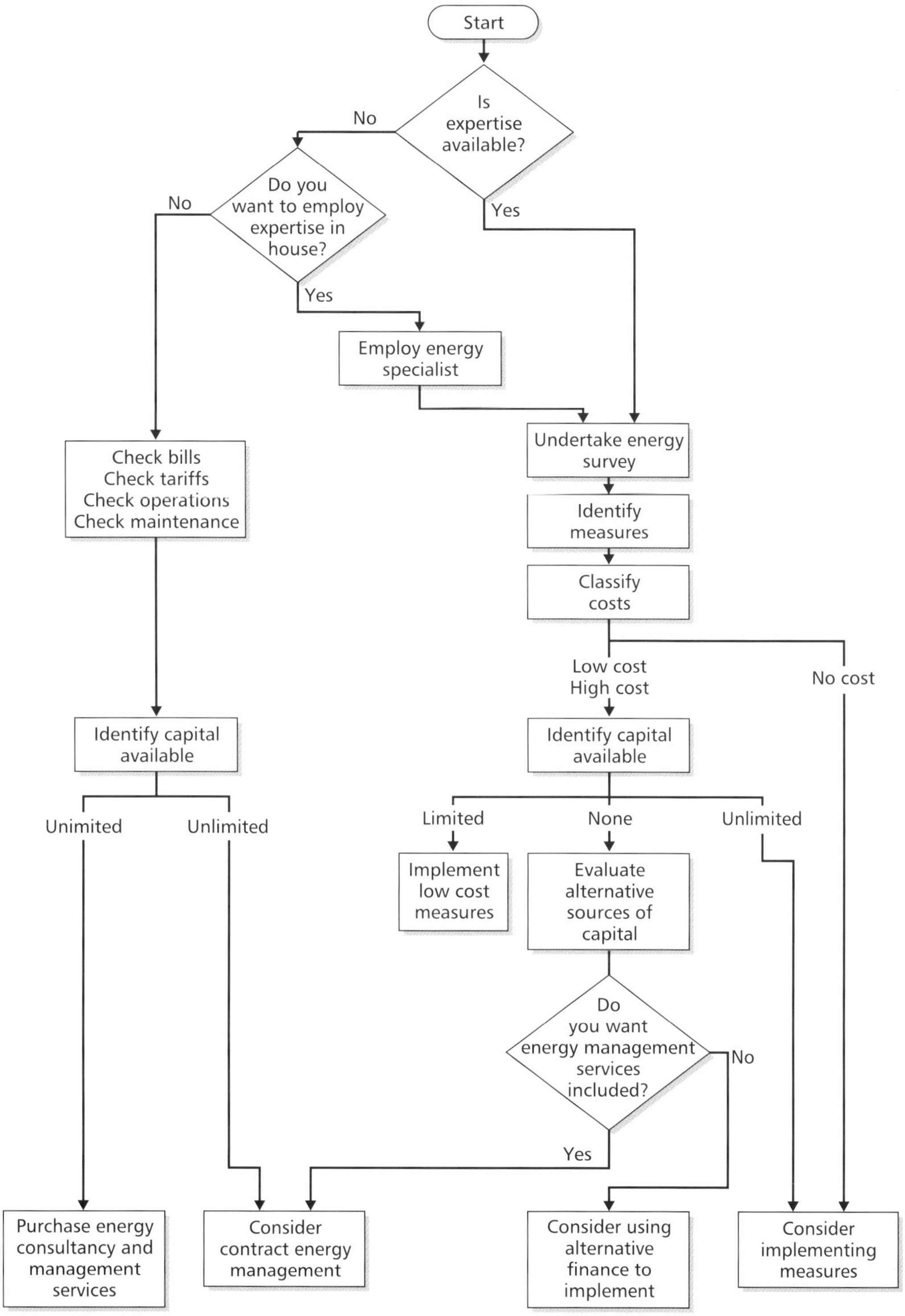

Figure 14.3 When to contract out energy management[15]

Figure 14.3 flowchart:

Start → Is expertise available?
- No → Do you want to employ expertise in house?
  - No → Check bills / Check tariffs / Check operations / Check maintenance → Identify capital available → Unimited → Purchase energy consultancy and management services; Unlimited → Consider contract energy management
  - Yes → Employ energy specialist → Undertake energy survey
- Yes → Undertake energy survey

Undertake energy survey → Identify measures → Classify costs
- Low cost / High cost → Identify capital available
  - Limited → Implement low cost measures
  - None → Evaluate alternative sources of capital → Do you want energy management services included?
    - No → Consider using alternative finance to implement
    - Yes → Consider contract energy management
  - Unlimited → Consider using alternative finance to implement
- No cost → Consider implementing measures

14.3.5 Purchasing policy

Purchasers of energy, sub-contracted services and equipment should be encouraged to consider energy efficiency as an important criterion.

14.3.5.1 Energy

The energy and purchasing managers should review periodically the arrangements for purchasing energy. There is a wide range of energy supply contracts available, with significant cost saving possible through judicious competitive tendering. Whilst this does not generally affect energy consumption, it can alter the energy supply tariff structures, and this can have a knock-on effect for energy management procedures.

14.3.5.2 External contracts

Where general services, e.g. catering, cleaning and security, are to be sub-contracted, it is vital to include energy efficiency in the contract. Compulsory competitive tendering and selecting the lowest cost tender rarely results in an energy efficient solution, unless it is clearly asked for in the brief. During the tendering procedure, it is advisable to check the contractor's ability to manage energy. This is particularly important when contracting:

— cleaning staff (switching lighting on and off)

Table 14.2 Advantages and disadvantages of CEM contracts

Contract type	Advantages	Disadvantages
Heat service	Simple payments based on energy use	No incentive for CEM company to reduce user's demand
	Full user control over amount of energy use	Cost savings strongly dependent on fuel prices
	User benefits directly from reduced consumption	Contracts of long duration
	Guaranteed supply	Usually limited to heat supply only
	Well established form of contract	
Shared savings	Performance basis encourages CEM company to achieve savings	Calculation of share of savings can be complicated
	Some savings guaranteed	Costs and savings not known in advance
	Incentive for user to increase savings	CEM companies may take unacceptable degree of control over energy supply
	Only savings achieved by CEM company's investment need to be shared	Unconventional contract and finance
	Flexible contracts allow higher rewards if user accepts more risk	No incentive to user to reduce consumption
		Control may be surrendered to CEM company
Fixed fee	Single, fixed payment	Not usually available as energy savings service on its own
	No complicated calculation	
	Cost known in advance	
	Single point of responsibility for all services included	
	Shorter contract lengths than other types	

— security staff (patrols can switch-off lighting and equipment)

— catering staff (control of ovens, hot plates and use of hot water).

14.3.5.3   Office equipment

Managers should select the most efficient office equipment possible, with the energy consumption and energy saving features established before purchase (see section 11). Manufacturers should provide the average power consumed under typical conditions, the peak nameplate rating, provision to switch to standby 'sleep' modes and the consumption in these modes. It should be noted that average power consumption is not necessarily related to the nameplate rating. Modern PCs tend to have 'energy star' ratings and purchasing managers should acquire only equipment which satisfy these requirements.

Purchasing efficient equipment also applies to desk lamps and fans, vending equipment, photocopiers and printers. This is particularly important when selecting catering equipment such as ovens and dishwashers.

14.3.5.4   High efficiency motors

All new and replacement plant should be specified with high efficiency motors as they now carry little or no additional capital cost. For new applications or spares, it is always cost-effective to buy high efficiency motors (see section 10). Motor rewinding and repair policies may also require review and amendment since it may be more economic to replace older motors by higher efficiency motors (see 19.7).

The efficiencies of energy efficient motors range from 2 to 6%. Ideally, purchasing specifications should define precise performance requirements for each motor by application and size, including minimum acceptable efficiency. If this is impractical, the user should specify 'premium', rather than 'high' efficiency motors.

14.4   Occupant involvement

14.4.1   Motivation and training

The value of making energy a management issue and relying on people, rather than purely technical solutions, cannot be over emphasised. By raising awareness about the campaign, energy managers can enlist staff and management support to achieve success. For example, a good housekeeping campaign will recognise the importance of cleaning and security staff, particularly as they are often the first and last people in the building. Implementing a good housekeeping policy can also promote staff awareness of their responsibility to the environment as a whole[16,17]. Equipment will only be switched off if staff fully understand the reasons.

Whilst monetary saving is a driving factor for management it is seldom a motivator for staff in general. Therefore, it is the responsibility of the energy manager to find ways of convincing staff that energy efficiency is worthwhile. Possible motivators and de-motivators are shown in Table 14.3. The influence of these motivators on the staff will differ depending on their positions in the energy management structure. It is, of course, particularly important to communicate success at all levels in order to maintain the momentum of the campaign.

Training is essential for all those that have responsibility for energy management, particularly energy managers, wardens and those responsible for reading meters[18].

Table 14.3 Examples of motivating and de-motivating factors

Motivators	Demotivators
Individual or group achievement	Unrealistic targets
Praise and recognition of success	Lack of support
Encouragement and support	Inadequate resources
Sense of individual control	Lack of recognition
Concern for environment	Failure to reward
Strong corporate image	Imposition of directives without explanation
Savings represent additional staff/equipment	Feeling of inability to influence or control

14.4.2   Occupant satisfaction

The comfort, health and safety of the occupants are primary aims of any building manager. However, well managed buildings can be both comfortable and energy efficient[19]. Occupant satisfaction is not only about providing the right temperature and light levels, but is also associated with peoples' ability to control their own surroundings. For example, delays in switching on the cooling system in response to warm weather may persuade occupants that their local environment is unsatisfactory.

The building manager will find that there are real energy saving benefits to be gained from securing the understanding and involvement of occupants. Staff should be:

— advised how to use the building and control the local services

— informed and encouraged to improve energy efficiency

— kept informed about any problems together with the actions being taken.

Health and safety regulations based upon European Workplace Directives place new responsibilities on building managers, clients and building professionals to maintain the indoor environment for buildings in which people work. These are:

— *The Workplace (Health, Safety and Welfare) Regulations 1992*[20]: affects ventilation, temperature and lighting standards.

— *The Health and Safety (Display Screen Equipment) Regulations 1992*[21]: affects the thermal and visual comfort of occupants using display monitors and requires the provision of adequate humidity in the space.

Guidance on complying with these regulations is available[22]. Whilst these regulations provide constraints for the building, the opportunity to install energy efficient services should not be missed where systems need to be replaced or upgraded in order to meet these regulations.

References

1   *A strategic approach to energy and environmental management* GPG 200 (London: Department of Environment, Transport and Regions) (1996)

2   *Organising energy management — a corporate approach* GPG 119 (London: Department of Environment, Transport and Regions) (1996)

3   *Organisational aspects of energy management* GIR 12 (London: Department of Environment, Transport and Regions) (1993)

4   *Energy efficiency in the workplace — a guide for managers and staff* GPG 133 (London: Department of Environment, Transport and Regions) (1994)

5   *Introduction to energy efficiency in buildings* Booklets EEB 1–13 (London: Department of Environment, Transport and Regions) (1994)

6   Field J, Soper J, Jones P G, Bordass W and Grigg P Energy performance of occupied non domestic buildings: Assessment by analysing end-use energy consumptions *Building Services Engineering Research and Technology* **18**[(1)] (1997)

7   *Developing an effective energy policy* GPG 186 (London: Department of Environment, Transport and Regions) (1996)

8   *Educated energy management* (London: E and F N Spon) (1991)

9   *Is your energy under control? A practical guide to assessment and action* GPG 136 (London: Department of Environment, Transport and Regions) (1994)

10   *Organisational aspects of energy management: a self-assessment manual for managers* GPG 167 (London: Department of Environment, Transport and Regions) (1995)

11   *Putting energy into total quality. A guide for energy managers* GPG 169 (London: Department of Environment, Transport and Regions) (1996)

12   *Choosing an energy efficiency consultant* (DETR) (1993)

13   *Energy audits and surveys* Applications Manual AM5 (London: Chartered Institution of Building Services Engineers) (1991)

14   *Energy audits for buildings* Fuel Efficiency Booklet No. 1 (London: Department of Environment, Transport and Regions) (1993)

15   *Contract energy management* Applications Manual AM6 (London: Chartered Institution of Building Services Engineers) (1991)

16   *Managing and motivating staff to save energy* GPG 84 (London: Department of Environment, Transport and Regions) (1993)

17   *Marketing energy efficiency — raising staff awareness* GPG 172 (London: Department of Environment, Transport and Regions) (1997)

18   *Energy management training* GPG 85 (London: Department of Environment, Transport and Regions) (1993)

19   Bordass W T, Bromley A K R and Leaman A J *Comfort, control and energy efficiency in offices* IP3/95 (BRE) (1995)

20   *The Workplace (Health, Safely and Welfare) Regulations 1992* (London: Stationery Office) (1992)

21   *The Health and Safety (Display Screen Equipment) Regulations 1992* (London: Stationery Office) (1992)

22   *Healthy workplaces: Guidance on complying with health and safety regulations* Guidance Note GN2 (London: Chartered Institution of Building Services Engineers) (1992)

Bibliography

Practical energy saving guide for smaller businesses ACBE 1 (London: Department of Environment, Transport and Regions) (1992)

Harris P *Preparing the company energy plan* (Energy Publications) (1989)

Financial aspects of energy management in buildings — a summary GPG 75 (London: Department of Environment, Transport and Regions) (1995)

Financial aspects of energy management in buildings GPG 165 (London: Department of Environment, Transport and Regions) (1995)

Energy managers handbook (London: NIFES/Graham and Trotman) (1985)

Reviewing energy management GIR 13 (London: Department of Environment, Transport and Regions) (1993)

Parsloe C J *The allocation of design responsibilities for building engineering services — a code of conduct to avoid conflict* TN 8/94 (Bracknell: Building Services Research and Information Association) (1994)

Gregory D *Building services in the year 2000* TN 5/85 (Bracknell: Building Services Research and Information Association) (1985)

Gilham A and Shakespeare C Good management — managing energy efficiently — the role of the building services engineer in facilities management *CIBSE National Conference 1995* (London: Chartered Institution of Building Services Engineers) (1995)

15 Acquisition and refurbishment

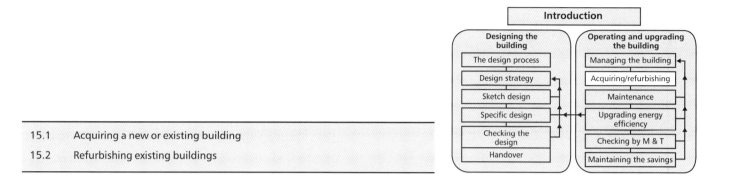

15.1   Acquiring a new or existing building

15.2   Refurbishing existing buildings

This section outlines the issues that need to be addressed when acquiring a new building or refurbishing an existing building (see the principles at the front of this Guide). These present major opportunities for improving energy efficiency[1,2].

15.1   Acquiring a new or existing building

Energy efficiency is seldom considered as part of the building procurement process even though purchase/rental can represent a long term commitment to high energy bills. Organisations should include energy efficiency targets in the brief to those searching for a building. Considering running costs over the building's lifetime will highlight the long-term commitment being made.

In larger and more complex buildings, it may be appropriate to carry out a brief energy audit and assessment of the potential for savings. This may highlight wasteful features that are difficult to improve in the foreseeable future, and areas in which savings can readily be made. It can also be advantageous to re-commission the building services when taking responsibility for a building in order to ensure that the design intent is being met.

Older plant may be less efficient and hence may become increasingly costly to operate and maintain. The need to replace plant should be taken into account in the procurement process, alongside any improvement in efficiency, when upgrading to new plant.

15.2   Refurbishing existing buildings

Refurbishment provides excellent opportunities for improving energy efficiency[1,2], although it can increase energy consumption where services are enhanced, e.g. by the introduction of air conditioning. Major refurbishment will involve a significant amount of design and, therefore, reference should be made to sections 2 to 13. Minor refurbishment may present opportunities for introducing the specific energy saving measures discussed in section 19.

DETR Good Practice Guide 35[3], which is supported by case studies[4,5], provides checklists that show what should be addressed in the refurbishment of offices, with appropriate benchmarks. A key decision is whether to provide air conditioning or to design it out[6], or adopt a mixed-mode approach (see section 4).

Building services installed during refurbishment should be fully commissioned before handover, and comprehensive operating and maintenance instructions should be provided (see section 13). Sub-metering of fuel supplies should also be provided as a basis for monitoring and targeting, as described under section 4.3.

15.2.1   Complete refurbishment

This generally involves total replacement of plant and major changes to the building fabric, possibly only retaining the facade or structural frame. It nearly always involves radical strategic changes to the building services, which provides major energy saving opportunities, including:

—   introducing passive measures to reduce external heat gains while maximising daylight, e.g. replacing windows and introducing atria and rooflights

—   changes to the ventilation strategy to minimise the use of mechanical ventilation

—   assessment of the need for air-conditioning, leading to reduction and, sometimes, complete avoidance[6]

—   upgrading fabric thermal performance to reduce energy requirements for heating through improved insulation and better heating controls

—   installing energy efficient plant, such as condensing boilers and CHP

—   installing energy efficient lighting and lighting control systems

— improving building services monitoring and controls, possibly through the introduction of BMS.

Complete refurbishment should achieve standards comparable to energy efficient new buildings[7], as discussed in 12.2.

15.2.2 Major refurbishment

This usually involves replacement of major plant and can include some changes to the fabric, e.g. window replacement. It often allows significant changes to building services strategies. Energy saving opportunities include:

— adding atria and sun spaces to increase natural ventilation and daylight[1]

— increasing the use of passive measures or mixed mode strategies in air-conditioned buildings

— maximising use of 'free' cooling

— removing (fully or partially) air conditioning through minor changes to fabric, lighting and controls, e.g. in shallow plan buildings on relatively quiet sites

— selecting efficient plant and flexible controls, including zone controls

— specifying an efficient and fully insulated hot water system, with consideration given to localised water heating where this will help to reduce standing losses.

Major refurbishment that upgrades the building envelope should enable energy use to be improved from 'typical' (medium consumption) to better than 'good practice' (i.e. low consumption), as discussed in 20.5[8].

15.2.3 Minor refurbishment

This generally involves refitting the interior and making minor alterations to space layout and plant. Energy saving opportunities include:

— changing space layout to enhance daylight, ventilation and zone controls

— improving lighting and switching arrangements, including automatic controls

— improving window performance by adding blinds etc.

— using of lighter coloured interior surfaces and furnishings to enhance the lighting efficiency

— improving perimeter services and window controls to avoid blockage by desks etc.

— introducing zoned areas for equipment etc. with high heat gains or special environmental requirements.

The aim in minor refurbishment should be to achieve 'good practice' (i.e. low consumption), as discussed in 20.5.

15.2.4 Passive refurbishment

Where possible, refurbishment should be based on passive solutions, e.g. daylighting and natural ventilation, to improve energy efficiency and reduce running costs. Passively refurbished buildings also offer potential environmental benefits[9,10] which can be used to promote the passive approach, including:

— more attractive, daylit interiors

— less dependence upon mechanical systems and ozone-depleting refrigerants.

— lower energy and maintenance costs

— good long term investment with less dependency on supplies of delivered energy

— less overheating, more comfort, and possibly a healthier internal environment

— opportunities for straightforward personal control of the local environment, particularly in cellular offices.

However, developers and investors are often worried about the marketability and financial returns from passive designs, especially for premium properties. Common concerns are:

— lower rental values; at present passive buildings enjoy no rental premium

— risks to thermal comfort, particularly if occupancy and equipment levels are high

— unfamiliar technologies may require changes of habits from management and occupants

— lack of flexibility in accommodating partitioning to suit occupiers' needs (partitions may block ventilation paths and interfere with control strategies).

Where these concerns are genuine, it helps to introduce contingency paths to allow extra services to be added easily, as necessary. For many building specifiers, wary of commitment to wholehearted passive redesign, this strategy offers a comforting 'halfway house' with an escape route[6,11,12], see 4.2.5.3.

Wherever passive measures are introduced, it is important for those who operate and occupy the building to fully understand the design and operational strategies. This will ensure that the building functions correctly in the passive mode. Otherwise, operators may assume that the measures have failed and allow extra services to be installed. Once this has occurred, it is unlikely that the building will revert to its passive mode of operation.

References

1   Buckley M (BRECSU), Burton S (ECD Partnership) and Bordass W (William Bordass Associates) *Passive refurbishment of offices, UK potential and practice Lyons, November 1994*

2   *Industrial building refurbishments: opportunities for energy efficiency* IP2/93 (Garston: Building Research Establishment)

3   *Energy efficiency in offices. Energy efficient options for refurbished offices — for the design team* GPG 35 (London: Department of Environment, Transport and Regions) (1993)

4   *Naturally comfortable offices — a refurbishment project* GPCS 308 (London: Department of Environment, Transport and Regions) (1997)

5   *Energy efficiency in offices — low cost major refurbishment. Policy Studies Institution, London* GPCS 1 (London: Department of Environment, Transport and Regions) (1989)

6   *Avoiding or minimising the use of air-conditioning — a research report from the EnREI Programme* GIR 31 (London: Department of Environment, Transport and Regions) (1995)

7   *A performance specification for the energy efficient office of the future* GIR 30 (London: Department of Environment, Transport and Regions) (1996)

8   *Introduction to energy efficiency in buildings* Booklets Energy Energy Efficiency Booklets Nos.1–13 (London: Department of Environment, Transport and Regions) (1994)

9   Halliday S P *Environmental code of practice for buildings and their services* ENCOP (Bracknell: Building Services Research and Information Association) (1994)

10   *Environmental code of practice for buildings and their services — Case studies* CS4/96 (Bracknell: Building Services Research and Information Association) (1996)

11   Jaunzens D and Bordass W T Building design for mixed mode systems *CIBSE National Conference 1995* (London: Chartered Institution of Building Services Engineers) (1995)

12   Bordass W T, Entwistle M J and Willis S T P Naturally-ventilated and mixed-mode office building: opportunities and pitfalls *CIBSE National Conference 1994* (London: Chartered Institution of Building Services Engineers) (1994)

Bibliography

Energy efficiency in refurbishment of industrial buildings. Parts warehouse GPCS 175 (London: Department of Environment, Transport and Regions) (1995)

Energy efficiency in refurbishment of industrial buildings. GEC Alsthom Large Machines Ltd., Rugby GPCS 188 (London: Department of Environment, Transport and Regions) (1995)

Booth W B and Williams R N Occupant satisfaction and environmental conditions following refurbishment of two air-conditioned office buildings to natural ventilation *CIBSE National Conference 1996* (London: Chartered Institution of Building Services Engineers) (1996)

Beggs C, Warwicker B, Winwood R, Edwards R and Bordass W T A developmental retrofit method for the utilisation of fabric thermal storage in existing buildings *CIBSE National Conference 1995* (London: Chartered Institution of Building Services Engineers) (1995)

Levermore G J *Staff reaction to building energy management systems* DLP 4 (Bracknell: Building Services Research and Information Association) (1989)

16 Maintaining the building

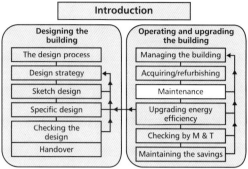

This section provides an overview of maintenance and its implications for energy management, in line with the principles at the front of this Guide. Section 17 covers more specific maintenance issues that affect energy efficiency. Detailed guidance on maintenance is also available from CIBSE[1], HVCA[2], and other sources[3,4].

16.0   General

Effective maintenance contributes to the realisation of an energy efficient building by ensuring the efficient operation of systems and equipment; it also prolongs the useful life of the plant. Each building is unique and maintenance regimes should be tailored to the particular building.

16.1   Planning maintenance

The overall approach should be set down in a clear concise policy for operation and maintenance.

16.1.1   Maintenance policy

The maintenance policy is the plan to provide and maintain the required environment for the occupants within the constraints of the owner's objectives and legal requirements.

Maintenance and energy policies should be co-ordinated with the support of top management (see section 14). Maintenance work can then include energy efficiency measures and checks, as appropriate.

Maintenance and energy management have the common objectives of:

—   ensuring that a building and its services continue to function reliably, efficiently and effectively

—   ensuring the health, safety and comfort of occupants

—   protecting and enhancing the value of investment in a building and its equipment.

16.1.2   Types of maintenance

Maintenance tasks generally fall into two main categories. These are:

—   reactive or breakdown maintenance

—   planned preventative maintenance.

Maintenance duties might also include checks on plant operational efficiency and the installation of new services and equipment. Maintenance staff or contractors can maintain and improve energy efficiency by:

—   servicing plant and equipment, e.g. boilers[5,6] to maintain optimum efficiency

—   repairing faults that cause direct energy wastage

—   identifying and implementing energy efficiency measures.

Most of the recommendations in section 17 are maintenance tasks and can often be funded, sometimes at marginal cost, from maintenance or utilities budgets.

16.1.2.1   Reactive maintenance

Although defects and emergencies are by their nature unplanned, they should not be identified and dealt with in the same way. Faults that result in loss of service tend to be reported promptly, whereas faults that result in energy wastage (but do not cause inconvenience) tend to be ignored. Building users should be encouraged to report all faults, whether or not they result in loss of service. This can help develop staff awareness and positive attitudes to energy efficiency. All reported defects should be assigned a priority and action taken accordingly.

Maintenance problems and energy losses that are not immediately evident can sometimes be detected by careful monitoring of energy use. Some can be identified directly

Table 16.1 Examples of planned maintenance tasks

Time based	Condition based
Annual service of boiler plant, clean adjust/replace items as necessary	Change air filters when pressure drop across filter exceeds given level
Daily/weekly/monthly checks for air, steam or water leaks	Clean gas side of boiler when flue gas temperature exceeds that in clean condition by, say 40°C
Complete daily/weekly/monthly log sheets to monitor plant performance	Grease motor bearings when bearing temperatures or vibration exceeds a certain level
Carry out weekly/monthly test of boiler efficiency	

Table 16.2 Advantages and disadvantages of contract and direct labour

Contract	Direct labour
More competitive price	More difficult to assess costs
More flexible workforce wit wide skills	Fixed workforce and fixed skills
May not be able to respond to all emergencies	Always available to respond to emergencies
Contract needs to be monitored	In-house supervision required
Specialist training and tools included	Need to provide specialist tools and training

by suitable BMS software. The use of energy monitoring and targeting systems in diagnosing faults is described in section 20.

Formal records should be kept of all repairs and breakdowns for management review. Monitoring equipment performance will help to identify malfunctions, which can then be rectified by reference to maintenance manuals. The timing and frequency of maintenance procedures is vital to the efficient running of equipment[7].

16.1.2.2 Planned preventative maintenance

Planned preventative maintenance should reduce the risk of breakdown or loss of performance of an item of equipment. It may be carried out at set intervals ('time based') or when pre-determined conditions occur ('condition based'). Table 16.1 gives some examples of tasks falling into these categories which have energy implications.

The frequency of planned preventative maintenance should be reviewed where monitoring suggests that a change would be worthwhile. An assessment of the likely effect on energy costs should be included as part of any review. The condition based tasks are generally carried out in response to the results of routine checks, measured against target values[8]. Performance monitoring of this type can be assisted by the use of building management systems[9,10].

16.2   Maintenance contracts

There is a growing reliance on contractors for the maintenance of building services plant. External contractors require tight specifications with performance targets to maintain energy efficiency. BSRIA[11] provides advice on all aspects that the client should consider when obtaining contract maintenance. It covers concepts, conditions, specifications, tender procedures, and the monitoring and control of the ongoing contract. Maintenance contracts frequently lack a clear explanation of operational responsibilities and standards. The result is that plant is often run liberally to avoid complaints, but energy efficiency suffers badly.

16.2.1   Performance specification

A brief from the client to the maintenance manager is required whether maintenance is carried out in-house or by external contractors. This should include budgets, levels of service, responsibilities, reporting procedures and policies such as energy, and health and safety. CIBSE Technical Memoranda TM17[1] provides a detailed checklist of issues that should be included.

Many contracts now include performance standards for particular items of equipment, e.g. a boiler must operate above a certain efficiency. This approach places a greater responsibility on the contractor to ensure that plant is maintained to a high level in order to achieve the required performance. This can be an effective way of building energy efficiency into the maintenance contract. However, requirements for efficient operation of the system as a whole are seldom included.

16.2.2   Use of maintenance contractors

Some of the advantages and disadvantages of using maintenance contractors are shown in Table 16.2.

An important issue in any maintenance contract is identifying those actions which should be undertaken by suitably qualified specialists as indicated in the manufacturer's documentation. The in-house capabilities can then be assessed to see if specialist contractors are required. Further guidance on the use of contractors is contained in CIBSE Technical Memoranda TM17[1].

16.3   Monitoring maintenance

While responsibility for maintenance should rest with those carrying it out, the client must institute some form of monitoring to ensure value for money and to identify any changes in the policy that need to be made. In particular, it is important to obtain feedback on whether the contractor is adhering to the maintenance policy and to determine the effectiveness of that policy in ensuring the energy efficiency of the plant.

16.3.1.1   Maintenance records

Maintenance records are a vital part of maintenance management and therefore have an important role in energy management. There are two broad categories of records:

— Installation records: include operating and maintenance (O&M) manuals[12], plant details, design performance data, maintenance

Table 16.3 Approximate costs for maintaining mechanical and electrical services

Building type	Cost ($£/m^2$)
Hospitals	12–14
Hotels	8–10
Offices, light industrial, university	6–9
Leisure	4–6
Major retail	3–5
Schools, residential homes	2–4

Note: based on BSRIA research 1991

instructions, commissioning data, record drawings and control set points. Documents should be updated when any modifications are made.

— Service records: include log sheets, job records, work orders, inspection and test results and service performance data. Periodic checks on performance of plant and equipment in service can indicate when action should be taken before serious energy wastage occurs. Details should be kept of the time and nature of corrective action. Other adjustments of plant or control settings should also be recorded for future reference.

The schedule of installed assets, the planned maintenance programme and the service history are often combined in a computer based information system. This greatly simplifies the task of extracting and analysing information. Full details of test results or data logged during maintenance work (meter readings, flow and return temperatures, boiler flue-gas temperatures, etc.) is more commonly kept in its original form on log sheets. Traditional log sheets can still be a useful source of information for energy management.

A BMS can help to collect this information and prepare inspection and maintenance routines for maintenance staff. A BMS can handle a greater volume of data in less time, and assists in monitoring complete systems, rather than individual assets, highlighting anomalies that would otherwise go unnoticed.

16.3.2   Checking maintenance standards

Building operators should monitor both technical and financial indicators to ensure that maintenance is effective[1].

Breakdown frequency provides a retrospective benchmark. A minimum period of data collection is necessary to provide a useful comparison. Judgements have to be made by the building owner over time, related to the expected life of the plant. Energy management through monitoring and targeting can also provide valuable information to assess the effectiveness of maintenance. Lack of maintenance or incorrect plant settings will increase energy consumption when compared with target figures.

As a rule of thumb, based on research by BSRIA[13] and data from Williams[14], the annual spend on building services maintenance should be about the same as that for energy. If the figures differ widely, something may be wrong,

especially if the energy spend is high and the maintenance spend low.

Table 16.3 provides a guide to the costs of maintaining mechanical and electrical services for various types of buildings. Cost indices, such as those provided by Building Maintenance Information (a division of the Royal Institution of Chartered Surveyors' Business Services) can be used to obtain current values.

References

1   *Building services maintenance management* Technical Memoranda 17 (London: Chartered Institution of Building Services Engineers) (1994)

2   *HVCA Standard Maintenance Specification* Volumes 1–4 (London: Heating and Ventilating Contractors' Association)

3   *Building services maintenance* RG 6/95 (Bracknell: Building Services Research and Information Association) (1995)

4   *Planned maintenance for productivity and energy conservation* (London: Fairmount Press) (1989)

5   *Maintaining the efficient operation of heating and hot water. A guide for managers* GPG 188 (London: Department of Environment, Transport and Regions) (1996)

6   Armstrong J *The effect of maintenance on boiler efficiency* TN 5/83 (Bracknell: Building Services Research and Information Association) (1983)

7   *BS 5720: 1979: Code of practice for mechanical ventilation and air conditioning in buildings* (London: British Standards Institution) (1979)

8   *Condition-based maintenance for building services* TN 1/95 (Bracknell: Building Services Research and Information Association) (1995)

9   Armstrong J *Planned maintenance and the use of computers* TN 1/85.1 (Bracknell: Building Services Research and Information Association) (1991)

10   Barnard N and Starr A *BEMS as condition based maintenance tools* TN(S) 4/95 (Bracknell: Building Services Research and Information Association) (1995)

11   Smith M H *Maintenance contracts for building engineering services* AG 4/89.2 (Bracknell: Building Services Research and Information Association) (1992)

12   Armstrong J H *Operating and maintenance manuals for building services installations* AG 1/87.1 (Bracknell: Building Services Research and Information Association) (1990)

13   Smith M H *Maintenance and utility costs — results of a survey* TM 3/91 (Bracknell: Building Services Research and Information Association) (1991)

14   Williams B *The Economics of Environmental Services* **11**(11) 13–23 (1993)

Bibliography

Building services maintenance RG 6/95 (Bracknell: Building Services Research and Information Association) (1995)

Parsloe C *Design for maintainability* AG 11/92 (Bracknell: Building Services Research and Information Association) (1992)

Butler H and Armstrong J *Maintenance management — results of a survey* TN 1/81 (Bracknell: Building Services Research and Information Association) (1981)

Armstrong J *Inspection of building services plant and equipment — a review of current practice* TN 6/86 (Bracknell: Building Services Research and Information Association) (1986)

Armstrong J *Fault finding procedures in the building services industry* TN 12/86 (Bracknell: Building Services Research and Information Association) (1986)

Starr A and Wynne R An introduction to condition based maintenance for building services *CIBSE National Conference 1994* (London: Chartered Institution of Building Services Engineers) (1994)

Stonard P *Instruments for building services applications* TN 14/86 (Bracknell: Building Services Research and Information Association) (1986)

Barnard N and Starr A *Vibration monitoring for building services* TN(S) 3/95 (Bracknell: Building Services Research and Information Association) (1995)

HVAC Applications: Building operation and maintenance ASHRAE Handbook (Atlanta, GA: American Society of Heating, Refrigeration and Air Conditioning Engineers) (1995)

Owning and operating costs CIBSE Guide B18 (London: Chartered Institution of Building Services Engineers) (1986)

Armstrong J H Life cycles or death throes? Revision to CIBSE Guide Section B18 — Owning and operating costs *CIBSE National Conference 1996* (London: Chartered Institution of Building Services Engineers) (1996)

Johansson M *Building services legislation directory* 3rd Edition RG 14/95 (Bracknell: Building Services Research and Information Association) (1995)

17   Maintaining for energy efficiency

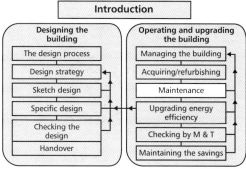

This section provides a checklist of specific maintenance issues that influence energy efficiency. The appropriate checks should be included in a planned maintenance programme that promotes energy efficiency. Manufacturers' instructions should always be followed, particularly in relation to safety. This section should be read in conjunction with HVCA Standard Maintenance Specification[1]. Section 16 and CIBSE Technical Memoranda TM17[2] provide strategic guidance on maintenance policy and management.

17.1   Good housekeeping as a maintenance issue

Significant reductions in energy consumption can be achieved through good housekeeping measures, e.g. switching off lights when not needed. A 'switch it off' policy requires no capital expenditure but requires the co-operation of all staff, especially maintenance staff who are responsible for a large part of good housekeeping. Motivating staff to save energy is covered in section 14. Further good housekeeping measures can be found in DETR's *Introduction to energy efficiency* booklets[3].

The following are typical good housekeeping measures:

— Adjust controls to match heating, cooling and lighting use to occupancy periods, and to ensure service levels meet the needs of occupants, i.e. avoid over-heating, over-cooling and excessive lighting levels.

— Establish responsibility for control setting, review and adjustment.

— Arrange partitioning and layout to make best use of natural lighting and building services.

— Concentrate out-of-hours occupancy in as few areas, or buildings, as possible and run plant in these areas only.

— Switch off non-essential office equipment when not in use.

— Close windows and doors when the building is unoccupied during the heating season.

— Ensure automatic door closers function properly.

— Discourage supplementary electrical space heating appliances except for out-of-hours use when, otherwise, central systems would have to be operated.

— Switch off miscellaneous extract fans when the building is unoccupied, unless continuing operation is essential.

— Use window shading devices during summer to minimise air conditioning loads. Close window shading devices during the heating season, and when dark outside to minimise radiation losses.

— Reduce heat generation from internal sources during the cooling season, i.e. lighting, machines, cooking equipment, etc.

— Ensure catering equipment is only on when necessary, particularly kitchen ovens, hot plates and dishwashers, but also local hot water urns, vending machines etc.

— Instigate a purchasing policy that considers energy consumption when buying new equipment.

— Ensure that security staff and cleaners practice a 'switch-it-off' policy

17.2   Building fabric

Maintenance of the building fabric is essential to avoid excessive infiltration and minimise heat losses. The following are examples of maintenance measures:

— Rehang misaligned doors and windows.

— Replace weather stripping or other sealant if damaged.

— Keep curtains and blinds clean and in good working condition.

— Ensure openable windows can be properly closed and latched, with a good seal.

— Replace broken or cracked glazing.

— Replace or upgrade damaged or missing insulation.

17.3 Controls

Regular checking/maintenance of controls to ensure correct setting and operation is fundamental to energy efficiency. Checks should be made to ensure that:

— controls are correctly commissioned and are set at the desired levels; also ensure that calibration of sensors and controls has not drifted

— the building environment is regarded as comfortable and that changes in building use have not occurred to warrant alterations in the controls

— zone controls meet the needs of the occupants and there are no occurrences of overheating, over cooling or annoyance due to automatic light switching

— plant operating times are optimised and time switches/optimisers operate in accordance with the intended settings, and provide appropriate flexibility in relation to occupancy patterns

— weather compensators and optimisers have been gradually adjusted over a long period in order to find the best settings

— occupants understand the use of local controls, e.g. that room thermostats and TRVs should be left alone once set, rather than used as on/off switches

— air conditioning terminal controls are linked to the central plant to give the lowest acceptable level for heating requirements, and the highest acceptable level for cooling

— central plant is modulating/sequencing to match the load while ensuring that controls are stable, i.e. not causing excessive cycling; unnecessary or standby plant should remain off, particularly during periods of low demand

— simultaneous heating and cooling does not occur except where maximum humidity control is essential.

The building manager should keep a current record of the control settings and display them near to the controls to assist in returning them to optimum settings if they are tampered with.

17.4 Ventilation systems

Good maintenance of ventilation and air conditioning plant can have a significant effect on the overall success of the ventilation strategy, energy efficiency, comfort and indoor air quality. Cleanliness, balancing and control are particularly important. The following items should be checked:

— Correct operation of window ventilation fittings and furniture.

— Cleanliness of fan blades and interior fan casing.

— Motor drives: where necessary, replace worn bearings and ensure correct drive alignment. Correct tensioning of belts is critical.

— Operation of volume control devices, i.e. speed controls, VAV boxes, dampers, etc: ensure that damper blades and linkages for proper operation and tight shut-off for accurate control.

— Cleanliness of equipment components.

— Pressure drops: ensure that they are in accordance with manufacturers' data, e.g. heating and cooling coils, filters, casing interior, etc; clean outlet/inlet grilles regularly.

— Ductwork insulation: repair or replace where necessary.

— Cleanliness of heat transfer surfaces.

— Absence of air 'short-circuiting'; absence of leaks in ducts as this increases heating/cooling load as well as fan consumption.

— Lubrication of fan/motor bearings.

— Regularly vent air from heat exchangers, particularly fan coil units, where they become noisy or output is reduced.

— Ensure correct operation of unitary air conditioning equipment, e.g. through-the-wall units and split systems; clean heat transfer surfaces and filters; ensure airflows are not obstructed and avoid unwanted air leakage around the outside of units.

17.5 Refrigeration systems

Refrigeration systems are often used intermittently to meet short periods of excessive heat gains. This places additional stress on components, requiring particular care in maintenance. Checks should be made to ensure that:

— refrigerant is free of moisture by regularly inspecting moisture-liquid indicator; clean filters and/or recharge refrigerant when necessary

— refrigerant charge is correct as low charge reduces heat transfer

— expansion valves are correctly set

— insulation on suction and liquid lines is in good order

— chilled water temperatures are increased when humidity or load conditions permit

— condenser water temperatures and/or flow rates are kept to a minimum

— compressor operating pressure and temperatures are correct, particularly suction pressure, discharge pressure and oil pressure; investigate any changes that occur

— compressor is not cycling excessively, as this may indicate inefficient operation

— Compressor noise level is not abnormal; excessive noise or vibration may indicate drive needs attention.

— compressor joints and shaft seals are not leaking (open machines only)

— chiller performance is monitored regularly by recording water inlet and outlet temperatures and flow rate (or water-side pressure drop) to ensure cleanliness of water-side heat transfer surfaces; investigate any variations from the norm

— refrigerant pressures, air flow rates and temperatures are set correctly to keep air cooled condenser performance high

— heat rejection equipment (e.g. cooling towers) performance is monitored by recording ambient wet-bulb temperature, water inlet and outlet temperatures and flow rate

— cooling towers are kept clean to minimise air-side and water-side resistance including tower-fill or packing, nozzles (water distribution system, tower basin, water intake screens/ strainers air intake screens etc).

More information on installation and maintenance procedures for good energy efficiency are given in DETR Good Practice Guides 36 and 42[4,5].

17.6 Lighting systems

Regular maintenance of lighting installations, including planned replacement of lamps, will sustain lighting levels and ensure continued efficiency. Cleaning lamps and luminaires, windows and internal walls is particularly important. Other checks should ensure that:

— efficient lamps and ballasts are used when replacement is carried out

— internal surfaces are decorated with light colours to obtain benefit from natural and electric lighting

— surfaces are kept clean

— the operation of controls is effective and they are suitable for space occupancy and use

— lights are switched off when not needed; research shows that leaving fluorescent lighting on unnecessarily for even a few minutes is not cost-effective; building managers should make occupants aware of this.

17.6.1 Cleaning and replacement

The reduction in light output due to luminaires and rooms getting dirty can be very significant. Uplighters with glass covers are particularly prone to a fast build up of dust, making frequent cleaning necessary. In addition, the light output from most lamps decreases as they age. The illuminance from a lighting installation, therefore, decreases with time, and lack of maintenance will affect energy consumption and the productivity of occupants.

Proper cleaning materials and techniques should be used to reduce losses caused by chemical action or scratching of

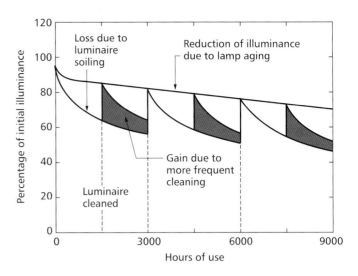

Figure 17.1 Effect of cleaning on bulk lamp changes[7] (reproduced from Thermie Maxibrochure *Energy efficient lighting in buildings*. Crown copyright (1993))

optics and electrostatic dust accumulation. Glass/acrylic diffusers generally have the longest useful life, whereas polystyrene tends to discolour with age and reduce the light output from a luminaire.

If discharge lamps are only replaced when they fail, this causes efficiency and illuminance to fall. In all but the smallest installation, it is sensible to replace the lamps as a group. This planned group replacement can also reduce maintenance labour costs. Optimising replacement periods is discussed in the CIBSE *Code for interior lighting*[6].

Replacement and cleaning can be planned to correspond with a holiday period to reduce disruption to staff. However, spot replacement may still need to be done if there is an early failure. The effect of bulk lamp changing, luminaire cleaning, room surface cleaning and redecoration can be seen in Figure 17.1[7].

17.7 Heating systems

Heating and hot water systems require regular maintenance in order to ensure efficient operation[8]. The following checks should be made:

— Check boiler operating pressures, temperatures, fuel consumption, and investigate any variations from the norm.

— Check flue gas analysis, adjust burners to achieve most efficient flue gas temperatures, CO_2, O_2 and excess air settings.

— Where heavy fuel oil is used, check oil storage temperatures to avoid overheating. Check oil line steam tracing for leaks and damage, and electric tracing for continuity. Check insulation on oil tanks and for leaks in oil lines.

— Check cleanliness of water- and fire-side heat transfer surfaces. Ensure that water treatment levels are maintained and the system is free from sludge and scale.

— Ensure that boilers are not cycling excessively, indicating inefficient operation.

— Check boiler and primary pipework insulation.

— On oil fired boilers, check condition of nozzles or cups of burners, cleanliness of oil line strainers and correct operation of oil heaters.

— On gas fired boilers, check wear and cleanliness of burners, burner gas pressure, operation of gas boosters, operation of governors and controls.

— On coal fired boilers, check performance of automatic stokers and controls, excessive unburned coal (indicating inefficient combustion) and minimum effective continuous combustion for proper kindling control.

— On electric boilers, check cleanliness and freedom from corrosion of elements/electrodes, wear and alignment/spacing of elements/electrodes, absence of loose connections.

— To avoid waste on steam boilers, meter feed water, steam output, blowdown and percentage condensate return.

— Repair steam leaks, without delay.

— Ensure cleanliness of heat transfer surfaces, filters and air paths through convectors, induction units, fan coil units etc.

— Ensure proper air venting in radiators, convectors, fan coil units etc.

— Ensure that frost protection systems are not set too high causing unnecessary operation of the heating system.

— Check that pump drives are in good condition, tighten belts/pulleys, replace worn bearings, and ensure correct drive alignment. Correct tensioning of belts is critical. Ensure pump noise/vibration is not abnormal, indicating incorrect operation.

— Check correct hot water storage temperatures are maintained, but only for the periods necessary.

— Ensure that spray taps and percussion taps operate correctly.

Electric heating systems require little or no maintenance, other than checking the settings of control and washing air filters. The unitary nature of electric heating enables an individual heater to be replaced, if needed, without affecting the integrity of the heating system as a whole.

17.8   Motors and drives

Correct maintenance of motors helps to keep operational efficiencies high. Checks should include the following:

— Lubricate motor bearings in accordance with manufacturers' instructions since inadequate lubrication results in excessive friction and torque, leading to overheating and power losses.

— Check motor shaft to load alignment to reduce running losses, bearing wear, noise and vibration; where necessary, tighten belts/pulleys.

— Clean motor fan inlets and frame surfaces so that generated heat can be removed effectively. An increase in the motor stator winding temperature of 1 K can result in up to 0.5% increase in the I^2R loss, as well as shortening the life of the motor insulation. Ensure good ventilation to prevent over heating.

— Replace worn brushes, belts, sheaves, bearings and gears, as necessary.

— Check loading on large motors compared with rating and consider replacement.

— Check loads are balanced across the three phases as unbalanced supply voltage can lead to a significant increase in motor heat losses and reduced life.

— Check the power factor at varying loads is within acceptable limits; consider power factor correction where necessary.

— Check electrical connections and contacts for corrosion and arcing, and attend to loose connections or bad contacts. Thermography of drive systems offers an early warning of over-heating and wasted energy, and can often help detect problems before there are signs of impending failure.

— Use motor circuit analysis (MCA) to measure the absolute and relative resistance, inductance, and capacitance of motor circuits and windings. MCA can also be used to predict circuit failure, enhancing a motor maintenance or replacement programme.

References

1   *HVCA Standard Maintenance Specification* Volumes 1–4 (London: Heating and Ventilating Contractors Association)

2   *Building services maintenance management* Technical Memoranda TM17 (London: Chartered Institution of Building Services Engineers) (1994)

3   *Introduction to energy efficiency in buildings* Booklets EEB 1–13 (London: Department of Environment, Transport and Regions) (1994)

4   *Commercial refrigeration plant: energy efficient operation and maintenance* GPG 36 (London: Department of Environment, Transport and Regions) (1992)

5   *Industrial refrigeration plant: energy efficient operation and maintenance* GPG 42 (London: Department of Environment, Transport and Regions) (1992)

6   *CIBSE Code for interior lighting* (London: Chartered Institution of Building Services Engineers) (1994)

7   *Energy efficient lighting in buildings* Thermie Maxibrochure (Building Research Energy Conservation Support Unit/OPET) (1993)

8   *Maintaining the efficient operation of heating and hot water. A guide for managers* GPG 188 (London: Department of Environment, Transport and Regions) (1996)

Bibliography

Armstrong J *The effect of maintenance on boiler efficiency* TN 5/83 (Bracknell: Building Services Research and Information Association) (1983)

Armstrong J H *Operating and maintenance manuals for building services installations* AG 1/87.1 (Bracknell: Building Services Research and Information Association) (1990)

Parsloe C *Design for maintainability* AG 11/92 (Bracknell: Building Services Research and Information Association) (1992)

Building services maintenance RG 6/95 (Bracknell: Building Services Research and Information Association) (1995)

Smith M H *Maintenance and utility costs — results of a survey* TM 3/91 (Bracknell: Building Services Research and Information Association) (1991)

Butler H, Armstrong J *Maintenance management — results of a survey* TN 1/81 (Bracknell: Building Services Research and Information Association) (1981)

Armstrong J *Planned maintenance and the use of computers* TN 1/85.1 (Bracknell: Building Services Research and Information Association) (1991)

Armstrong J *Inspection of building services plant and equipment — a review of current practice* TN 6/86 (Bracknell: Building Services Research and Information Association) (1986)

Armstrong J *Fault finding procedures in the building services industry* TN 12/86 (Bracknell: Building Services Research and Information Association) (1986)

Stonard P *Instruments for building services applications* TN 14/86 (Bracknell: Building Services Research and Information Association) (1986)

Condition-based maintenance for building services TN 1/95 (Bracknell: Building Services Research and Information Association) (1995)

Barnard N and Starr A *Vibration monitoring for building services* TN(S) 3/95 (Bracknell: Building Services Research and Information Association) (1995)

Barnard N and Starr A *BEMS as condition based maintenance tools* TN(S) 4/95 (Bracknell: Building Services Research and Information Association) (1995)

HVAC Applications: Building operation and maintenance ASHRAE Handbook (Atlanta, GA: American Society of Heating, Refrigeration and Air Conditioning Engineers) (1995)

Owning and operating costs CIBSE Guide B18 (London: Chartered Institution of Building Services Engineers) (1986)

Armstrong J H Life cycles or death throes? Revision to CIBSE Guide Section B18 — owning and operating costs *CIBSE National Conference 1996* (London: Chartered Institution of Building Services Engineers) (1996)

de Saules T *Handover information for building services* TN 15/95 (Bracknell: Building Services Research and Information Association) (1995)

18 Retrofitting energy saving measures

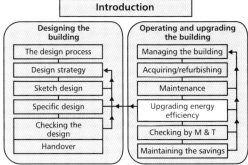

This section provides an overview of the process of retrofitting energy efficiency measures when upgrading existing buildings (see the principles at the front of this Guide). It is aimed predominantly at the energy manager/consultant. Section 19 provides a checklist of specific measures that can be introduced. Where measures require significant amounts of design, reference should be made to the relevant section in Part A.

18.0   General

The key to retrofitting cost-effective measures in existing buildings is to:

— identify high energy users

— establish the potential for energy saving through measurement, audits etc.

— identify practicable measures to achieve these savings

— establish the financial case for introducing these measures, as well as other benefits

— implement the savings in a planned way with the least disruption to the building

— monitor the savings to confirm they have been achieved and to ensure they are maintained (see sections 20 and 21).

Energy consumption of existing buildings can often be reduced by about 20% by introducing simple and cost-effective measures, usually with payback periods of less than 5 years. Any cost savings add directly to the profitability of organisations once the initial capital cost has been repaid. Identifying and implementing retrofit energy saving measures can, therefore, be highly cost-effective often with significant spin-off benefits including reduced environmental emissions and higher productivity[1].

Measures range from changes to working practices through low cost/no cost items to more significant alterations to the building and its services[2,3]. Many of these measures may require little or no design input and can be implemented by the building manager using contractors. Refurbishment is an ideal opportunity to improve energy efficiency, as discussed in section 15.

18.1   Developing a programme

While it is possible to introduce *ad hoc* measures, it is usually more beneficial to develop a prioritised programme to ensure best use of the funds available and that supports the original design intent, while minimising disruption to the building.

18.1.1   Commitment and co-operation

An energy efficiency programme requires commitment from senior management. A senior member of staff must lead activities, and be responsible for ensuring the continued commitment and co-operation of management and staff (see section 14). The energy manager should initiate the following actions:

— Identify those measures and expected benefits that can produce energy savings with minimal expenditure.

— Produce a cost-benefit analysis for all measures that incur capital expenditure or changes in operational requirements.

— Obtain agreement on priorities, level of funding and economic criteria.

— Explain the impact of proposed energy efficiency measures on occupants and their work.

— In tenanted buildings, identify those aspects of the programme that are related to conditions in the lease and list the advantages to the owner and the tenants.

— Highlight the results achieved by others in the field of energy efficiency.

18.1.2 Planning

Since planning is essential, the first action should be to produce a fully costed plan of action, and obtain agreement to proceed with the programme, either as a whole or in stages.

All the original design information on the building and its services, plus the records, drawings, and maintenance and operating manuals, should be collected and reviewed in order to provide a good understanding of the original design intent (see section 14).

A simple audit of annual energy consumption based on invoices will establish if actual energy use is in line with expectations and targets (see section 20). It should then be possible to prepare an initial budget and action plan for discussion with maintenance and operations staff, for subsequent approval by owners and tenants. The action plan should include the following items:

— Preparation of a more detailed energy audit and building survey[3-7].

— Identification of measures where energy savings could be made.

— The effects of energy saving measures on the internal environment and activities within the building.

— Cost-benefit assessment of proposed measures.

— A list of priorities for the proposals.

— Involvement of maintenance staff and building occupants in additional activities.

— The implementation of the programme including timescales and disruptions which could occur to normal operation.

— Identification of external sources of information which could be needed in assessing the returns achieved in the programme, e.g. meteorological data, case studies of energy usage in similar buildings.

— The planning of a monitoring and recording system to assess the effect of the programme.

Figure 18.1 shows the main stages in the retrofit process and indicates where professional assistance might be considered.

18.2 Identifying measures

Energy audits and surveys provide the information needed to make decisions on which are the most cost effective measures[3-7].

18.2.1 Energy surveys and audits

18.2.1.1 Energy audits

Like a financial audit, an energy audit is an attempt to allocate a value to each item of energy consumption over a given period, and to balance these against overall energy use[3-7].

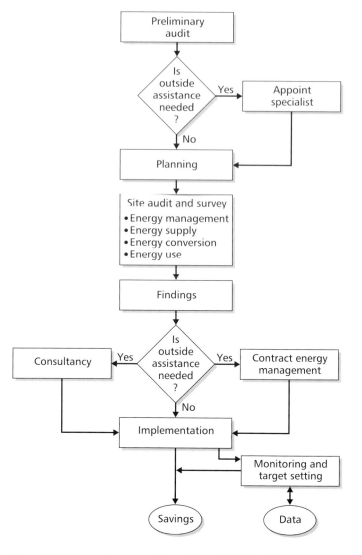

Figure 18.1 The retrofit process (adapted from CIBSE Applications Manual AM5[3])

An energy audit, however imprecise, should be undertaken early in any energy efficiency programme to identify where energy is being used. It is then possible to direct energy efficiency action towards the highest consumers. Energy audits can bring to light and eliminate hitherto unknown mistakes (such as incorrect billing) and/or unnecessary uses of energy. Auditing should become progressively more accurate and can use all the analysis techniques shown in section 20.

Where a whole stock of buildings is being considered, simple performance indicators (e.g. (kW h)/m^2 for fossil fuel and electricity) can be used to set up league tables of the highest consumers. Investigations should then target the worst buildings first, ultimately leading to detailed energy surveys where high consumption can not be easily explained and rectified (see section 20).

18.2.1.2 Energy surveys

An energy survey[3-7] is an on-site technical investigation of the supply, use and management of energy to identify specific energy saving measures. Two basic levels of survey, concise and comprehensive, are shown in CIBSE Applications Manual AM5[3] with standard specifications

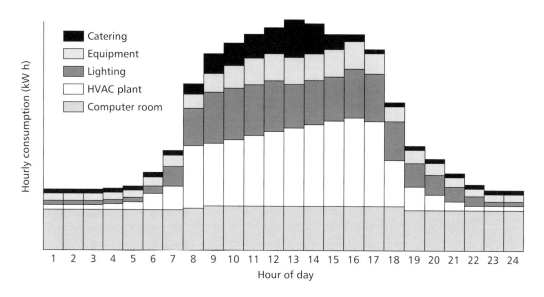

Figure 18.2 Identifying individual uses within the demand pattern[4] (reproduced from DETR Fuel Efficiency Booklet No.1. Crown copyright (1993))

of what a survey should cover. These can be used to brief the survey team.

The survey should cover the main items affecting energy use, including the following:

— the building: levels of insulation, ventilation, air infiltration etc.

— the pattern of use: periods of occupancy, the types of control, the temperatures and humidities maintained, the use of electric lighting, the activities and processes being undertaken, including their operating temperatures, insulation etc.

— the main building services: primary heating, cooling and air handling plant

— electric lighting: quality, illuminance, luminance efficiency, extent to which daylight could reduce energy use, flexibility of control etc.

— the transport of energy within the building: fans and pumps, insulation of hot water and steam pipes and air ducts, evidence of leakage etc

— the plant room: state and condition, insulation of boilers, tanks, pipe work, recovery of condensate, plant efficiency checks etc.

The survey should also assess energy management, determining who is responsible for energy management in each department. The assessment should include how energy consumption is reviewed, recorded and analysed. A check should be made as to whether the analysis correlates with departmental activity.

Measurements should be made systematically with correctly calibrated instruments. Guidance on instrumentation is given below. In the absence of instrumentation, it is possible to estimate energy use from nameplate and manufacturers' data, combined with an assumed proportion of full load operation. Such estimates are, however, second-best to actual measurement. Early in the energy efficiency programme, the larger energy-using systems should be instrumented, enabling actual energy consumption to be measured.

Comprehensive surveys should aim to reach a detailed breakdown of the constituent parts of typical load patterns. This allows the principal components to be identified and, in particular, the base load, as indicated in Figure 18.2. This is particularly helpful in indicating possible opportunities for reducing energy consumption.

Recent work[8] has emphasised the importance of accurate key data such as floor area, and the benefit of assessing the consumption of different energy sources separately, particularly electricity and fossil fuels. This work has provided a method for achieving a more accurate apportionment of end-uses by:

— using the most reliable data sources available

— reconciling the apportionment results with all useful metered data and avoiding *ad hoc* adjustments

— assessing the reliability of data and of the apportionment; if justified, seeking more data

— using specific techniques to obtain more details on uncertain loads.

These methods[8] require little or no extra work but can provide more useful and reliable information in understanding the building's detailed performance.

18.2.1.3 Instruments and measurements

Good instrumentation and measurement is an essential part of investigating and implementing retrofit measures. Measurements taken as part of energy surveys can indicate the potential for savings but it is also important to include metering in the implementation package in order to monitor the future savings achieved. A BMS can provide a useful source of measurements although the accuracy of any information needs to be assessed carefully. More detailed information on consumption can be obtained through spot check measurements, demand profile recording and metering selected items of plant[9].

Table 18.1[3] shows some common portable instruments found useful during surveys. All should have valid calibration certificates to ensure confidence in the results.

Table 18.1 Useful survey instruments

Instrument	Purpose/application
Electrical load profile recorder	Indicates pattern of overall building load or local use (e.g. 24 h, 7-day); recordings can include (kVA h), V, A, power factor, dependent on type; useful for analysis, auditing and tariff review.
Clip-on power meter	Useful for auditing and checks on lighting circuits, motor consumption and small power usage
Data logger (or chart recorder)	Inputs can include space temperature, duct air temperature, water temperature and relative humidity; pulsed outputs can also be used to provide gas/oil/water consumption, and indications of system and control performance
Boiler combustion test kit	Flue gas analysis; temperature, O_2, CO_2, CO, smoke number; spot check on boiler efficiency to highlight need for burner adjustment, boiler cleaning, etc.
Light meter	Spot checks on illuminance levels
Digital temperature indicator	Surface and immersion probes; spot checks on space/water/duct temperatures; surface temperatures for assessment of quality of pipework and vessel insulation
Sling hygrometer	Spot checks on wet and dry bulb space temperatures
Anemometer (or pitot tube and manometer)	Air flow rate to calculate supply/extract volumes, air change rates

Meters installed in an area or on an individual plant can be used to record consumption. The cost of sub-metering can usually be justified on major loads, particularly where little information on energy use is currently available (see section 4).

18.2.2   Level of detail required

The level and extent of an energy audit/survey should be determined by the likely potential for savings and the necessary investment in time and resources. In a small building with a relatively low energy bill, it may not be worth investing a great deal of time and effort in a survey. Large, complex buildings or sites will usually merit a detailed investigation of all areas of energy use[3].

A simple walkabout survey is often sufficient to identify some low-cost/no-cost measures and some areas requiring further study. A detailed survey will be required to identify and assess more complex and costly measures.

18.2.3   Integrating the measures

Energy analyses or surveys often identify stand-alone measures that will save energy on specific items. However, the wider effects of any measures should be considered carefully in relation to the whole building and the original design intent. Often, one set of problems can be exchanged for another. For example, turning off humidifiers on air conditioning plant to reduce electricity consumption may lead to control problems and complaints of dryness.

It is essential that these measures are co-ordinated so that they form an integrated package, avoiding conflict between one measure and another. For example, the introduction of fast response lighting controls alongside the introduction of high pressure discharge lamps with long strike-up times will result in significant problems. Equally, better building insulation without good heating controls may simply result in overheating.

Integration should also avoid double counting of savings. For example, if a boiler is upgraded and improved boiler controls are introduced then the savings from the controls should be based on the consumption expected after boiler replacement.

New measures should also be carefully integrated with the ability and resources of the existing management since additional burdens may prevent savings actually being achieved in practice.

18.2.4   Reporting the results

For action to be taken, recommendations for energy efficiency measures must reach the correct level of management, be presented in a form that assists, and offer a good case for investment. Energy analyses or survey reports should include:

—   a management summary suitable for non-technical managers

—   observations and data

—   an analysis of costs and non cost benefits

—   conclusions and interpretation of the findings

—   clear recommendations.

The energy account is often best presented in tabular form in a similar manner to a financial account. A graphical presentation can also be adopted, e.g. a pie-chart or Sankey diagram as shown in Figure 18.3[3].

The audit and survey report should include future targets (see section 20), including emissions targets in (kg CO_2)/m^2 per annum (see 12.3).

Survey recommendations can range from simple non-technical measures to those needing major investment, and possibly more detailed investigation. A report can also include recommendations for savings solely in energy cost, e.g. tariffs or control of electrical maximum demand. Such recommendations can often help the supplier reduce their primary energy consumption.

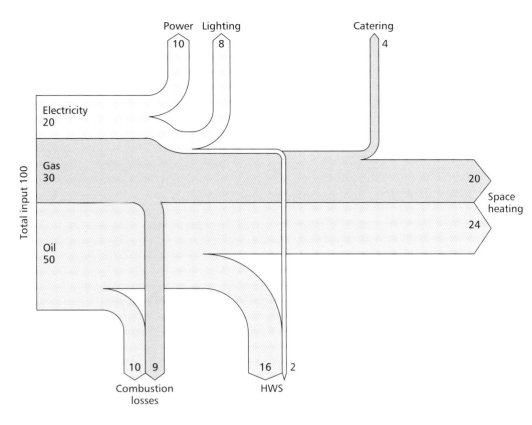

Figure 18.3 Sankey diagram showing where energy is being used[3]

Table 18.2 Specimen summary of recommendations

Ref	Location	Description of recommendation	Fuel type	Net annual savings		Implementation costs (£)		Simple payback (years)
				(£)	(GJ)	Extra study and design if applicable	Total	
Totals (and overall payback period)								

Measures can be summarised and ranked in as much detail as the data allows, as shown in the specimen summary illustrated in Table 18.2.

18.3 Assessing energy saving measures

18.3.1 Option appraisal

Before making a change to an existing system, it is important to consider all the available options, particularly where major investment is involved, e.g. new boilers or a BMS. A full option appraisal will ensure that the most cost-effective and efficient plant is chosen[10,11]. Option appraisal can provide a number of benefits:

— correct sizing of plant to meet the real demands of the building, often leading to lower capital costs

— improved comfort levels through increased levels of control taking account of the needs of staff

— lower running costs through the installation of more efficient plant with better controls

— easier maintenance and improved reliability by using modern plant and careful choice of systems

— higher environmental standards by considering the environmental benefits of each option

— a formal justification for the recommendations made, including a well researched fall-back option in case the first recommendation is rejected by management.

— an opportunity to investigate other forms of financing such as contract energy management.

Table 18.3 Example format for an option appraisal worksheet

Option appraisal worksheet			
	Option 1	Option 2	Option 3
Plant output (kW)			
Hours run			
Seasonal efficiency			
Energy consumption (kW h)			
Fuel cost (p/(kW h))			
Annual running cost			
Capital cost			
Payback period			
Environmental emissions			
Other benefits			

Option appraisal compares possible solutions to a particular problem in order to arrive at the optimum solution to provide the required comfort conditions. The appraisal includes capital and operating costs, and environmental impact, as well as practical issues like flueing and plant location and the flexibility to cope with changes in building use and occupancy.

Option appraisal is a highly iterative process. Some options will be eliminated during the process due to the constraints on the project, such as economics or practical problems like the size of the plant room. Conversely, others may become known during the analysis. It is important, therefore, to consider even what appear to be the most unlikely options. The appraisal should be treated as a flexible process of development; nothing should be fixed until final recommendations are made.

Strategic issues should be considered, including:

— Should the plant be centralised or decentralised?

— Where will the plant be located?

— What fuels are available on site?

— Is in-house maintenance available or will it be contracted out?

— Are there complaints from staff about comfort levels?

Future changes which may influence demand should also be considered, for example, use or occupancy patterns, alterations to the buildings including additions, refurbishments, demolitions etc.

The process starts by comparing the rough payback and non-cost benefits of each option. The worksheet shown in Table 18.3 illustrates a suitable format for estimating the paybacks and lists the information that will be required at this stage[10]. The aim is then to focus on the most feasible and economic options by gradually increasing the accuracy of costings and the engineering detail for those most favoured. The preferred options can be further refined by considering the practical problems e.g. flue heights, floor loadings etc.

18.3.2 Investment criteria

For low cost/low risk measures with quick returns, simple methods of appraisal are generally acceptable. Appraisals of large or long-term investments should take account of interest rates, inflation, project life and risk. Energy efficiency measures should be assessed on the same basis as other investments, taking into account the wider benefits that can accrue. Analysis of the sensitivity to changes in, for example, ambient temperature (as measured by degree-days), equipment performance or energy prices is also advisable.

The full implementation costs should always be considered including equipment, material and labour costs, consultants' fees, builders work and any disruption costs. In-house staff time, whether carrying out work directly or supervising the work of others should also be included.

Some of the methods used in investment appraisal are outlined below[12–14].

18.3.2.1 Simple payback

The crudest test of cost-effectiveness is simple payback period, which is the time taken for the initial capital expenditure to be equalled by the saving in energy cost.

This ignores interest rates and the benefit of continuing savings to the end of the life of the plant. A persistent and unthinking use of this method of testing cost-effectiveness may lead to under investment and a failure to seize good investment opportunities where payback periods are somewhat longer than anticipated.

The method is generally adopted for measures showing a return within five years, measures involving only minor investment, or for an initial assessment of measures that involve more substantial investment.

It should be made clear whether costs and savings are based on firm quotations or budget estimates. Where alternative measures are being compared, the marginal capital cost should be used to indicate the payback of one measure versus the other.

18.3.2.2 Discounted cash flow

Large projects and long term measures require the preparation of a cash flow statement to evaluate their true economic worth. Discounted cash flow (DCF) takes into account the timing of capital and revenue costs and savings. The decision on when to apply DCF methods should reflect normal business policy.

Such methods require the use of discount rates[12–14]. These discount rates differ widely between organisations but are usually between 5% and 20%. This is, in effect, saying that such a return on capital can be obtained by an alternative investment and an energy efficiency investment must yield a return no less than this. Discounted payback, or the break-even period, can be calculated in a similar way to simple payback except that discount rates are taken into consideration.

When the net annual saving is less than the real or notional interest charges, i.e. the discount rate, the capital can never be recovered. Some organisations may wish to take into account predictions of future energy prices. The discount rate should then be reduced by the predicted annual percentage increase of energy costs. Alternatively, they may wish to assess the effect of falling energy prices, in which case the discount rate would be increased.

18.3.2.3 Net present value

Net present value (NPV) indicates the discounted cash flow over the life of the project[12–14].

The effects of taxation and capital allowances can be taken into account, as can changes in energy prices. The true worth of the proposed measure can then be seen as a sum of money in present day values.

18.3.2.4 Internal rate of return

Internal rate of return (IRR) provides an alternative approach to NPV, representing the rate of interest that money would have to earn elsewhere to be a better investment; the higher the IRR, the better the project.

IRR is defined as the discount rate at which the net present value of the project reduces to zero. There is no direct way of calculating IRR. The interest rate at which the NPV becomes zero is determined by successive approximations[12–14].

18.3.3 Life cycle costing

In addition to direct financial returns, there are nearly always wider benefits that should be taken into account, including:

— improved manageability, for example through better control and monitoring

— reduced maintenance and staff costs after replacing or upgrading plant

— reduced harmful emissions to the atmosphere, e.g. less CO_2, NO_x etc; this is particularly important to organisations with environmental policies

— improved management information and decision making

— improved services, comfort and productivity.

The last point is often missed but is commonly one of the greatest benefits. Results from building surveys[1], have shown a combination of benefits comprising optimum levels of energy efficiency, people satisfied with their environment, and high productivity. This does not mean that installing measures will always directly improve productivity, but rather that well managed buildings tend to have satisfied occupants who pay attention to energy management.

Total life cycle costing involves evaluating all costs and benefits over the entire physical life of the asset, providing a more realistic basis for comparison. However, there is a risk of overestimating benefits and exposing the project to an unnecessary level of risk from market effects. In particular, it should never be used as a means of enhancing the value of a project that has a poor payback.

18.4 Implementing savings

A works programme, as shown by the example in Table 18.4, can help to prioritise measures and to assist in

Table 18.4 Example energy efficiency works programme

Proposed project	Location	Priority	Works order no.	Estimated cost	Estimated rate of return	Organisation actioned	Project manager	Date work ordered	Expected completion date	Comments

managing project implementation. It should show the cost, responsibility and timing of each recommended measure.

Large scale energy saving projects need significant supervision to an extent that an independent project manager may be required.

One effective method is the rolling programme in which savings from the first energy saving measures are re-invested to produce further savings. Part of the initial investment can sometimes be raised by capitalising fuel cost savings from good housekeeping measures that need little or no capital expenditure.

Energy managers should publicise the programme and explain its importance and implications. Implementation should be planned so that measures are introduced with minimum disruption to normal activities but achieve savings at the earliest opportunity. Repetitive solutions may benefit from pilot projects to provide valuable experience and identify any pitfalls. Monitoring equipment should be installed as part of implementation in order to quantify the savings actually achieved. The implementation programme should be regularly reviewed, and all personnel should be kept informed of progress and the results achieved.

References

1   Bordass W T, Bromley A K Rand Leaman A J *Comfort, control and energy efficiency in offices* BRE Information Paper IP3/95 (BRE) (1995)

2   *Introduction to energy efficiency in buildings* Energy Efficiency Booklets Nos. 1–13 (London: Department of Environment, Transport and Regions) (1994)

3   *Energy audits and surveys* CIBSE Applications Manual AM5 (London: Chartered Institution of Building Services Engineers) (1991)

4   *Energy audits for buildings* Fuel Efficiency Booklet No. 1 (London: Department of Environment, Transport and Regions) (1993)

5   *Energy audits and surveys* IP12/92 (Garston: Building Research Establishment) (1992)

6   *Energy audit and survey guide: for building managers and engineers* GPG 28 (London: Department of Environment, Transport and Regions) (1991)

7   *Energy audit and survey guide: for building financiers and senior managers* GPG 27 (London: Department of Environment, Transport and Regions) (1991)

8   Field J, Soper J, Jones P G, Bordass W and Grigg P Energy performance of occupied non domestic buildings: Assessment by analysing end-use energy consumptions *Building Services Engineering Research and Technology* **18**(1) (1997)

9   Stonard P *Instruments for building services applications* TN 14/86 (Bracknell: Building Services Research and Information Association) (1986)

10   *Heating system option appraisal — an engineer's guide for existing buildings* GPG 187 (London: Department of Environment, Transport and Regions) (1996)

11   *Heating system option appraisal — a manager's guide* GPG 182 (London: Department of Environment, Transport and Regions) (1996)

12   *Owning and operating costs* CIBSE Guide B18 (London: Chartered Institution of Building Services Engineers) (1986)

13   *Financial aspects of energy management in buildings — A summary* GPG 75 (London: Department of Environment, Transport and Regions) (1995)

14   *Financial aspects of energy management in buildings* GPG 165 (London: Department of Environment, Transport and Regions) (1995)

Bibliography

Is your energy use under control? A practical guide to assessment and action GPG 136 (London: Department of Environment, Transport and Regions) (1994)

Organisational aspects of energy management: a self-assessment manual for managers GPG 167 (London: Department of Environment, Transport and Regions) (1994)

Choosing an energy efficiency consultant (London: Department of Environment, Transport and Regions) (1993)

Practical energy saving guide for smaller businesses ACBE 1 (London: Department of Environment, Transport and Regions) (1992)

Energy managers handbook (London: NIFES/Graham and Trotman) (1985)

Reviewing energy management GIR 13 (London: Department of Environment, Transport and Regions) (1993)

Energy efficiency in the workplace — A guide for managers and staff GPG 133 (London: Department of Environment, Transport and Regions) (1994)

Heslop P *Training staff to cut energy costs* (Energy Publications) (1986)

Energy Management Training GPG 85 (London: Department of Environment, Transport and Regions) (1994)

Educated energy management (London: E and FN Spon) (1991)

Energy efficiency handbook (London: Heating and Ventilating Contractors Association) (1987)

Bordass W, Bunn R, et al. PROBE: Some lessons learned from the first eight buildings *CIBSE National Conference 1997* (London: Chartered Institution of Building Services Engineers) (1997)

19 Specific energy saving measures

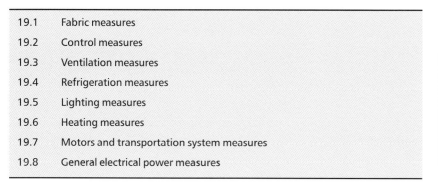

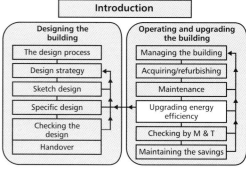

This section provides a checklist of the main retrofit energy saving measures to consider when upgrading energy efficiency in existing buildings[1] (see the principles at the front of this Guide). It should be read in conjunction with sections 17 and 18.

19.1   Fabric measures

As a retrofit measure, major energy saving building fabric measures are best applied when repairing or refurbishing the fabric. Major alterations are usually difficult to justify on energy saving grounds alone due to high capital costs and the resultant extended paybacks. Consequently, these projects often go ahead for other reasons, such as the need to deal with the deterioration of the existing fabric. When this is the case, it presents an opportunity to improve significantly the fabric energy efficiency in which case paybacks should be related to the marginal cost of including a superior specification.

Section 4 covers some of the sketch design issues, and maintenance issues are discussed in section 17. For further detail on fabric issues, reference should be made to DETR Fuel Efficiency Booklet No 16[2].

19.1.1   Identifying problems

Problems can be identified by the following methods:

— *thermography*: detects damaged or missing insulation and air leakage by identifying areas of fabric with high temperature in winter

— *building pressure testing*: establishes the magnitude of infiltration leakage paths through the building fabric[3]; used in conjunction with smoke pencils or thermography, pressure testing can identify primary leakage paths

— *building simulation*: computer models are used to highlight major areas of heat loss and predict the effect of fabric changes on energy use.

19.1.2   Draught proofing

Draught proofing is often one of the most cost-effective means of improving building fabric since uncontrolled air infiltration can be one of the most significant heat losses from buildings, particularly those that are well insulated. The options are shown below.

External doors and entrances:

— Add draught lobbies to busy entrances, although capital cost may be high.

— Install weather stripping on doors or replace, if worn or broken.

— Use automatic door-closers on external doors, or entrances to unconditioned or unheated spaces.

— Provide signs and instructions for the operation of doors; and a reminder to keep closed.

— Consider using expandable entrance enclosures to connect to the back of delivery vehicles, or use automatic doors.

— Where there is regular traffic, consider using fast acting automatic doors, which give a pay back period of around 2 years[4].

— A simple and cheap option for factory doors is to use transparent plastic curtains which research[4] indicates can reduce heat loss through factory doors by up o 50%.

— Consider making delivery entrances smaller.

Windows and skylights:

— Upgrade windows by repairing window furniture, seals and ventilators.

— Install weather stripping or replace if worn or broken; this gives a payback of under 2 years.

— Seal gaps between window frames and walls.

— Provide signs and instructions on how to use the windows, window furniture and ventilators, e.g. keep windows closed while the building is being heated or cooled.

Walls and roofs:

— Seal or draught proof at exterior joints, e.g. between walls and roof, and wall panels.

— Seal building openings at service penetrations, e.g. for piping and electrical conduits.

— Fit external covers or flaps to the outside air connections of window and wall fans, and unit air conditioners, thereby preventing infiltration when they are not in use.

19.1.3   Insulation

Upgrading insulation levels reduces heat loss and improves energy efficiency.

DETR Fuel Efficiency Booklet 16[2] contains methods of calculating the most economic thickness of insulation. Careful consideration should be given to avoiding any risk of interstitial condensation[5], particularly in the case of existing composite wall structures which already incorporate some insulation. The options are shown below.

Wall insulation:

— Install external wall insulation: low risk of thermal bridges occurring, although the visual impact is significant. It is often expensive due to installation requirements e.g. scaffolding.

— Add internal wall insulation: no effect on the external appearance, but building use will be disrupted and there is a danger of thermal bridging at the junctions of building elements, e.g. where a floor slab penetrates an external wall.

— Install cavity wall insulation: often a more cost-effective measure than internal or external insulation, with a payback of about 3–5 years; it also causes less disruption to building use. It is only possible where there is a suitable cavity, there is no danger of interstitial condensation and there is no risk of damp penetration due to driving rain.

Roof insulation:

— Add insulation within the roof cavity (cold roof): can be very cost-effective often with paybacks under 3 years, although for flat roofs there is a danger of condensation.

— Apply insulation above the structure (warm roof): preferred option where there is no roof cavity. Careful detailing is necessary to avoid moisture penetration.

Floor insulation:

— Add insulation to the exposed surfaces of floors, e.g. where the first floor overhangs the floor below, or is over unheated or unconditioned floors. Ground floor insulation is most appropriate when the floor is renewed.

19.1.4   Windows

The options for windows are as follows:

— Specify double or triple glazing for replacement windows and consider low emissivity glass and multiple glass combinations (see section 4).

— Consider selective films/coatings on existing glazing: can help minimise solar gains (to avoid cooling loads) and reduce radiative heat loss, although they may have an adverse effect on daylighting levels.

— Replace existing clear glazing with special solar control glazing where solar gain is likely to cause overheating.

— Reduce the glazed area (if considered excessive) without compromising daylighting levels.

— Fit external or mid-pane shading devices to eliminate unwanted solar gains in the summer.

— Use internal shading to reduce glare, although this is unlikely to reduce solar gains significantly.

19.2   Control measures

Upgrading controls is often the single biggest improvement that can be made to enhance the energy efficiency of existing buildings. Modern microprocessor controls are more accurate and more flexible, giving closer control and greater functionality and therefor better comfort conditions and lower running costs.

Even well-designed building services will perform badly if controls are inadequate, incorrectly installed or mis-understood by the building operators. Many problems with building services can be traced back to poor control of the systems.

Overall control strategies should always be considered when upgrading specific controls or diagnosing building services problems since they can sometimes be the root cause of symptoms that appear unrelated. Control strategies are covered in section 5 and maintenance issues are covered in section 17. Further guidance on controls can be found in the CIBSE Applications Manual AM1[6], in CIBSE Guide B3[7], DETR Fuel Efficiency Booklet No. 10[8], BSRIA Applications Handbook AH 1/90[9] and DETR GIR 40[10] and 41[11].

19.2.1   Diagnosing control faults

A number of studies[12] have indicated common control problems that can reduce performance and increase energy consumption, with systems either defaulting to on when they could have been off, or operating inefficiently. The following can cause problems

(a)   Excessive operation, in which whole-building systems are brought on to service small loads, for example when:

— the whole chilled water system is brought on to service a few small machine rooms

— heating (or, most wastefully, air conditioning) is brought on early, or left on overnight, to avoid a few rooms otherwise being uncomfortable for out-of-hours use.

Demand based control systems are the most energy efficient. However, where small areas are required frequently for out-of-hours use, plant dedicated to that area can be more economic to operate.

(b) Unwanted operation, when systems run long hours, or constantly, owing to:

— controls being over-ridden for a short-term purpose and not reset

— automatic controls (e.g. frost thermostats) bringing on systems unnecessarily due to poor settings or calibration, or incorrect interlocks

— time controls getting out of phase after a power failure.

User friendly overrides are essential, normally providing a fixed period of operation.

Time controls should have battery back-up or spring reserve as appropriate. System settings should be regularly checked where interference, or drift, is likely. Interlocks should be checked from record wiring diagrams or for DDC/BMS through the software logic. These problems are far less likely to occur with modern DDC controls or BMS, provided it has been correctly specified and commissioned.

A simple way of improving failure detection is to include a few diagnostic checks, either regular manual checks or within the BMS, which will identify major departures of important items of plant from the design intent and report exceptions. These checks need tailoring to the building in question, but will commonly include:

— monitoring daily hours run by major items of plant during periods when they should be off

— identifying simultaneous operation of potentially conflicting items of plant, e.g. chillers and heat recovery systems

— monitoring efficiencies of heat recovery devices and creating an alarm if the actual to anticipated efficiency in operation is less than say 65%

— raising an alarm if the supply air temperature for ventilation plant used for night cooling is more than say 3°C warmer than the outside air temperature.

19.2.2 Upgrading and tuning controls

Before upgrading or tuning controls, a check should be made that controls are operating in accordance with their declared characteristics or that current operating requirements are met by the existing characteristics. Upgrading options are shown below.

Time controls:

— Set timeswitches in relation to occupancy and use of the service: where suitable, introduce timeswitches on energy using equipment, e.g. vending machines (some items may need power during standby periods).

— Upgrade major time controls to optimum start/stop controls and ensure that existing optimisers are actually minimising start up periods.

— Where override facilities are introduced to allow extensions to the occupancy period, these should always be self-resetting, e.g. a push button, to override the time controls for a preset fixed period of time. Incorporate an indication lamp to show that the system has been overridden, thereby indicating misuse. Override controls are inappropriate for systems with a slow thermal response, e.g. underfloor heating.

Plant capacity controls:

— Introduce sequence controls where appropriate and check that the sequence selection of boilers and chillers provides a minimum output matched to the load.

— Check that plant is not cycling excessively as this can reduce performance. Frequent cycling can normally be prevented using standard controls (see 9.3.2.1). Boiler-delay or anti-dry-cycling controls for heating systems should be avoided.

— Introduce variable speed drives where appropriate for central plant fans and pumps to minimise the power required during periods of low demand (see 10.2).

Temperature controls:

— Check for overheating or over cooling and investigate the underlying reasons. Consider gradually lowering the flow temperature until overheating ceases.

— If the building overheats in some areas in order to maintain design conditions elsewhere, check the balance of the system and ensure that the circuit temperature is suitable for the emitter characteristic.

— Provide separately compensated zones where structure, orientation (solar gain), occupation, or emitters have different characteristics.

— Where small areas have different uses, consider time controlled local zone valves.

— Consider compensation of chilled water systems via reset of chillers.

— Consider separate provision of cooling (chilled water or DX) for de-humidification duties, rather than cooling all chilled water systems via reset of chillers.

— Check that local temperature controls are able to meet the needs of the staff and can respond to changes in occupancy etc.

— Consider varying set point temperatures depending upon external conditions. Use a fixed differential between inside and outside air temperature, e.g. a summer set point of say 3°C below external temperature.

Terminal unit controls:

— Ensure settings are maintained at the lowest acceptable level for heating requirements, and the highest acceptable level for cooling requirements.

— Check the stability of terminal unit/controls: instability may be due to the proportional band being too narrow (adjust controls) or to incorrect selection of the unit and/or the controls (seek specialist advice).

19.2.3 Integrating the controls

19.2.3.1 Zoning arrangements

Services are often required at different times and levels (e.g. temperature or illuminance) in different areas of a building. Systems should be zoned according to occupancy, the layout of the services, building aspect and use so that each zone can be separately controlled. The options for zoning are as follows:

— Provide separately compensated zones where structure, orientation (solar gain), occupation or emitters have different characteristics.

— Consider time-controlled local zone valves where small areas have different uses.

— Zone light switches and automatic lighting controls, e.g. reset and/or photoelectric controls, in relation to daylighting and occupancy patterns.

— Consider decentralising primary cooling and heat generating plant to match the needs of each zone.

19.2.3.2 Simultaneous heating and cooling

Measures available to avoid simultaneous heating and cooling are as follows:

— Set heating system and local controls correctly to avoid unauthorised local overrides by occupants, e.g. windows being opened to reduce the excess heating temperatures.

— Ensure that there is a dead band between heating and cooling.

— Ensure that, in addition to a dead band, P+I controllers have additional methods to prevent simultaneous heating and cooling, such as software or hardwired interlocks.

— Automatically reset the cold air supply temperature of reheat systems (other than VAV) to the highest to satisfy the zone requiring the coolest air. This minimises the effects of simultaneous heating and cooling in systems that supply more than one zone and use reheating for temperature control.

— Automatically reset the preheated air supply temperature in re-cool systems to the lowest to satisfy the zone requiring the warmest air. This minimises the effects of simultaneous heating and cooling in systems that supply more than one zone and use re-cooling for temperature control.

— Multi-zone dual duct systems will require the control described above for both the hot deck and the cold deck. Where simultaneous heating and cooling is unavoidable, either reclaimed heat or free cooling should be used wherever possible. This type of control can be complex and often needs BMS control to minimise energy use.

— Fully integrated air conditioning with other systems within the building to minimise energy

consumption. Attempts are sometimes made, on the grounds of energy efficiency, to shut down perimeter heating before the variable volume system is allowed to increase the cooling input. This may result in a better theoretical energy balance, but the occupants will often complain about cold down draughts from the windows. Setting the compensated circuit to the minimum temperature to avoid cold down draughts will be more satisfactory than turning the circuit off.

19.2.4 Introducing building management systems

Introducing a building management system (BMS) as a retrofit measure can be a good way of upgrading the overall control strategy and improving both energy efficiency and comfort. BMSs can provide additional management benefits through improved monitoring of comfort conditions, plant operation and energy consumption (see section 5). Issues for introducing a BMS are as follows:

— Retrofitting a BMS can be expensive; payback periods are widely variable dependent upon how efficiently the plant has been operated but can be in excess of 5 years based on energy savings alone. The overall viability of a BMS should take into account the additional benefits and wider management implications, such as gaining full control over large and complex buildings or large multi-building sites. Many buildings cannot be run effectively and efficiently without a BMS.

— The building user must be prepared to employ and train staff to operate the BMS and hence utilise all its facilities. If this aspect is neglected, poor performance and even complete failure of systems can result. Although installing a BMS may result in a net reduction in the level of manpower required to operate plant, the benefits to be accrued are directly proportional to the effort put in to running the system. Where site staff are not available to operate a BMS, off-site bureau services can be very cost-effective.

— BMSs are not a panacea for all ills and will not compensate for badly designed or badly maintained plant. However, BMSs can be used to identify poor design, operation and maintenance.

— Regularly review systems to ensure that they are being used most effectively. Even a well installed and commissioned BMS can easily fall into misuse leading to a rise in energy consumption, if appropriate time is not spent in managing the system.

— A phased approach to implementation should be considered when introducing a BMS to an existing site in order to spread capital costs and minimise site disruption. Future system development and the capacity for additional control monitoring points should be considered, as and when the need arises.

— Excessive alarms and monitoring can result in an information overload with so much information being generated by the BMS that little is actioned and the key information is hidden.

19.3 Ventilation and air conditioning measures

Ventilation is often responsible for the largest energy loss in well-insulated buildings; it therefore offers significant scope for retrofit energy saving measures. The checklists below indicate some of the measures that can be introduced. Further detail on ventilation issues is available in section 6, CIBSE Application Manual AM10[13], CIBSE Guide B3[7], DETR GIR 31[14] and BRE Digest 399[15]. Where the measures alter the overall ventilation strategy or require a significant level of design, reference should be made to section 4.

19.3.1 Natural ventilation

The potential measures for natural ventilation are as follows:

— Check that window ventilation systems are readily usable and operate correctly.

— Ensure natural ventilation is not obstructed by partitions.

— Ensure that heat and smoke relief vents are closed in winter.

— Ensure hot air is re-circulated from high level if stratification occurs during heating.

— Consider the introduction of cooling using external air at night.

19.3.2 Mixed-mode

Mixed-mode operation can be more energy efficient approach than full air conditioning. However, it needs to be introduced with care, and the overall ventilation strategy needs to be reassessed beforehand (see section 4). The options for mixed-mode operation are as follows:

— For changeover mixed-mode, turn the air conditioning system off in the mid-season, opening windows for ventilation and cooling. Make sure that occupants understand when these various modes are in operation to avoid windows being opened when the air conditioning is on.

— Zoned mixed-mode also provides a retrofit option for reducing mechanical ventilation by only serving the areas that actually require air conditioning.

19.3.3 Mechanical ventilation and air conditioning

Whatever steps are taken, the aim should be to reduce the need for ventilation and cooling, commensurate with the required environmental conditions (see section 4). Where air conditioning is essential, ensure that it operates efficiently. The issues for mechanical ventilation and air conditioning are as follows:

— Ensure plant is not oversized; BSRIA Guidance Note GN11/97[16] covers the monitoring, assessment and remedial action that should be taken where plant is likely to be oversized.

— Check that the minimum necessary air change rates are maintained.

— Consider switching off humidifiers when minimum humidity is not critical.

— Simultaneous heating and cooling should not occur except where close humidity control is essential.

— Check controls are set so that higher space temperature can be used in summer and lower space temperatures in winter.

— Ensure the cooling system is shut down in winter, when there are no cooling loads.

— Ensure heating is shut down whenever there are no heating loads, especially where internal heat gains are such that heating plant operation is unnecessary.

— Perimeter heating should be operated at the lowest temperature consistent with eliminating down draught.

— Fans, particularly those for toilet ventilation systems, should be switched off when the building is unoccupied. Where possible, they should operate in response to demand, e.g. controlled by presence detectors.

— Unless close control of humidity is required, allow the relative humidity to vary from 40% to 65%. Occasionally, over dry air can cause problems with static electricity and with respiration.

— Turn off reheat in all areas during the summer except where process or equipment requirements necessitate close humidity control.

— Readjust and rebalance systems to minimise over cooling and overheating which results from poor zoning, poor distribution, improper location of controls, or improper control.

— Review motor sizing and consider introducing variable speed drives to modulate fan speeds where loads vary significantly.

— Air curtains generally use more energy than they save and are not an efficient means of controlling heat loss through large openings.

— Ensure maximum use is made of re-circulated air and fresh air for 'free' cooling as appropriate. Introduce variable re-circulation where appropriate; using return air that retains an element of heating/cooling is the best form of energy recovery. Using automatic variable air dampers to control the amount of fresh air drawn into the system minimises the amount of air to be heated/cooled and consequently reduces energy consumed.

— Minimise air leakage from ductwork to prevent wasting fan power and the heating/cooling content of treated air; this also prevents unwanted heat gains/losses to other areas.

— Insulating ductwork is particularly important where treated air ducts pass externally or through unconditioned spaces[17,18]. DETR Fuel Efficiency Booklet 8[17] provides a means of estimating the most economic thickness of insulation.

19.3.3.1   Constant volume systems

A reappraisal of existing ventilation requirements can result in reduced ventilation rates, and hence a downsizing of motors and fans. Reducing the air volume handled by the fan saves energy, taking care to ensure that poor air distribution or fan instability does not result - and limiting the temperature range of the supply air. Re-commissioning of central-fan air volumes should be by changing pulleys to vary fan speed rather than by closing dampers. Variable speed fan drives can often be used instead of overall system regulation dampers (see section 10).

Single zone systems

These systems have a separate air handling plant for each zone and temperature control is achieved by means of a sensor situated within the controlled space. Consider the following measures:

— Reduce the air volume handled by the fan where appropriate.

— Switch off humidifiers when minimum humidity is not critical, or set humidity control to a maximum of 40%, as appropriate.

— Avoid simultaneous heating and cooling except where de-humidification is essential.

— Adjust or modify the control system so that higher space temperature can be used in summer and lower space temperatures in winter.

— Convert to variable air volume where practicable.

Multi-zone terminal reheat systems

Multi-zone systems use a single air-handling plant to meet the requirements of several zones simultaneously. These systems provide air at a predetermined temperature to air zones, where secondary terminal reheaters raise the supply air temperature to suit space load requirements. Each zone therefore receives its own individually controlled air supply. Consider the following measures:

— Reduce the supply air volume where appropriate.

— Shut off reheat coils in summer, and raise the supply air temperature, as necessary.

— Install controls that ensure the control of common heating and cooling coils is based on the zone requiring the greatest load. This ensures that, while sufficient capacity is available for temperature control, excessive capacity is avoided.

— Convert to a variable air volume system where practicable, or heating and cooling coils for each zone.

Dual duct systems

A dual duct system provides space temperature control by mixing the two air streams; one hot, one cold. Consider the following measures:

— Reduce air volume flow to all mixing boxes to the minimum acceptable level.

— Lower the hot deck temperature.

— Raise the cold deck temperature.

— Shut down the cooling system in winter when there are no cooling loads. Operate hot deck as a single duct system.

— Shut down heating system in summer when there are no heating loads. Operate cold deck as a single duct system.

— Convert to a VAV dual duct system; this should provide significant energy savings.

19.3.3.2   Induction systems

The options for induction systems are as follows:

— Re-balance the system if the orifices have become enlarged due to cleaning.

— Reset the primary air heating and secondary chilled water temperatures according to load and season.

— Consider upgrading central plant and induction unit controls.

— Investigate the possibility of conversion of two-pipe changeover and three-pipe systems to four-pipe operation to minimise change-over and mixing losses.

19.3.3.3   Room fan coil systems

The options for fan coil systems are as follows:

— Reduce air volumes to the minimum acceptable level.

— Provide control interlocks between heating and cooling systems at each unit and within each zone to prevent simultaneous use.

— Convert zoned two-pipe and three-pipe systems to central four-pipe systems to minimise change-over and mixing losses.

19.3.3.4   Variable air volume systems

The options for variable air volume systems are as follows:

— Use variable speed drives or variable pitch axial fans to control the air volume, rather than inlet guide vanes.

— Ensure that the static pressure sensor is located correctly so that the air volume reduces in relation to demand.

— Set terminal re-heat to operate only when the VAV terminal has turned down to the minimum amount for reasonable air distribution.

— Ensure that any perimeter heating is operated at the lowest temperature consistent with eliminating down draught.

— Automatically reset supply air temperature, where appropriate, to suit heating and cooling requirements.

19.3.3.5   Self-contained systems

Self-contained systems include unitary air conditioning,

unitary heat-pumps and room-unit systems. The options are as follows:

— Provide control interlocks between heating and cooling systems at each unit and within each zone to prevent simultaneous use.

— Replace old existing units with modern units or heat pumps with a higher efficiency rating.

— Improve local user controls to enable operation to match local requirements.

— Provide centralised automatic stop/start control (with manual over-ride) of multiple units.

— Ensure units operate only in occupied zones.

19.3.3.6   Industrial ventilation systems

The options for industrial ventilation systems are as follows:

— Introduce destratification fans where the upper part of the space is overheating.

— Use localised extraction for equipment emitting pollutants (e.g. welding, paint spraying etc.) in order to minimise ventilation losses.

— Improve hood design to reduce quantity of air handled and consider using unheated local outdoor make-up.

— Use 'ball-blankets' etc. on open tanks to limit evaporation and hence reduce ventilation rates.

19.3.4   Heat recovery

Heat recovery systems use heat energy that would otherwise be rejected to waste.

Options for heat recovery are as follows:

— Consider air-to-air heat recovery devices which transfer sensible heat (but possibly, depending on the device, total heat) from the exhaust air stream to the fresh air inlet. Several devices are available, the most common being run-around coils, plate heat exchangers and thermal wheels[19].

— Consider preheating incoming air through atria, conservatories, roof spaces etc. or using waste heat from air-cooled condensers, e.g. industrial refrigeration and computer rooms.

— Check that any additional electrical energy input required, e.g. fan power to overcome resistance of heat exchangers or coils, does not negate the energy saved, bearing in mind that it uses electricity rather than the fossil fuel energy. Note that extra fan power is needed whenever the system is in operation, although the degree of heat recovery varies throughout the year. Include the additional fan or pump running costs when calculating the viability of the scheme.

— Use effectiveness as a measure of the heat recovered, as shown in Figure 19.1.

— Consider re-circulation, which is essentially a form of heat recovery, and in common use. The effectiveness is equal to the re-circulation

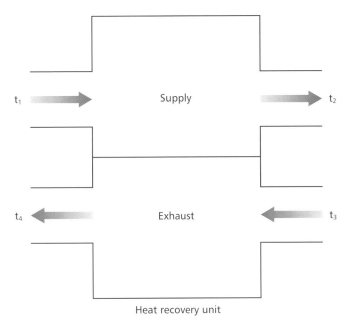

t_1 = supply air temperature (dry-bulb) into unit (°C)
t_2 = supply air temperature (dry-bulb) out of unit (°C)
t_3 = exhaust air temperature (dry-bulb) into unit (°C)
t_4 = exhaust air temperature (dry-bulb) out of unit (°C)
W_s = supply flow rate
W_c = exhaust flow rate
W_{min} = minimum value of W_s pr W_c

$$\text{Sensible effectiveness} = \frac{W_s\,(t_1 - t_2)}{W_{min}\,(t_1 - t_3)} = \frac{W_e\,(t_4 - t_3)}{W_{min}\,(t_1 - t_3)}$$

Figure 19.1 Heat recovery effectiveness

percentage, e.g. 10% fresh air gives a 90% heat recovery effectiveness.

19.3.4.1   Run-around coils

These comprise finned-tube copper coils located in supply and exhaust air streams connected by pipe work through which is pumped water, or antifreeze solution. The advantages and disadvantages are summarised in Table 19.1.

Typical thermal effectiveness is 45–65% depending on the number and spacing of coil rows and the temperatures prevailing. The additional air resistance and pumping energy should be taken into account, as should temperature conditions across the whole season when assessing viability.

19.3.4.2   Thermal wheels

These cylindrical drum heat exchangers rotate slowly between supply and exhaust air streams, absorbing heat from the warmer air and transferring it to the cooler air. Typical effectiveness is 60–85% depending on the media construction in the thermal wheel. A sensible heat exchanger may recover up to about 65% sensible heat, whilst the hygroscopic exchanger can recover around 80% total heat (i.e. sensible plus latent heat). The advantages and disadvantages are summarised in Table 19.2.

Table 19.1 Advantages and disadvantages of run-around coils

Advantages	Disadvantages
Supply and exhaust airflows are separated, thus avoiding any possibility of cross contamination	Direct transfer of latent heat is not generally possible
Can be used where the supply and exhaust ducts are not in close proximity	Overall heat recovery effectiveness is not likely to be greater than 65%
Seasonally reversible, providing preheating in winter and pre-cooling in summer	Frost protection should be provided
Multiple supply and exhaust systems can be incorporated in a single loop where appropriate	
Easy to fit with minimum disturbance	
Use conventional finned tube technology	

Table 19.2 Advantages and disadvantages of thermal wheels

Advantages	Disadvantages
Can be controlled by varying the rotational speed	Possibility of cross contamination from exhaust to supply (can be minimised using a purge section)
Possible to recover both latent and sensible heat using hygroscopic materials	Difficult to clean
Highest heat recovery effectiveness of all devices; efficiency may be as high as 65% in sensible heat reclaim and 80% in enthalpy terms for the hygroscopic type	Supply and extract ducts must be adjacent

19.3.4.3   Plate heat exchangers

Cross-flow plate heat exchangers are inexpensive, have low hydraulic resistance and require no motive power. Effectiveness can be in the range 30–70%, depending on the spacing of the plates, but is typically less than 50%. The advantages and disadvantages are summarised in Table 19.3.

Placing the fan on the downstream side of the device on the supply side and the upstream side on the exhaust side maximises the ability to pick up the fan energy.

19.3.4.4   Heat pipes

The heat pipe makes use of a closed fluid cycle within a sealed tube to give a reversible heat recovery system. With this system, supply and exhaust air ductwork must be connected adjacent.

19.3.4.5   Heat pumps

Heat pumps should be used only where it is necessary to take advantage of small temperature differences between supply and exhaust air or where it is appropriate to convert rejected latent heat into sensible heat. Energy is required to drive the compressor, although high COPs are possible (see 6.3.3 and 9.1.5).

19.3.5   Ventilation controls

19.3.5.1   'Free' cooling

'Free' cooling (or 'enthalpy control') should be considered to reduce energy consumption. Enthalpy sensors detect the cooling capacity of the external air and then modulate the dampers to draw in more air than the basic fresh air requirement. This 'free' external cooling can significantly reduce the energy required for mechanical cooling (see 6.3.4 and 6.4.4).

Table 19.3 Advantages and disadvantages of plate heat exchangers

Advantages	Disadvantages
Simple static devices; easy to commission and maintain	No modulation, so rate of heat recovery cannot be controlled unless a by-pass duct is provided (i.e. overheating could occur when heating requirements are small); over-recovery of heat also possible if there is a building cooling requirement (i.e. could result in heat being dumped into a cooled space, thereby increasing the cooling load)
Minimal risk of cross contamination unless mechanical damage occurs	
May be constructed so as to be easily removed for cleaning	
	Supply and exhaust ducts must be adjacent, and ductwork needs to be arranged to allow heat transfer through the plates

19.3.5.2   Night cooling

Night cooling can be introduced as a retrofit measure to make use of the lower night-time air temperatures and the thermal capacity of the building. However, it is essential to ensure that the system is well controlled and fully integrated into the existing cooling and ventilation strategies. The cost of any energy should be balanced against the cooling energy saved (see 4.2.5).

19.3.5.3   Terminal and room controls

Good control of individual room and equipment controls is essential for the efficient use of energy. Options are as follows:

— Check the operation and settings of controls regularly, in order to maximise energy savings as well as comfort improvements.

— Upgrade to direct digital control (DDC) and electronic controls that can bring significant benefits; they are generally more accurate and responsive than older controls. An upgrade may be an opportunity to consider a more integrated control strategy, perhaps using a BMS.

19.4   Refrigeration measures

Where it is necessary in UK buildings, cooling is generally only required for parts of the year. However, plant is often found operating unnecessarily or inefficiently to supply small loads. There is a significant energy saving potential in upgrading refrigeration systems and controls, or installing smaller plant to serve such loads.

Where measures alter the overall cooling strategy or require a significant level of design , reference should be made to section 7. Minimising cooling requirements is also covered in sections 3, 4 and 6.

Energy issues related to the maintenance of refrigeration systems are covered in section 17. For further detail on refrigeration issues, reference should be made to CIBSE Guide B14[20], DETR Fuel Efficiency Booklet No 11[21] and DETR Good Practice Guides 36[22], 37[23] and 38[24].

19.4.1   Minimising cooling loads

Options for minimising cooling loads are as follows:

— Reduce solar gains by using coated glasses, blinds and shading (see section 4). A cheaper alternative is to add reflective plastic coating to existing windows, although this may reduce daylight penetration and hence increase artificial lighting use.

— Reduce gains from lighting by using more efficient lighting and lighting controls. Air handling luminaires can reduce cooling loads by removing heat before it enters the occupied zone. This is particularly applicable in deep plan buildings where lighting is a major source of heat gain (see sections 6 and 8).

— Reduce gains from office equipment by using more energy efficient PCs, printers, photocopiers, etc. (see section 11).

19.4.2   Refrigeration plant

The use of refrigerants having zero ozone depletion potential may cause significant reductions in energy efficiency and refrigerant capacity. Information on strategies to respond to the need to phase out CFCs is given in CIBSE Guidance Note GN1[25] and BRE Information Paper IP 14/95[26].

Options for refrigeration plant are as follows:

— Ensure that plant is not oversized; BSRIA Guidance Note GN13/97[27] covers the monitoring, assessment and remedial action that should be taken where plant is likely to be oversized.

— Replacement of inefficient compressors is unlikely to be cost effective unless there is very poor efficiency or excessive part load operation. However, a smaller machine to meet part load conditions could be cost effective. Very low loading of compressors should be avoided. As a rule of thumb, compressors should not operate at less than 50% of their full load.

— Check that the best form of heat rejection equipment has been chosen. A cooling tower will give a better coefficient of performance, but the extra costs of its maintenance, as well as the water and water treatment tend to mean that it is only economical for large systems.

— Consider the opportunity for recovering heat from refrigeration plant (see 7.2.2).

— If waste heat is available, investigate the possibility of recovering or using it as the input for an absorption machine, see 7.4.3.

— If an absorption machine is already being used, check to ensure all sources of waste heat are being employed.

— Check the condition and thickness of pipework insulation.

— Reduce condenser water temperature on water-cooled systems.

— Consider the possibility of using water direct from the cooling tower to give free cooling, thus avoiding the use of the chiller (see 7.1.3).

19.4.3   Refrigeration controls

The options for refrigeration controls are as follows:

— Ensure refrigeration plant is switched on only during periods when cooling will be required. Consider optimum start/stop or demand based controls where possible.

— Use efficient compressor capacity controls. Avoid hot gas by-pass and suction throttling where possible (see 7.6.1). Consider use of variable speed drives for capacity control of compressors (see 10.4).

— Ensure that the maximum acceptable chilled water flow temperature is maintained through automatic reset or direct compensation of the chiller. Significant savings can often be achieved during milder weather since the system can be operated at higher temperatures.

— Check sequence controls and sequence selection to ensure chillers are operating at maximum efficiency where possible, e.g. one compressor operating at full load will be more efficient than three operating at 33% load. In modular plants, the COP can sometimes increase at part load, since the reduced temperature lift can occasionally outweigh the compressor inefficiencies caused by unloading.

19.5   Lighting measures

In most buildings, lighting is the largest single component of the electrical consumption and, in offices, often the biggest single energy cost. The energy consumption of the lighting can be reduced by upgrading lamps, luminaires, ballasts and lighting controls. Where measures alter the overall lighting strategy or require a significant level of design, reference should be made to section 8.

Energy issues related to lighting maintenance are covered in section 17. For further detail on lighting issues, refer to CIBSE Code for interior lighting[28], DETR Fuel Efficiency Booklet No. 12[29], Thermie Maxibrochure: Energy efficient lighting in buildings[30] and CADDET Analyses No. 6[31].

19.5.1   Luminance refurbishment and replacement

It is not only older installations that can benefit from refurbishment or replacement. Installations that are only 5 to 10 years old can also benefit, since the installation of modern equipment can often result in substantial energy savings in addition to improved visual conditions[32].

Options are as follows:

— Use modern luminaires with efficient reflectors; this allows fewer lamps or luminaires to be used to produce a given illuminance.

— Consider refurbishment before replacement. To assess viability, select a representative area. Clean and re-lamp the luminaires within the selected area, clean the wall and ceiling surfaces if possible and then measure the average illuminance over the working plane using a light meter (see *CIBSE Code for interior lighting*[28]). This will give a reliable indication of the initial illuminance that the existing equipment and installed load could achieve without further modification. Calculate the maintenance factor (see 8.1.2) to arrive at the design maintained illuminance that would be achieved.

— Downrate lamps or remove lamps from multi-lamp fluorescent luminaires; this may be possible where illuminance is significantly higher than the design requirement. Where the illuminance is lower than design levels, appropriate measures should be taken to increase it to the design level, even though this may increase energy consumption (see 19.5.2).

19.5.2   Improving luminaires

General measures for improving luminaires are as follows:

— Ensure that the combination of light source, control gear and luminaire is the most efficient to meet the functional and aesthetic requirements of the system.

— Replacement of luminaires may not always be cost-effective on the grounds of energy efficiency alone, although there are measures that can be taken to improve the overall performance of lighting systems. For example, the simple expedient of replacing old and yellowed prismatic or opal diffusers, linked with the measures listed in 19.5.3, can be very effective.

19.5.2.1   Task lighting

The use of local lighting (see 8.1) at workstations with a lower background illuminance can provide an energy efficient alternative to a high general lighting level.

Options are as follows:

— Lighting consumption can be reduced significantly due to the lower installed load and the close proximity of task lighting switches.

— Introducing localised lighting may be appropriate in some areas and allow a reduction in the general background lighting.

19.5.2.2   Specular reflectors

Specular reflectors are available to upgrade existing luminaires. Energy savings of 30–50% can be achieved, with payback periods of less than three years, due to the relatively low capital cost. However, not all luminaires are suitable for this modification, in particular because it can change the visual appearance of the space.

The following simple checks should be carried out before proceeding with the complete installation:

— Measure the illuminance at several points over an area lit by an existing luminaire that has been cleaned and fitted with a new lamp.

— Repeat this procedure with the specular reflector fitted to the same or an identical luminaire.

— Calculate the average illuminance from each set of measurements. Check also that the distribution of illuminance has not changed to an extent that could adversely affect the uniformity of illuminance or the appearance of the space.

19.5.3   Lamp replacement

A change to a more efficient lamp type will reduce energy consumption. Some changes involve little or no capital expenditure, others may require the addition, or change, of control gear. Changing luminaire type and/or position will be less cost-effective. A summary of lamp characteristics is shown in 8.3[33]. The options for lamp replacement are as follows:

(a)   *Tungsten*:

— Replace tungsten lighting with compact fluorescent lamps (see 8.3.4). A payback period of 35 years is possible, depending on use[34].

— Tungsten spotlights can also be replaced with low voltage (LV) tungsten-halogen systems. Although this requires some re-wiring and the installation of transformers, it can be cost-effective in many circumstances, e.g. shops, museums etc. Tungsten-halogen lamps are susceptible to over voltage which can significantly shorten life; this is particularly important for LV tungsten-halogen lamps on a track system with a shared transformer which may have poor regulation when under loaded.

(b)   *Fluorescent*: replace older 38 mm diameter fluorescent tubes with 26 mm diameter type. Direct substitution of 38 mm diameter lamps by 26 mm lamps can be made in many existing luminaires with switch-start control gear. They cannot be used with starter-less circuits (see 8.3.3)

(c) *Mercury and sodium*: replace high pressure mercury, MBF or MBTF lamps with high pressure sodium SON, or high pressure mercury MBI lamps. Energy savings are typically up to 20% with payback periods of less than three years (see 8.3.5).

19.5.4 Control gear

The options for control gear are as follows:

— Replace standard glow-switch starters by electronic starters; 'soft' starting extends the economic life of the fluorescent tube, thus reducing maintenance costs. Energy savings can be 15–20%, with payback periods of 5–10 years (see 8.4).

— Low-loss ballasts may be satisfactorily incorporated into new installations, or the installation of electronic high frequency control gear (with or without dimming) can achieve savings.

19.5.5 Lighting controls

The addition of lighting controls can be a highly cost-effective retrofit measure, giving energy savings of 20–50% with payback periods of 2–5 years[35] (see 8.5).

Options for lighting controls are as follows:

— Self-contained luminaires, each with its own sensor and control, may be a more practical and economic solution than centralised control.

— Staff awareness campaigns may fail; control systems that are obtrusive are counter-productive and may even be sabotaged by the occupants. Minimise such problems by making staff aware of the purpose of the control system, how it works and how they can interact with it. Consult staff before introducing new controls.

19.6 Heating measures

Heating is the single biggest component of the total energy consumption in most buildings and therefore often provides significant potential for energy saving through upgrading primary plant, distribution systems and heating controls. Where measures alter the overall heating strategy or require a significant level of design, guidance is given in section 9.

Energy issues related to heating maintenance are covered in section 17. For further details on heating issues, reference should be made to CIBSE Guide B1[36], DETR Fuel Efficiency Booklets[37-41], DETR General Information Reports GIR 40 and 41[10,11], and Good Practice Guides 132 and 143[42,43].

Ensure that plant is not oversized; BSRIA Guidance Note GN12/97[44] covers the monitoring, assessment and remedial action that should be taken where plant is likely to be oversized.

19.6.1 Minimising heating demand

The options for minimising heating demand are as follows:

— Keep distribution system losses as low as possible. Pipework and ductwork lengths should be kept to a minimum. In particular, long deadlegs in hot water systems should be avoided.

— Check the provision of thermal insulation. *Building Regulations* stipulate that hot water storage vessels should be insulated to restrict standing losses to 1 W/litre, or insulated with at least 50 mm of insulation with a thermal conductivity of 0.045 W/(m K). Pipework that does not contribute usefully to a space heating requirement should be insulated with at least 40–50 mm of insulation with a thermal conductivity of 0.045 W/(m K). Existing insulation should be upgraded to at least these levels. Wet or damaged insulation is ineffective and should be replaced immediately, particularly in hot water circulation systems that operate all year round.

— Add extra insulation, further reducing distribution losses, with typical payback periods of less than 3 years. Valves and storage vessels should always be insulated.

19.6.2 Boilers

Boiler replacement can lead to a 5–25% improvement in energy consumption depending on the inefficiency of the existing plant.

19.6.2.1 Low temperature hot water boilers

Using high efficiency boilers can raise seasonal efficiency to over 80%; the use of condensing boilers can raise the efficiency further to 85–92% (see 9.1.1).

The options for low temperature hot water (LTHW) boilers are as follows:

— In the case of multiple boilers, allow the plant to match the load more closely and hence maximise plant efficiency. A mixture of condensing and high efficiency boilers helps minimise capital costs although with very little reduction in the seasonal efficiency of the overall plant, thus optimising the payback period (see 9.1.4).

— Introduce effective measures to minimise standing losses with traditional heavyweight high water content boilers. Older boilers can have standing losses of up to 7%. When older boilers shut down, large amounts of cold air can enter the boiler gas side. This leakage should be eliminated by an automatic shut-off damper on the burner or on the boiler flue off-take, suitably interlocked with the burner operation.

— Consider decentralising plant. In many cases the replacement of old centralised steam heating plant with local modern LTHW boilers and the elimination of extended steam distribution systems has provided considerable savings. This has often included the separation of heating and hot water plant to improve summer hot water efficiencies. Decentralisation is discussed in 9.1.1.3.

— Provide common flow and return header system to ensure simple and reliable sequence control from return water temperature by providing a constant flow pumped primary circuit. Do not fit automatic isolation valves, or individual pumps on boilers, as these can cause the primary circuit flow to vary (see 9.3.2.5). Ensure that the boiler circuit flow is not affected by variable flow from other circuits (see 9.3.1).

19.6.2.2 Medium temperature hot water and steam boilers

The options are as follows:

— Introduce oxygen trim controls to maintain the correct air-to-fuel ratio and thus optimise combustion efficiency. Generally economic for large modulating boilers, these controls constantly measure the oxygen level in the flue gases and alter the air inlet damper to ensure the correct excess air level. Savings of 3–5% can be achieved and, although the capital cost is high, it is outweighed by the fuel saved in large boilers.

— Use variable speed control for the combustion air fan. For large modulating boilers, the average electrical demand of the combustion air fan motor can be reduced by up to 60% using a variable speed drive (VSD), see DETR Good Practice Case Study No. 35[45].

— Pre-heat combustion air using heat recovery equipment (see 19.3.4). If the combustion air temperature is raised by 20 K, the thermal efficiency of a boiler is increased by 1%.

— Consider economisers that recover waste heat from boiler flues using heat recovery equipment (see 19.3). This is often cost-effective as a retrofit measure in very large plant. Install condensing economisers on gas fired boilers to raise efficiency even further.

— Around 3–5% of fuel consumption can be lost in blowdown from steam boilers. Blowdown can be automatically controlled to maintain the total dissolved solids at their optimum value, thus minimising losses.

— There are a number of cost-effective methods of recovering heat from blowdown which are covered in DETR Fuel efficiency booklet No. 2[46]. Stagger or automatically time the blowdown cycle to spread the availability of waste heat recovery more evenly. Where more than one boiler is operated on an intermittent system, the cost-effectiveness of waste heat recovery is improved because the equipment required will be smaller and will run for a higher proportion of the time.

19.6.3 Combined heat and power

Combined heat and power (CHP) should be considered where loads are suitable[47] (see 9.1.3). Usually, there needs to be a simultaneous requirement for heat and power for at least 4,500 hours per year to make CHP cost-effective[48,49].

The following should be considered for CHP:

— CHP plant requires careful sizing making a detailed feasibility study necessary.

— CHP can be installed in conjunction with boiler plant, but it should always take the lead role. In multiple building sites, the heat load may be significant enough to consider large scale CHP, e.g. gas turbines.

19.6.4 Warm air systems

A significant temperature differential (4–6 K) can often exist between the ceiling and the occupied space in large volume buildings, e.g. factories.

The options for warm air systems are as follows:

— De-stratifying the air by forcing the warmer air down towards the occupied space reduces the heating requirements at working level. De-stratification fans are usually controlled thermostatically such that they operate once the temperature in the upper area reaches a pre-set level. Fan speeds are low to avoid perceptible down draughts and noise, thus fan energy requirements are also small.

— An air-jet circulation system is an alternative to de-stratification. This system draws warm air from the upper space and distributes it through a duct before blowing it vertically down at high speed to various locations. This stream entrains cooler air, preventing stratification and reducing energy requirements, although fan power is significant.

19.6.5 Radiant systems

The options for radiant systems are as follows:

— Radiant tube and plaque systems can be a cost-effective replacement for warm air systems in buildings with high air change rates, e.g. factories (see 9.2.3).

— Ensure that radiant systems have good controls using black bulb sensors to ensure comfort levels and savings.

— Electric, quartz radiant heaters can be used for spot heating where requirements are highly inter-mittent. They have a very rapid response time and can be used in conjunction with occupancy sensors to control heat output but maintenance costs can be high.

19.6.6 Electric systems

The options for electric systems are as follows:

— Existing systems should be replaced by fossil fuel heating where a life-cycle cost evaluation demon-strates that it would be cost-effective. Compare with benchmarks in terms of CO_2 emissions rather than delivered energy.

— It may be cost-effective to retain electric heating in part of a building otherwise heated by a fossil fuel system where a limited area is heated at different times from the rest.

— Where electric heating is retained, install good time and temperature controls. Where heating needs vary, ensure that suitable heat emitters and controls have been chosen to allow the heat output to track variations in heat requirement.

— If electric storage heaters are retained, ensure that charge controllers are set correctly to minimise overheating on mild days.

19.6.7 Hot water services

19.6.7.1 Hot water services in general

The options for hot water services in general are as follows:

— Minimising hot water consumption reduces energy consumption. Install spray taps, percussion taps, tap restrictors and showers instead of baths. Fix leaks and dripping taps as soon as they are detected.

— Consider whether the volume of hot water stored can be reduced, and whether pipe runs are longer than necessary.

— Turn off circulating pumps when the building is unoccupied.

— Calculate and install the economic thickness of insulation on storage tanks and pipework.

— Ensure that stored hot water is not overheated.

— Ensure that thermostats are set correctly on electric immersion heaters and individual time controls are installed. Ensure immersion heaters for summer use are not left on through the winter.

19.6.7.2 Hot water controls

The options for hot water controls are as follows:

— Always employ time-control to ensure that hot water is only heated when required.

— Timeswitches should control the primary and secondary circulation pumps.

— Always use thermostatic controls to maintain hot water at the required temperature, e.g. a cylinder thermostat or a thermostat built into the storage water heater. Hot water should always be stored at $(60 \pm 2.5)°C$ to avoid legionella (see 9.3.8).

19.7 Motor and transportation system measures

Significant energy savings can be realised by upgrading motors and motor controls[50]. When designing new systems with motors or replacing an existing motor, reference should be made to section 10. Maintenance and operation is discussed in section 17.

Further details on the energy efficient use of motors can be found in DETR Good Practice Guide 2[51], DETR Fuel Efficiency Booklet No. 9[52] and General Information Report GIR 41[11]. Heat gains from electric motors are given in CIBSE Guide A7[53].

The motor load should always be minimised by good system design prior to motor selection (see 10.1). Effective system regulation and control are essential for efficient operation.

Electric motors and drives can account for a significant part of the energy demand in buildings. A modest sized 11 kW induction motor costing £300 can build up a running cost of over £8,000 in intermittently occupied buildings with seasonal system operation over ten years, and up to £30,000 with continuous operation over the same period.

The particular options for motors are as follows:

— Higher efficiency motors should always be considered as they often have no additional capital cost and offer efficiency and economic benefit in virtually all situations (see 10.2 and 14.3.5).

— Motors should be sized correctly to avoid the increased losses resulting from part-load operation.

— Use direct drives rather than belt drives where practicable.

— Where belt drives are used, consider modern flat, synchronous, or ribbed-belt drives rather than traditional V-belts, to reduce drive losses (see 10.3).

— Systems should be carefully designed to minimise pressure loss and hence reduce energy consumption.

— Efficient system regulation, achieved by matching fan and pump characteristics to the system (normally via speed change), can provide significant energy savings compared with increased system resistance. Energy savings are typically 20% for 10% flow regulation and 40% for 20% regulation.

— Variable flow control can provide significant opportunities for energy saving. Building services are sized for peak loads and, for most of their working life, operate well below their full output. Typically, only 20% of full volume energy is required to move air and water at 50% of maximum volume.

— The use of variable speed drives should always be considered for efficient system regulation and variable flow control (see 10.4).

19.7.1 Assessing motor performance

The potential benefits of an investment in high efficiency motors or improved drives can be established by firstly checking the actual operating parameters for existing systems. At the outset, establish an inventory of motors operating on the site, then undertake measurements, simple observations and tests on selected drives. These tests should be repeated following implementation of any energy saving upgrade, to ensure that savings have been achieved.

The load determines the actual power drawn by the motor but the size of the motor does not necessarily relate to the power being drawn. For example, a 20 kW motor may be driving a 5 kW load very inefficiently.

The rated motor power is the shaft power, i.e. the useful power it can provide to turn the load. However, due to the motor's internal losses, the power drawn by the motor at full load is greater than the rated shaft power. For example, a 30 kW motor which is 92.5% efficient at full load will, at full load, draw a power of (30/0.925) = 32.4 kW.

Motor performance can be assessed using the following techniques:

— Estimate the actual running cost by multiplying the rated power of the motor by the number of hours running per year, and by the average cost of electricity in £/(kW h). This ignores the motor efficiency and actual load conditions but provides a quick estimate of potential running costs and gives a useful guide as to where best to concentrate efforts on a site with many motor drives. For example, an 11 kW motor running for 5000 hours and costing 5p/(kW h) would have a potential annual running cost of £2,750.

— Spot-check current measurement using a clip-on instrument. The kVA drawn by the motor is given by $(V \times I \sqrt{3})/1000$. If the current drawn is close to the full load current as stated on the rating plate, it is likely that the motor is operating near to full load rated power. However, if the measured current is well below the full load value, all that can be said with certainty is that the power will be significantly less than the calculated kVA.

— Data logging is more accurate than spot-checks and reflects the variation of motor load with time. Two methods are available:

   (a) *Current recording*: measures current over time. A data logger with the ability to analyse the information and present it in the form of frequency curves is preferable.

   (b) *Power recording*: requires voltage connections to be made in addition to those required for current measurements and therefore is less convenient and more expensive. However, it may be appropriate where a large capital investment is being considered, such as the installation of a variable speed drive.

— Fit (kW h)-meters or run-time meters: particularly suitable for assessing savings on machines using large amounts of power.

Two examples of estimating running costs are shown below. Motor efficiencies are taken from manufacturers' data.

Example 19.1

Motor rated output: 30 kW; full-load efficiency: 87%; part-load motor output: 20 kW; calculated motor efficiency: 85%; annual hours run: 2000 h; energy cost: 5 p/(kW h). The annual cost of energy for continuous running cost under actual load is given by:

$$\frac{(20 \times 2000)}{0.85} \times 0.05 = £\,2,353$$

Example 19.2

As for Example 1, but with the annual hours run divided into 500 hours at full load, 1000 hours at 20 kW and 500 hours at an idling load of 5 kW. Under this last condition, the calculated efficiency has fallen to 75%.

The annual cost of energy for continuous running cost under actual load is given by:

$$\frac{(30 \times 500)}{0.87} + \frac{(20 \times 1000)}{0.85} + \frac{(5 \times 500)}{0.75} \times 0.05 = £\,2,205$$

If the motor can be switched off during the idling periods then a cost saving can usually be made.

Note: for simplicity, these calculations ignore the electricity tariff, involving maximum demand charges etc. This calculation also neglects the effect of low power factor, which is common to lightly loaded motors, because its impact on savings/costs would be negligible unless the majority of motors on the site were similarly loaded. Also ignored are the marginal costs associated with starting currents.

19.7.2 Minimising motor loads

There is little point in optimising the motor and its control if the driven equipment and the system it supplies are wasteful. The means of reducing the load are often inexpensive and provide an excellent starting point (see also section 10).

19.7.2.1 Transmission efficiency

Measures relating to transmission efficiency are as follows:

— Use direct drives rather than belt drives, where practicable.

— Where belt drives are used, consider modern flat, synchronous, or ribbed-belt drives rather than traditional V-belts, to reduce drive losses.

— Replace all belts on a multiple belt drive, even if only one has failed.

— Check for correct pulley alignment.

— Ensure that the motor and load shafts are parallel.

— Check belt condition and re-tension on regular basis according to manufacturers' instructions, particularly with V- and wedge belts.

19.7.2.2 Pumping systems

Measures for pumping systems are as follows:

— Select an efficient pump and operate it close to the point of most efficient operation.

— Consider variable flow systems that can provide significant energy savings.

— Ensure that the system is efficiently regulated by matching pump to system, rather than system to pump which is inherently inefficient.

— Maintain pumps properly; without maintenance, pump efficiency can fall to 10% of its value when new.

— Install a smaller impeller or trim the existing one if consistently under loaded.

— Minimise pressure drops: design for 2 m/s maximum flow in water.

— Minimise the number of sharp bends.

— Use low friction piping and consider coating the pump with friction reducers.

— Check that inlet pressures are satisfactory.

— Avoid unnecessary throttling.

— Establish a condition monitoring programme for large pumps in order to determine the optimum time for refurbishment.

19.7.2.3 Fan systems

Measures for fan systems are as follows:

— Select the most efficient fan for the application.

— Consider variable flow systems, which can provide significant energy savings.

— Ensure that the system is efficiently regulated by matching fan to system, rather than system to fan which is inherently inefficient.

— Clean blades regularly.

— Keep filters clean and avoid unnecessary pressure drops in ducting.

— Cut off the extract systems from unused machinery by fitting dampers.

— Where there is a bank of fans, switch units on and off to suit the demand.

19.7.3 Motor sizing, selection and repair

Consider replacing standard motors with high efficiency motors as part of a purchasing policy[54] (see 14.3.5).

Measures for motor sizing, selection and repair are as follows:

— Ensure that motors are sized correctly for the application and consider replacement where over-sizing is identified (see 10.2).

— It is seldom economic to repair standard induction motors much below 11 kW, and some companies draw the line at a much higher figure, up to perhaps 37 kW[55]. The effect on the environment of scrapping old motors and replacing them with new is outweighed by the reduction in carbon dioxide emissions through improved efficiency.

— Tests have shown that rewinding a motor can reduce its efficiency permanently by between 0.5% and 2%. Some motors are so badly damaged before they arrive at the repair shop that they should be scrapped rather than repaired.

19.7.4 Transportation measures

Detailed guidance on the management and operation of transportation systems in buildings is provided in CIBSE Guide D[56] and *Guidance on the management of lifts and escalators*[57]. Where lifts, escalators and conveyors are to have a major refurbishment or are being replaced entirely then reference should be made to section 10.

Transportation systems should be upgraded every 15–20 years to improve passenger service, increase reliability and performance, and reduce energy consumption.

19.7.4.1 Lifts

Specific measures for lifts are as follows:

— Review the traffic patterns and consider the suitability of the lift controls to the application. Upgrading controls, particularly group controls, could reduce journeys and hence minimise energy consumption.

— Consider the possibility of shutting-down some lifts at the end of the working day. This avoids two lifts being in service where one is adequate.

— In multiple lift installations, it may be advantageous to omit the feature where unused lifts are directed to specific floors outside normal operating hours.

— Consider replacing older drives with energy efficient motors. In particular, old 'Ward-Leonard' AC/DC systems are very inefficient and lead to high energy ensumption.

19.7.4.2 Escalators and conveyors

Unlike lifts, escalators and conveyors operate continuously once they have been started. The energy efficiency measures are as follows:

— Delay starting escalators for as long as is practicable at the beginning of the working day.

— Stop single escalators when convenient after normal working hours

— Programme multiple escalators to operate in accordance with the predicted traffic pattern. A balance needs to be struck between staff involvement and the energy saved.

19.8 General electrical power measures

Small power loads are an increasingly significant component of the total energy use in buildings. In particular, they have an important effect on the energy consumed in air conditioning and can influence the need to upgrade air conditioning due to increased internal heat gains (see section 11). There is significant potential to reduce the energy consumption of small power loads through sound purchasing policies and good housekeeping (see 14.3.5 and 17.1).

Further details on small power loads can be found in DETR Energy Consumption Guide 35[58], Good Practice Guide 118[59] and BSRIA Technical Note TN 8/92[60].

19.8.1 Reducing energy consumption of small power loads

Measures for reducing the energy consumption of small power loads are as follows:

— Limit the proliferation of non-essential equipment, e.g. kettles, electric heaters, desk fans. The provision of local hot water urns, adequate heating, and opening windows all help to discourage staff from using such appliances.

— Install time controls for vending and food dispensing equipment avoid machines being on overnight.

— Switch off photocopiers and other office equipment out of hours. In addition, the use of energy saving features, such as standby switches, can reduce energy consumption by up to 40%[59]. However, the use of standby mode out-of-hours is not energy efficient.

— Install automatic sensors for warm air hand dryers; dryers rated at 3 kW or greater are significant consumers of energy.

19.8.2 Reducing cooling loads

All the energy consumed by appliances represents heat gain in the space where the appliance is located, acting to increase staff discomfort if no action is taken to dissipate the heat. Usually, this is achieved by increasing ventilation rates or cooling, which often leads to increased energy consumption (see section 6). Office equipment and appliances can therefore generate a double energy penalty. Cooling loads can be reduced by the following measures:

— Review the need for new office equipment in the light of its effect in increasing heat gains (see section 11)[58].

— Review the existing office equipment in the light of its effect on heat gains.

— Review the location of office equipment in relation to the air conditioning system to avoid 'hot-spots' where the air conditioning cannot cope.

— Position office equipment in groups, served by dedicated heat rejection plant. Providing a single room for fax machines, photocopying and printing machines, kettles, refrigerator etc. means that this room only may require air conditioning, rather than the entire office.

19.8.3 Information technology

Surveys suggest that for most general purpose office buildings, the power demand of general IT equipment is likely to be in the range 10–15 W/m^2, or about 200 W/person. However, for intensive users, this load may increase to as much as 50 W/m^2.

The introduction of large-scale IT can produce substantial increases in electricity consumption. Where equipment is replaced the following factors should be considered:

— Establish a purchasing policy to introduce 'energy star' computers wherever possible since this can have a significant effect on energy consumption (see 14.3.5). Make sure the facility is enabled on equipment as it is commissioned.

— Make use of energy saving features, including automatic standby and switch-off modes.

— Retrofit energy saving devices where appropriate, even though some may be less effective than others. Total purchase and installation costs should be compared with the real reduction in energy use by the equipment over its remaining life.

— Introduce a 'switch-off' policy, even for some printers which take time to warm-up. Always switch off at night and weekends unless required. Research in Canada has indicated that computer operational time can be reduced by as much as 60%. Switching off monitors at lunch time, or when users are away from their desks, can save two thirds of the normal energy consumption.

— Minimise hours of use to keep energy consumption under control. Equipment left on permanently can consume up to four times the energy of that which is on only during working hours.

References

1   *Introduction to energy efficiency in buildings* Energy Efficiency Booklets Nos. 1–13 (London: Department of Environment, Transport and Regions) (1994)

2   *Economic thickness of insulation for existing industrial buildings* Fuel Efficiency Booklet No. 16 (London: Department of Environment, Transport and Regions) (1993)

3   Potter I N, Jones T J and Booth W B *Air leakage of office buildings* Technical Note TN 8/95 (Bracknell: Building Services Research and Information Association) (May 1995)

4   *Retail warehouses — the potential for increasing energy efficiency* Information Paper IP8/90 (Garston: Building Research Establishment) (1990)

5   *Condensation in roofs* Digest 180 (Garston: Building Research Establishment)

6   *Automatic controls* CIBSE Applications Manual AM1 (London: Chartered Institution of Building Services Engineers) (1985)

7   *Ventilation and air conditioning* CIBSE Guide B2/3 (London: Chartered Institution of Building Services Engineers)

8   *Controls and energy savings* Fuel Efficiency Booklet No. 10 (London: Department of Environment, Transport and Regions) (1993)

9   *Standard specification for BEMS* Volume 2 — version 3.1 Applications Handbook AH1/90 (Bracknell: Building Services Research and Information Association) (1990)

10 *Heating systems and their control* General Information Report GIR 40 (London: Department of Environment, Transport and Regions) (1996)

11 *Variable flow control* General Information Report GIR 41 (London: Department of Environment, Transport and Regions) (1996)

12 Bordass W T, Bromley A K R and Leaman A J *Comfort, control and energy efficiency in offices* Information Paper IP3/95 (Garston: Building Research Establishment) (1995)

13 *Natural ventilation in non-domestic buildings* CIBSE Applications Manual AM10 (London: Chartered Institution of Building Services Engineers) (1997)

14 *Avoiding or minimising the use of air conditioning — a research report from the EnREI Programme* General Information Report GIR 31 (London: Department of Environment, Transport and Regions) (1996)

15 *Natural ventilation in non-domestic buildings* Digest 399 (Garston: Building Research Establishment) (1994)

16 *Oversized air handling plant* Guidance Note GN 11/97 (Bracknell: Building Services Research and Information Association) (1997)

17 *The economic thickness of insulation for hot pipes* Fuel Efficiency Booklet No. 8 (London: Department of Environment, Transport and Regions) (1993)

18 *BS 5422: 1990: Method for specifying thermal insulating materials on pipes, ductwork and equipment (in the temperature range –40°C to +700°C)* (London: British Standards Institution) (1990)

19 *Air-to-air heat recovery* CIBSE Research Report RR2 (London: Chartered Institution of Building Services Engineers) (1995)

20 *Refrigeration and heat rejection* CIBSE Guide B14 (London: Chartered Institution of Building Services Engineers) (1986)

21 *The economic use of refrigeration plant* Fuel Efficiency Booklet No. 11 (London: Department of Environment, Transport and Regions) (1993)

22 *Commercial refrigeration plant: energy efficient operation and maintenance* Good Practice Guide GPG 36 (London: Department of Environment, Transport and Regions) (1992)

23 *Commercial refrigeration plant: energy efficient design* Good Practice Guide GPG 37 (London: Department of Environment, Transport and Regions) (1992)

24 *Commercial refrigeration plant: energy efficient installation* Good Practice Guide GPG 38 (London: Department of Environment, Transport and Regions) (1992)

25 *CFCs, HCFCs and halons: Professional and practical guidance on substances which deplete the ozone layer* CIBSE Guidance Note GN1 (London: Chartered Institution of Building Services Engineers) (1993)

26 *Phase-out of CFCs and HCFCs: options for owners and operators of air conditioning systems* Information Paper IP14/95 (Garston: Building Research Establishment) (1995)

27 *Oversized cooling and pumping plant* Guidance Note GN 13/97 (Bracknell: Building Services Research and Information Association) (1997)

28 *CIBSE Code for interior lighting* (London: Chartered Institution of Building Services Engineers) (1994)

29 *Energy management and good lighting practice* Fuel Efficiency Booklet No. 12 (London: Department of Environment, Transport and Regions) (1993)

30 *Energy efficient lighting in buildings* Thermie Maxibrochure (Building Research Energy Conservation Support Unit/OPET) (1993)

31 *Energy efficient lighting in commercial buildings* CADDET Analyses Series: 6 (Sittard: Centre for the Analysis and Dissemination of Demonstrated Energy Technologies)

32 *Energy efficient lighting — a guide for installers* Good Practice Guide GPG 199 (London: Department of Environment, Transport and Regions) (1996)

33 *Lamp guide* (London: Lighting Industry Federation) (1994)

34 *Lamp converting to compact fluorescent lighting — a refurbishment guide* Good Practice Guide GPG 159 (London: Department of Environment, Transport and Regions) (1995)

35 *Electric lighting controls — a guide for designers, installers and users* Good Practice Guide GPG 160 (London: Department of Environment, Transport and Regions) (1997)

36 *Heating* CIBSE Guide B1 (London: Chartered Institution of Building Services Engineers) (1986)

37 *Economic use of fired space heaters for industry and commerce* Fuel Efficiency Booklet No. 3 (London: Department of Environment, Transport and Regions) (1993)

38 *Degree days* Fuel Efficiency Booklet No. 7 (London: Department of Environment, Transport and Regions) (1993)

39 *Economic use of oil-fired boiler plant* Fuel Efficiency Booklet No. 14 (London: Department of Environment, Transport and Regions) (1993)

40 *Economic use of gas-fired boiler plant* Fuel Efficiency Booklet No. 15 (London: Department of Environment, Transport and Regions) (1993)

41 *Economic use of coal-fired boiler plant* Fuel Efficiency Booklet No. 17 (London: Department of Environment, Transport and Regions) (1993)

42 *Heating controls in small, commercial and multi-residential buildings* Good Practice Guide GPG 132 (London: Department of Environment, Transport and Regions) (1996)

43 *Upgrading controls in domestic wet central heating systems — a guide for installers* Good Practice Guide GPG 143 (London: Department of Environment, Transport and Regions) (1994)

44 *Oversized heating plant* Guidance Note GN 12/97 (Bracknell: Building Services Research and Information Association) (1997)

45 *Variable speed drive on a boiler fan* Good Practice Case Study GPCS 35 (London: Department of Environment, Transport and Regions)

46 *Steam* Fuel Efficiency Booklet No. 2 (London: Department of Environment, Transport and Regions) (1993)

47 *Combined heat and power in buildings* Applications Manual AM12 (London: Chartered Institution of Building Services Engineers) (in preparation)

48 *Small scale combined heat and power for buildings* Good Practice Guide GPG 176 (London: Department of Environment, Transport and Regions) (1996)

49 *Guidance notes for the implementation of small scale combined heat and power* Good Practice Guide GPG 1 (London: Department of Environment, Transport and Regions) (1993)

50 *Energy efficiency in offices — a technical guide for owners and single tenants* ECON 19 (London: Department of Environment, Transport and Regions) (1997)

51 *Guidance notes for reducing energy consumption of electric motors and drives* Good Practice Guide GPG 2 (London: Department of Environment, Transport and Regions)

52 *Economic use of electricity in buildings* Fuel Efficiency Booklet No. 9 (London: Department of Environment, Transport and Regions) (1993)

53 *Internal heat gains* CIBSE Guide A7 (London: Chartered Institution of Building Services Engineers) (1986)

54 *Purchasing policy for higher efficiency motors* Good Practice Case Study GPCS 222 (London: Department of Environment, Transport and Regions) (1994)

55 *The repair of induction motors - best practices to maintain energy efficiency* AEMT Good Practice Guide (Nottingham: DETR/Association of Electrical and Mechanical Trades)

56 *Transportation systems in buildings* CIBSE Guide D (London: Chartered Institution of Building Services Engineers) (1993)

57   *Guidance on the management of maintenance for lifts and escalators* (London: Lift and Escalator Industry Association/Chartered Institution of Building Services Engineers) (1994)

58   *Energy efficiency in offices — small power loads* ECON 35 (London: Department of Environment, Transport and Regions) (1993)

59   *Managing energy use. Minimising running costs of office equipment and related air-conditioning* Good Practice Guide GPG 118 (London: Department of Environment, Transport and Regions) (1997)

60   Parsloe C and Hejab M *Small power loads* Technical Note TN 8/92 (Bracknell: Building Services Research and Information Association) (1992)

Bibliography

Bordass W, Bunn R *et al*. PROBE: Some lessons learned from the first eight buildings *CIBSE National Conference 1997* (London: Chartered Institution of Building Services Engineers) (1997)

Holmes M J and Hamilton G *Heat recovery with run around coils* Technical Note TN 2/78 (Bracknell: Building Services Research and Information Association) (1978)

Gregory D P *Adaptive building envelopes* Technical Note TN 3/86 (Bracknell: Building Services Research and Information Association) (1986)

Johnson P Are you using too much insulation? *CIBSE National Conference 1995* (London: Chartered Institution of Building Services Engineers) (1995)

Heat losses through ground floors Digest 145 (Garston: Building Research Establishment)

Choosing between cavity, internal and external wall insulation GG5 (Garston: Building Research Establishment)

Cavity insulation Digest 236 (Garston: Building Research Establishment)

Industrial building refurbishments: opportunities for energy efficiency Information Paper IP2/93 (Garston: Building Research Establishment)

Pike P G *BEMS performance testing* Applications Guide AG 2/94 (Bracknell: Building Services Research and Information Association) (1994)

Levermore G J *Building energy management systems. The basics* DLP 1 (Bracknell: Building Services Research and Information Association) (1988)

Levermore G J *Control with a building energy management system* DLP 2 (Bracknell: Building Services Research and Information Association) (1988)

Levermore G J *Staff reaction to building energy management systems* DLP 4 (Bracknell: Building Services Research and Information Association) (1989)

Levermore G J *Presenting a case for a building and energy management system* DLP 6 (Bracknell: Building Services Research and Information Association) (1989)

Loyd S *Combined heat and power — an annotated bibliography* LB 112/90 (Bracknell: Building Services Research and Information Association) (1990)

Halliday S P *Building services and environmental issues — the background* IR 1 (Bracknell: Building Services Research and Information Association) (1992)

Halliday S P *Environmental code of practice for buildings and their services* ENCOP (Bracknell: Building Services Research and Information Association) (1994)

Environmental code of practice for buildings and their services — case studies CS4/96 (Bracknell: Building Services Research and Information Association) (1996)

Heat rejection systems — some methods and their operating costs TA 1/93 (Bracknell: Building Services Research and Information Association) (1993)

Kew J *Heat pumps for building services* Technical Note TN 8/85 (Bracknell: Building Services Research and Information Association) (1985)

Armstrong J *Fault finding procedures in the building services industry* Technical Note TN 12/86 (Bracknell: Building Services Research and Information Association) (1986)

Natural ventilation in non-domestic buildings CIBSE Applications Manual AM10 (London: Chartered Institution of Building Services Engineers) (1997)

Facilities managers' energy primer EP46 (Garston: Building Research Establishment) (1997)

Crisp V H C, Littlefair P J, Cooper I and McKennan G *Daylighting as a passive solar energy option: an assessment of its potential in non-domestic buildings* BR129 (Garston: Building Research Establishment) (1988)

Lighting controls and daylight use Digest 272 (Garston: Building Research Establishment)

O'Reilly J J N *Better briefing means better buildings* BR95 (Garston: Building Research Establishment) (1987)

Harrison H W, Keeble E J *Performance specifications for whole buildings* BR32 (Garston: Building Research Establishment) (1983)

Project information for statutory authorities Digest 271 (Garston: Building Research Establishment)

Beggs C B, Warwicker B A study of the environmental impact of fabric thermal storage in UK office buildings *CIBSE National Conference 1994* (London: Chartered Institution of Building Services Engineers) (1994)

Bordass W T, Entwisle M J and Willis S T P Naturally-ventilated and mixed-mode office buildings: opportunities and pitfalls *CIBSE National Conference 1994* (London: Chartered Institution of Building Services Engineers) (1994)

Channer G R A mixed mode ventilation system for an office tower which addresses the problems of infiltration, internal comfort and energy consumption *CIBSE National Conference 1994* (London: Chartered Institution of Building Services Engineers) (1994)

Permanent star running of a lightly loaded motor GPCS 267 (London: Department of Environment, Transport and Regions) (1996)

Compressor motor controllers on refrigeration plant GPCS 27 (London: Department of Environment, Transport and Regions)

Two-speed motors on ventilation fans GPCS 219 (London: Department of Environment, Transport and Regions) (1994)

20 Monitoring and targeting (M&T)

This section sets out some of the important issues in monitoring and targeting energy consumption in buildings, in line with the principles at the front of this Guide. Monitoring and targeting (M&T) is a disciplined approach to energy management that ensures that energy resources are used to the maximum economic advantage. It provides mechanisms for the long-term control of energy use and for highlighting planned improvements in the efficiency of energy use.

20.0   General

Good M&T should aim to:

— establish current consumption

— compare current consumption with historical data and benchmarks

— set future targets

— compare current consumption with the targets

— identify trends in consumption.

Where consumption is identified as excessive or above norms, action should be taken quickly (see sections 18 and 19). Further details on M&T can be found in DETR Good Practice Guide GPG 31[1], Energy – Containing the costs[2], BSRIA Distance Learning Package DLP5[3], DETR Fuel Efficiency Booklets Nos. 7[4] and 13[5].

20.1   The M&T process

The M&T process first establishes a standard of energy performance for each area of energy accountability, which might be a department, a process or a cost accounting unit. For energy savings to be made, each accountable area needs to improve on the standard performance; this is the purpose of targeting. A target is selected to be an achievable improvement in performance. The process of monitoring and targeting is illustrated in Figure 20.1.

The process is broken down into the following four stages:

— *Data collection*: energy consumption data is usually obtained from meter readings and fuel bills.

— *Data analysis*: although it is possible to collect the data and analyse it manually, a modern system

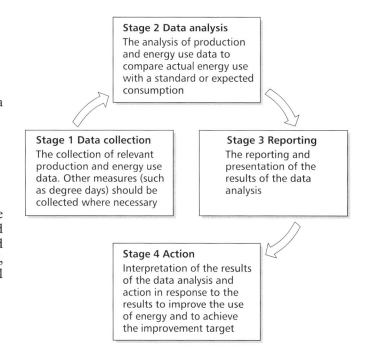

Figure 20.1 Overview of the M&T process

would use a computer to carry out the analysis and generate reports. The analysis would provide a comparison of consumption in each accountable area with the established standard as a means of controlling energy use. Also, by making comparisons with the target for an area (see 20.5), it is possible to identify the potential for further savings and plan improvements in the efficiency of energy use. Checks should be made to confirm the accuracy and quality of the data during collection and input. Some form of reconciliation should be carried out to ensure a fit between the data and the

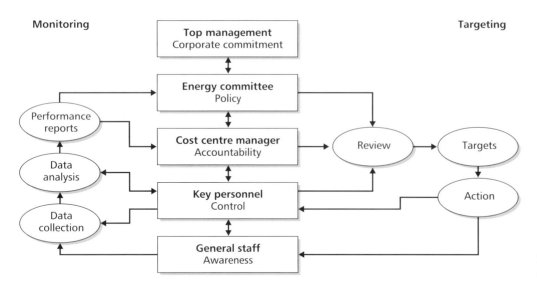

Figure 20.2 M&T operating at different levels of management

results. A comparison of current consumption with historical data, benchmarks and targets can then be carried out.

— *Reporting*: to be effective, the M&T process must include management reports on energy use based on areas of energy accountability. The management reports generated by the system provide the stimulus both to improve performance and to quantify the improvements made.

— *Action*: it is essential that a management structure exists to make effective use of the reports generated by the M&T system. Those responsible for energy will need to plan future actions and obtain rapid feedback on the outcome.

This is a highly iterative process of successive measurement and comparison. M&T should be undertaken to a level of detail that relates to the size of the energy bill. The operation of an M&T scheme requires a clear energy policy and the organisational structures described in section 14.

20.2   Setting up an M&T system

It can be advantageous to set up energy cost centres. These may relate to a complete building or a distinct area or service within that building. Each cost centre should have a manager accountable for energy use who receives regular information on energy performance. Figure 20.2 shows the involvement in M&T at different levels in the management structure.

A manual M&T system may suit buildings having energy bills of less than £10,000 per year. Such a system may consist of checking invoices, plotting monthly energy consumption and comparing it with the same period in previous years. Annual totals could also be compared with benchmarks and a basic target.

A simple spreadsheet may be appropriate when managing energy bills of up to, say, £100,000 p.a. Above this figure, an M&T software package may be more appropriate. The diversity of the estate also needs to be taken into account. For example, 10 buildings with a total bill of £100,000 will

require more data and analysis than a single building costing the same amount. Since proprietary software is available, it is seldom cost-effective to develop bespoke in-house systems for circumstances where nothing more than a simple spreadsheet is required.

The advantages and disadvantages of specialist M&T software are discussed in DETR Good Practice Guide GPG 31[1]. This also provides a checklist of features for consideration when selecting an M&T system.

Many M&T software systems cease to be used because they require excessive amounts of information when a few important indicators would suffice. Equally, over detailed reporting can cause staff to ignore vital information. The number of buildings or cost centres, and the way information is to be collected needs to be established with care.

There is little to be gained from carrying out detailed analysis when only limited consumption data is available, e.g. quarterly invoices. Equally, detailed 'CUSUM' calculations and regression analyses are more appropriate if weekly energy consumption is available.

The ability to respond quickly is an important factor in the success of an M&T system. Data collection and input should be rapid. Exception reports indicating excessive consumption should be generated speedily to allow early action. Organisations should establish how they will respond to what the system highlights, and how this will integrate with the existing management information system.

Specialist training is essential and a minimum of two members of staff should be able to use the system. They should also be aware of their essential role in highlighting exceptional consumption and the potential for savings.

Most BMSs can carry out automatic logging, meter recording and simple analysis, which can be automatically fed directly into M&T software. This provides a rapid comparison between meter readings and invoice data.

M&T systems should undergo periodic review, auditing and development to:

— examine the system operation

— check the quality of data inputted

— ensure the reporting is adequate to support the decisions taken

— identify where improvements can be made

— determine the level of benefits achieved.

Targets should be set for the performance of the system, e.g. throughput times and reporting.

20.3   Data quality

Good quality data is the foundation of a successful M&T system. Careful validation during the data collection and inputting process is essential[6,7].

Time spent entering, analysing and reporting the data should not be underestimated. Savings may be made by using existing routes. For example, accounts departments that enter cost information could also enter energy data. Utility companies may be able to provide computer disks to users with many accounts.

It is common to find sophisticated analysis being carried out on suspect data without any validation. Simple checks to improve quality and accuracy include the following:

— How do the data compare with previous readings?

— Is the number of digits correct?

— Do the figures fall within acceptance bands?

— Are correct units used?

— Do meter readings reconcile with invoices?

— Are invoices estimated?

Training or guidance for meter readers can also help increase confidence in the results.

Since consumption needs to be compared over similar periods, the date of the meter readings is often crucial. Different definitions can also be the cause of errors. For example, if floor areas are used as an indicator to compare different buildings, it is important to ensure that the same definitions of floor area are used, e.g. net, gross or treated (see section 12).

Coal and oil invoices often cause problems in M&T systems because they show bulk deliveries and therefore cannot provide a picture of the energy consumption patterns. It is more useful to meter the fuel that goes to the boilers etc.

20.4   Analysis techniques

The main aim of data analysis is to:

— highlight when corrective action is needed

— indicate when performance has been good and should be replicated

— evaluate the significance of changes in performance

— measure progress towards targets.

Three main methods of assessing the building performance are generally used. With these methods, actual energy consumption is compared with the following:

— *Benchmarks*: a comparison is made with a standard consumption benchmark (see Table 20.1) to establish how the building compares with typical and best practice buildings.

— *Performance lines*: these lines (e.g. variation of heating consumption with degree-days) make it possible to check whether the services continue to function in relation to key variables.

— *Historical data*: a comparison with a previous measurement to ascertain whether previously adopted energy efficiency measures have been effective, and to identify the need for further improvement

20.4.1   Performance indicators

The overall performance of a building can be crudely expressed as a performance indicator, usually in $(kW\,h)/m^2$ per year for fossil fuel and electricity. The analysis is normally performed on annual data, allowing comparison with published benchmarks to give an indication of efficiency[8]. Some of these benchmarks are shown in Table 20.1.

Although performance indicators for buildings are generally rated in terms of floor area, building volume and the amount of trade (e.g. number of meals) are sometimes used as normalising factors. Indicators, adjusted according to weather and/or occupancy are often called normalised performance indicators (NPIs). This 'normalisation' is intended to improve comparison between buildings in different climatic regions or with different occupancy patterns. However, it should be used with care as it can often distort the data and mask real patterns in consumption.

Where normalisation is essential and provided that consistent procedures are used, a valid comparison can be made of the NPI for a given building over successive years. However, care must be taken as errors in floor area, hours of occupancy etc. are common, particularly in large estates of buildings.

Table 20.1 provides separate benchmarks for electricity and fossil fuels to allow for the widely different costs and CO_2 emissions per unit of energy delivered. Each unit of electricity results in two to three times as much CO_2 being emitted as the direct use of fossil fuels in the building. In addition, a unit of electrical energy is more expensive than a unit obtained through the consumption of fossil fuels in the building's heating system. It is recommended, therefore, that separate indicators are used for electricity and fossil fuel consumption. Where a single indicator is required, the electricity and fossil fuel consumption should each be converted to a CO_2 emission figure and the two numbers added together (see 12.3).

Performance indicators give only a broad indication of building efficiency and therefore must be treated with caution. It should not be assumed that a building with a 'good' performance indicator is in fact being operated as efficiently as is possible, or offers no scope for cost-effective

Table 20.1 Energy consumption benchmarks for existing buildings

| Building type | Energy consumption benchmarks for existing buildings ((kW h)/m² treated area p.a.) | | | |
| | Low consumption (equal or less than benchmark) | | High consumption (equal or greater than benchmark) | |
	Fossil fuels	Electricity	Fossil fuels	Electricity
Offices:				
— naturally ventilated, cellular	79	33	151	54
— naturally ventilated, open plan	79	54	151	85
— air conditioned standard	97	128	178	226
— air conditioned prestige	114	234	210	358
Industrial:				
— general manufacturing	125	50	325	85
— factory office	100	55	225	100
— light manufacturing	90	31	300	70
— storage and distribution	80	20	185	43
Retail:				
— 'DIY' stores	150	130	195	160
— non-food shops	80	200	130	260
— department stores	150	240	220	290
— small food shops	80	400	100	500
— supermarket	160	670	290	920
Hotels:				
— small	240	80	360	120
— holiday	260	80	400	140
— luxury	300	90	460	150
Schools:				
— primary and middle	126	20	173	28
— secondary	136	24	174	30
Sports and recreation:				
— without pool	215	75	325	85
— with pool	360	150	540	205
— pool only	775 (2950)†	165 (550)†	1120 (4300)†	235 (900)†
Nursing and residential homes	247	44	417	79
Hospitals:				
— teaching and specialist	339	86	415‡	106‡
— acute and maternity	422	78	510‡	108‡
— cottage	443	55	492‡	78‡
— long stay	401	48	518‡	72‡

† per m² of pool surface area
‡ derived from GJ/(100 m²) benchmarks assuming 2.9 m floor-to-ceiling height

savings. Overall performance indicators can mask underlying problems with individual end uses of energy (see Figure 12.1).

20.4.2   Regression analysis

It can be helpful to carry out an analysis to determine the relationship between energy use and the drivers that influence it. For example, heating consumption varies with degree-days, as shown in Figure 20.3.

Analysis of energy data often shows simple linear relationships, as shown in Figure 20.4. The correlation and base load data obtained from such plots can provide useful information on energy use, particularly relating to control and standing losses[1-5]. Once the performance line is established, consumption measurements can be easily compared with past results. The intersection of the sloping

line and the Y-axis indicates the base load consumption. This is a technique often used to identify hot water loads in buildings.

Initial attempts at producing a thermal performance line for a building sometimes reveal very poor performance or a wide scatter of points. This is invariably due either to poor adjustment, or to inadequacy or malfunction of the heating system controls. In any event, remedial action should be taken. The correlation may also be poor if heating accounts for a small proportion of the fuel requirement.

A good thermal performance line can usually be produced if the controls are functioning and are reasonably adjusted. However, this does not mean that the building is operating efficiently, merely that its performance is consistent. Once established, the performance line can be used as a 'performance target' for the future operation of the building. Should any sudden significant deviation in fuel

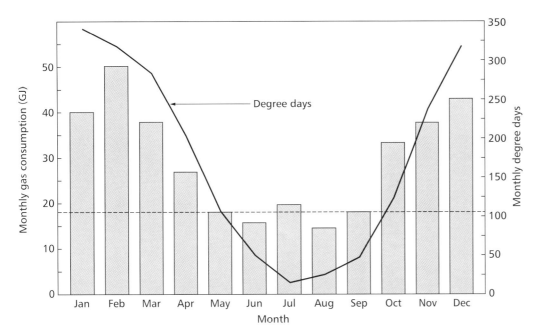

Figure 20.3 Histogram of monthly fuel consumption versus degree-days[20]

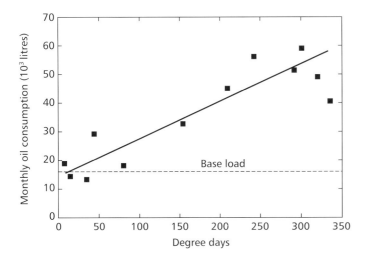

Figure 20.4 Energy consumption versus degree days showing base load[20]

consumption occur, indicated by a change in the slope of the line, it should be investigated and corrective action taken. The best fit thermal performance line should be re-calculated annually[1–5].

20.4.3 Trend logging and CUSUM analysis

Figure 20.5 shows that simple histograms can help to identify trends and make comparisons against the previous years consumption patterns. More complex ways of representing results can establish trends more clearly, such as the CUSUM technique[4,5,9].

To construct a CUSUM graph, the baseline consumption is required. By calculating the cumulative sum of the differences of actual consumption from this base line, a trend line can be plotted to indicate performance and changes in performance as shown in Figure 20.6. A downward trend indicates savings beyond the base consumption and an upward slope indicates excessive

consumption. The numerical value of CUSUM give the aggregate savings made to date, and the slope of the CUSUM line gives information on the performance trend.

20.5 Setting targets

One of the objectives of an M&T system is to set targets that will stimulate management to make improvements. These targets must be realistic and achievable, taking into account the likely savings from improvements in 'housekeeping', maintenance and other efficiency measures. Management should use a consultation process to agree individual targets, rather than simply impose arbitrary figures. Targets should be set for each cost centre, to stimulate positive management action, and be reviewed annually.

20.5.1 The 'top down' approach

Targets are often crudely set as part of an overall energy policy, for example, 'a 15% reduction in energy use to be achieved over five years'. Individual building targets can be set using the same 'top down' approach, e.g. 'an attempt will be made to save 10% in building 1 next year, but only 5% in building 2 as there is less scope for savings'. This broad-brush approach provides a means of starting the targeting process but, to be successful, requires agreement at all levels.

20.5.2 Standard benchmarks

A number of typical yardsticks or benchmarks exist for different kinds of building and these can be used as a target. Although they are very general, they give a more absolute measure of how certain types of buildings should perform, rather than a relative comparison with past performance. Based on historical data from large numbers of buildings, benchmarks shown in Table 20.1 have been formulated for existing buildings throughout a number of sectors[10–18]. More recent data are provided by Jones[19].

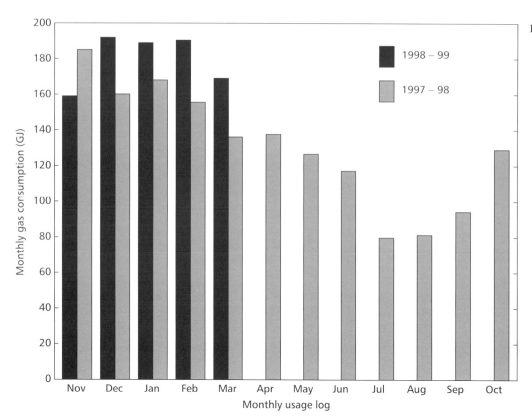

Figure 20.5 Monthly trend logging

Separate benchmarks are set for fossil fuel and electricity, since they have very different costs and CO_2 emissions. Most existing buildings should aim to have lower consumption figures than those in the 'low consumption' column. However, in inherently inefficient buildings, it may not be practicable or economic to bring the building up to this standard. In these circumstances, realistic targets should be set between the 'low consumption' and 'high consumption' benchmarks, the larger figures providing a useful upper limit. The 'low consumption' figures correspond to the 'good practice' upper limits introduced in section 12. New buildings should aim to achieve lower consumptions than these figures.

These benchmarks will change as better quality data is gathered and as the energy efficiency of buildings improves. However, they provide a useful upper limit for building operators. The shortfall between the actual consumed energy and the benchmark provides an indication of the potential for improvement. Analysis of the breakdown of energy use indicates where efforts should be directed to realise the improvement.

20.5.3 Targets based on historical records

Most targets are based on the historical consumption of each particular building. These targets may simply be the consumption for the previous year, an average over three years, or the consumption weather-corrected for a period such as the twenty-year average weather conditions. This method of targeting will not highlight any intrinsic problems in the building or its use but it does provide a target that is specific to the building being considered.

20.5.4 Targets based on key variables

As discussed in 20.4, energy consumption can be related to the most important variables, e.g. weather, number of meals, etc. Developing a performance line equation (i.e. an equation of the form: $y = mx + c$) can provide a target. For example, in Figure 20.7, the intercept theoretically represents the base load consumption, e.g. hot water. In practice, space heating is discontinued before the number of degree-days falls to zero and the true base load is higher than the intercept. The slope shows how the space heating demand relates to degree-days. The outlying point observed in winter, when the number of degree-days is highest, might be explained by a shutdown or plant breakdown. Targets could be set to reduce both the intercept and slope of the performance line.

The scatter of points often reflects the accuracy of control. A wider scatter suggests that control is poor, but it can also be caused by a fluctuating base load. Good correlation could result from consistent control. However, that does not necessarily mean that the control settings are optimised, since they could have been maintained consistently at the wrong level.

20.5.5 The 'bottom up' approach

Targets can also be derived by using a 'bottom up' approach, i.e. estimating end-use energy consumption in order to develop a building target. This approach provides a building specific target, but requires a number of assumptions and estimates[5]. By subtracting estimates of what each service should use from the actual consumption, it is assumed that any remainder must represent energy waste or potential savings. However, the accuracy of the energy breakdown determines the accuracy of the likely savings.

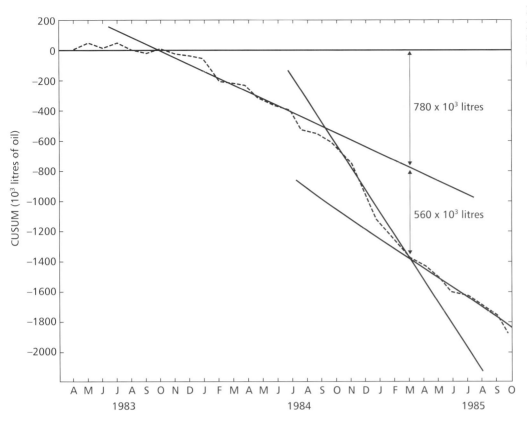

Figure 20.6 Example of a CUSUM plot showing cumulative energy savings[4] (reproduced from DETR Fuel Efficiency Booklet No. 7. Crown copyright (1993))

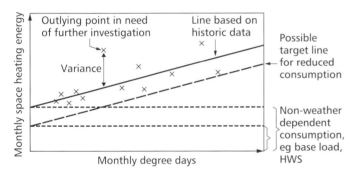

Figure 20.7 Typical linear relationship between degree days and space heating

20.5.7 Process energy

In many cases, particularly industrial buildings, the energy consumption for manufacturing and associated requirements may be substantially higher than, and may overshadow or directly affect, that needed for environmental services. An example is the use of process waste heat to offset space heating requirements. Computer rooms in offices could be treated as a process use, as could large medical equipment in hospitals. Areas with processes or exceptional use should always be separated for the purposes of estimating consumption targets.

A 'bottom up' approach can help identify the building's specific uses of energy and give a better estimate of possible savings. For example, total electrical consumption might indicate poor performance against established benchmarks. However, after removing the process loads for the computer room, the energy use by HVAC services and lighting may appear far more acceptable.

Typical energy use for individual building services throughout a range of buildings are shown in CIBSE Applications Manual AM5[20] and in a series of DETR Energy Consumption Guides[10–14,21].

20.5.6 Building modelling

Manual systems[22–25] and dynamic simulation software can be used to model buildings and hence derive targets. However, most of these systems are best used for comparing changes in a building design rather than predicting absolute energy consumption.

References

1   *Computer aided monitoring and targeting for industry* Good Practice Guide GPG 31 (London: Department of Environment, Transport and Regions) (1995)

2   *Energy — containing the costs* (London: Department of Environment, Transport and the Regions/Chartered Institute of Management Accountants) (1992)

3   Levermore G J *Monitoring and targeting with a building energy management system* BSRIA Distance Learning Package DLP 5 (Bracknell: Building Services Research and Information Association) (1989)

4   *Degree days* Fuel Efficiency Booklet No. 7 (London: Department of Environment, Transport and Regions) (1993)

5   *Waste avoidance measures* Fuel Efficiency Booklet No. 13 (London: Department of Environment, Transport and Regions) (1995)

6   Field J, Soper J, Jones P G, Bordass W and Grigg P Energy performance of occupied non domestic buildings: Assessment

by analysing end-use energy consumptions *Building Services Engineering Research and Technology* **18**(1) (1997)

7   Field J W and Soper J H B Understanding energy performance of commercial and high street buildings *CIBSE National Conference 1997* (London: Chartered Institution of Building Services Engineers) (1997)

8   *Introduction to energy efficiency in buildings* Booklets Energy Efficiency Booklets Nos. 1–13   (London: Department of Environment, Transport and Regions) (1994)

9   Harris P   *Energy monitoring and target setting using CUSUM* (Cheriton Technology Publications) (1989)

10   *Energy efficiency in offices — a technical guide for owners and single tenants* ECON 19   (London: Department of Environment, Transport and Regions) (1997)

11   *Energy efficiency in industrial buildings and sites* ECON 18 (London: Department of Environment, Transport and Regions) (1993)

12   *Energy efficiency in hotels — a guide for owners and managers* ECON 36   (London: Department of Environment, Transport and Regions) (1993)

13   *Saving energy in schools — the headteacher's and governor's guide to energy efficiency* ECON 15   (London: Department of Environment, Transport and Regions) (1991)

14   *Saving energy in schools — the 'school energy manager's' guide to energy efficiency* ECON 16   (London: Department of Environment, Transport and Regions) (1991)

15   *Energy efficiency in sports and recreation buildings — a guide for owners and managers* ECON 51   (London: Department of Environment, Transport and Regions) (1996)

16   *Energy consumption guide for nursing and residential homes* ECON 57   (London: Department of Environment, Transport and Regions) (1996)

17   *Introduction to energy efficiency. Health care buildings* EEB 4 (London: Department of Environment, Transport and Regions) (1997)

18   *Energy efficiency action pack — for retail premises* Good Practice Guide GPG 190   (London: Department of Environment, Transport and Regions) (1996)

19   Jones P G and Cheshire D Bulk data for benchmarking non domestic building energy consumption *CIBSE National Conference 1996* (London: Chartered Institution of Building Services Engineers) (1996)

20   *Energy audits and surveys* CIBSE Applications Manual AM5 (London: Chartered Institution of Building Services Engineers) (1991)

21   *Energy efficiency in public houses. Guidance on the benefits of energy efficiency in public houses for the brewer, licensee and customer* ECON 13   (London: Department of Environment, Transport and Regions) (1992)

22   Baker N V and Steemers K *The LT Method 2.0. An energy design tool for non-domestic buildings* (Cambridge Architectural Research/Building Research Energy Conservation Support Unit) (1994)

23   *Calculation of energy demands and targets for the design of new buildings and services* CIBSE Building Energy Code Part 2 (a) Heated and naturally ventilated buildings (London: Chartered Institution of Building Services Engineers) (1981)

24   *Air conditioned buildings* CIBSE Building Energy Code 2 (London: Chartered Institution of Building Services Engineers) (in preparation)

25   *Fundamentals* ASHRAE Handbook (Atlanta, GA: American Society of Heating, Refrigeration and Air Conditioning Engineers) (1997)

Bibliography

Is your energy use under control? A practical guide to assessment and action Good Practice Guide GPG 136   (London: Department of Environment, Transport and Regions) (1994)

Controlling energy use in buildings General Information Report GIR 47 (London: Department of Environment, Transport and Regions) (1997)

Practical energy saving guide for smaller businesses ACBE 1 (London: Department of Environment, Transport and Regions) (1992)

Energy managers handbook (London: NIFES/Graham Trotman) (1985)

Educated energy management (London: E and F N Spon) (1991)

Putting energy into total quality. A guide for energy managers Good Practice Guide GPG 169 (London: Department of Environment, Transport and Regions) (1996)

Monitoring and targeting in large manufacturing companies Good Practice Guide GPG 91 (London: Department of Environment, Transport and Regions) (1994)

Cheshire D N, Jones P G and Moss S Quality of data — an energy performance database *CIBSE National Conference 1997* (London: Chartered Institution of Building Services Engineers) (1997)

Mortimer N D *et al.* An energy based classification system for non domestic buildings *CIBSE National Conference 1997* (London: Chartered Institution of Building Services Engineers) (1997)

A B Birtles and P Grigg Energy efficiency in buildings: Simple appraisal method *Building Services Engineering Research and Technology* **16**(4) (1995)

Grigg P F, Moss S A and Birtles A B Assessing non domestic building design using an energy performance index method *CIBSE National Conference 1997* (London: Chartered Institution of Building Services Engineers) (1997)

21 Maintaining the savings

This section summarises how and when checks should be made to ensure that energy efficiency measures have been installed and are operating correctly, and that the savings originally predicted are actually being achieved. It should be read in conjunction with sections 18 and 20. The PROBE studies[1] show the importance of post project evaluations.

21.1   Post project evaluation

Following the implementation of energy saving measures, post project evaluation is desirable to establish that measures have been correctly installed and are achieving the predicted savings. Small measures may require only a cursory check but larger projects, e.g. those involving combined heat and power, require a thorough assessment. Evaluations should establish:

—   actual savings

—   final capital cost

—   impact on occupants

—   management implications

—   maintenance issues

—   other benefits achieved

—   practical pitfalls.

It may also be possible to compare actual savings with the savings achieved in published case study material. Problems identified well after implementation are often traced back to poor installation.

The energy manager should also provide a post project evaluation report to senior management on the effectiveness of the investment. For those managing a number of buildings, the evaluations can also help to indicate whether similar measures should be incorporated in other parts of the stock, while highlighting pitfalls to be avoided.

21.2   Continual monitoring

Continual monitoring helps to maintain the level of savings achieved over successive years. This requires:

—   installing monitoring equipment where information is required to assess energy usage and savings

—   instituting a measuring and analysis scheme and allocate tasks to personnel

—   maintaining records of energy use and comparing them with targets

—   checking records against utility bills to ensure cost savings are achieved

—   reporting results to the building operator on a regular basis.

The following maintenance and management procedures also play a large part in ensuring continued savings:

—   Review maintenance and operating procedures to ensure that efficiency of plant and system operation is sustained.

—   Keep all personnel informed of progress and of results achieved.

—   Keep a record of changes to the building and its use that may effect savings.

—   Regularly review the monitoring programme and modify actions where necessary.

A formal monitoring system is invaluable when assessing performance and looking for further improvements, including environmental impact[2]. The whole programme for improving energy efficiency may fall into disrepute if savings cannot be proved. Confirming the results of investment helps to justify future investment. Energy performance monitoring and targeting is examined in more detail in section 20.

References

1   Bordass W T, Bunn R, et al. PROBE: Some lessons learned from the first eight buildings *CIBSE National Conference 1997* (London: Chartered Institution of Building Services Engineers) (1997)

2   Bartlett P, Bishop T and Durrant H *The office toolkit. The guide for facilities and office managers for reducing costs and environmental impact* BR 285 (Garston: Building Research Establishment) (1995)

Bibliography

Energy audits and surveys CIBSE Applications Manual AM5 (London: Chartered Institution of Building Services Engineers) (1991)

Energy audits and surveys Information Paper IP12/92 (Garston: Building Research Establishment) (1992)

Energy audit and survey guide: for commercial and industrial buildings. Energy audit and survey guide: for building managers and engineers Good Practice Guide GPG 28 (London: Department of Environment, Transport and Regions) (1991)

Energy audit and survey guide: for commercial and industrial buildings. Energy audit and survey guide: for building financiers and senior managers Good Practice Guide GPG 27 (London: Department of Environment, Transport and Regions) (1991)

Appendix A1: CIBSE policy statements

A1.1 Energy

It is the Institution's policy to encourage the installation of those building services systems which minimise the consumption of energy.

The main objectives of this policy are:

— to mitigate the demands placed on the world's reserves of fossil fuels

— to reduce pollution of the environment caused by their consumption

— to promote the use of renewable and sustainable energy sources.

Whilst actively pursuing this policy it is accepted that any energy conservation measures must demonstrate that they are cost effective, can maintain set standards and do not give rise to any adverse consequences.

To meet these aims the Institution intends to:

— provide support to the UK Government in its promotion of energy conservation measures

— encourage the design of buildings which minimise energy consumption

— advise owners/occupiers of buildings on methods for reducing energy consumption

— support research into the development of energy efficient systems

— encourage the use of energy recovery/recycling systems

— advise CIBSE members of the policy and of the need for them to support it actively.

A1.2 Combined heat and power (CHP)

CHP is a highly efficient technology, which generates electricity and puts to good use heat that would otherwise be wasted. It is already widely used in UK buildings and in the right circumstances is a very cost-effective means of meeting a given energy demand. CHP also reduces harmful emissions to the environment.

It is CIBSE policy to encourage Institution members to consider CHP for use in all suitable applications. This is in line with current CIBSE policy statements on energy and global warming and also the Government's target of 5% GWe of installed CHP capacity by the year 2000.

CHP systems can contribute to space heating, domestic hot water and cooling requirements. They can be installed as a retrofit measure in existing buildings or as part of new building work. CHP can also satisfy some or all of the standby generation needs of a site.

To ensure a successful installation and to maximise energy and cost savings, the following points should be considered when evaluating CHP:

(1) Simple cost and low cost energy saving measures should always be considered as a means of reducing energy wastage before sizing CHP plant.

(2) CHP design should be fully integrated with the site's electrical and thermal demands and other plant.

(3) The need for proper maintenance of plant to ensure reliable operation and to minimise environmental emissions is essential.

Significant financial savings arise when CHP is appropriately installed since energy is provided at a much higher efficiency than conventional means of supply. In evaluating performance criteria for buildings, it is important to recognise that with CHP, primary energy savings arise on a national basis, rather than on an individual site. Comparing CHP systems with other ways of providing a given heating and electrical requirement should therefore be carried out on the basis of primary energy and cost savings.

CIBSE recognises that, where appropriate, CHP is a very effective measure in reducing the energy costs and environmental impact of buildings.

A1.3 Air conditioning

The policy of the CIBSE aims to encourage the adoption of low-energy design solutions wherever possible in fulfilment of environmental and functional requirements.

In circumstances where energy input is necessary to maintain the required environmental conditions, systems should be designed, operated and maintained to maximise energy efficiency, to minimise environmental impact and to avoid causing hazards to health.

If the requirement for air conditioning has been fully established, the following principles should be adopted:

(1) The system should be energy-efficient (with due regard being given to the inclusion of cost-effective energy saving methods such as free cooling) and controlled to minimise energy use.

(2) Operation and maintenance strategies should be devised and the necessary regimes adopted to deliver economy, efficiency and effectiveness in the working of systems throughout their life cycles.

(3) System design, construction and commissioning should be carried out in accordance with current national and European standards, codes of practice and statutory requirements.

(4) Cooling system refrigerants should be used in accordance with the policy laid down in CIBSE Guidance Note GN1: *CFCs, HCFCs and halons* (1993).

Generally, the design of buildings, services, equipment and process needs should optimise energy economy and performance.

A1.4   Global warming

The 'greenhouse effect' is the absorption of infrared radiation from the Earth's surface by certain gases naturally present in the atmosphere. This is a natural effect, without which global temperatures would be so low that life would be unsupportable. However, man-made greenhouse gasses, released into the atmosphere, are disturbing the natural balance resulting in rising global temperatures. Estimates indicate that 70% of the excess warming arises from CO_2 with methane, CFCs and nitrous oxide contributing most of the remainder. Scientists are uncertain of the extent and impact of the global warming but economic, political and technical implications are expected to be profound.

Unless action is taken now, the emission of greenhouse gases through man's activities will increase and accelerate the rise of global temperatures. Reports are already calling for international agreement to limit carbon dioxide emissions, similar to the Montreal Protocol which restricts the use of chlorofluorocarbons in order to reduce damage to the atmospheric ozone layer.

The Institution recognises the complex nature of global warming, the control agreements and specific legislation to limit the release of artificial greenhouse gases. All members have an obligation to acquaint themselves with developments in this field and to apply this information in their day-to-day activities.

CIBSE recommends that members take the following positive steps to reduce global warming.

— Consider the relative merits of alternative energy sources in the light of their greenhouse gas emissions.

— Advise clients and the professional team on the selection of the best design solution for energy-efficient structures, plant and systems using environmentally friendly resources.

— Advise clients on modifications to existing plant to incorporate developments with improved performance.

— Review operating and maintenance procedures to limit progressive deterioration of plant performance and building conditions.

— Examine standard specifications and remove features now recognised as potential hazards.

— Remain vigilant to the possibilities of eliminating chlorofluorocarbons.

— Promote the use of air conditioning only where necessary.

Throughout these activities, consider the potential for reducing the demand for primary fuels which generate greenhouse gases, as follows.

— Optimise building orientation, form, facade design, thermal insulation and passive energy utilisation to conserve energy.

— Consider all the available alternative energy sources.

— Specify efficient plant, accurately sized for the optimum duty.

— Design buildings for good access to plant for maintenance.

— Recognise opportunities for using combined heat and power generation plant.

The Institution was established to promote good engineering practice. The immediate application of good practice, with due care and regard for the environment, now takes on a greater significance and urgency if future generations are to be spared the full consequences of a warmer world. The quest for improved living standards should not be at the expense of our environment.

Appendix A2: Conversion factors and properties of fuels

Table A2.1 Conversion factors for energy units

Original units	Multiply quantity in original units by factor to give quantity in units below			
	joule	kilowatt hour	therm	Btu
joule	1	0.2778×10^{-6}	0.948×10^{-9}	0.948×10^{-3}
kilowatt hour	3.6×10^{6}	1	34.12×10^{-3}	3.412×10^{3}
therm	105.5×10^{6}	29.31	1	1×10^{5}
Btu	1.055×10^{3}	0.2931×10^{-3}	1×10^{-5}	1

Table A2.2 Conversion factors for miscellaneous quantities

Quantity	Units	Multiply by stated factor to give quantity in SI units	
		Factor	SI units
Calorific value (volume basis)	Btu/ft^3	3.726×10^{-2}	MJ/m^3
Calorific value (mass basis)	Btu/lb	2.326	kJ/kg
Density	lb/ft^3	1.602×10^{1}	kg/m^3
Force	lbf	4.448	N
Heat flow rate	Btu/h	2.931×10^{-1}	W
Heat flow rate intensity	Btu/(h ft^2)	3.155	W/m^2
Heat flow rate per unit length	Btu/(h ft)	9.615×10^{-1}	W/m
Heat flow rate (refrigeration)	ton	3.517×10^{3}	W
Mass:			
—	ton	1.016	tonne
—	pound	0.454	kg
Power	hp	7.457×10^{2}	W
Pressure:			
—	lbf/in^2	6.895	kPa
—	bar	1×10^{2}	kPa
Specific heat capacity	Btu/(lb °F)	4.187	kJ/kg
Specific volume	ft^3/lb	6.243×10^{-2}	m^3/kg
Thermal conductivity (λ-value)	Btu/(h ft^2 °F)	1.442×10^{-1}	W/(m K)
Thermal transmittance (U-value)	Btu in/(h ft^2 °F)	5.678	W/(m^2 K)
Volume:			
—	ft^3	2.832×10^{-2}	m^3
—	gallon	4.546	litre
Volumetric flowrate	ft^3/min	4.719×10^{-1}	litre/s

Table A2.3 Prefixes and multiplying factors for SI units

Symbol	Prefix	Multiplying factor
T	tera	10^{12}
G	giga	10^{9}
M	mega	10^{6}
k	kilo	10^{3}

Table A2.4 Calorific values of typical fuels

Fuel	Calorific value (MJ/kg)	
	Gross	Net
Class D fuel oil†	45.0	42.2
Natural gas‡	38.6	34.7
LPG:		
— butane	49.5	46.0
— propane	50.0	46.5
Solid fuels (washed smalls):		
— anthracite	29.65	28.95
— dry steam coal	30.60	29.65
— coking coals (medium volatile)	30.80	29.75

† to BS 2869
‡ at 15°C, 101.3 kPa

Table A2.5 Carbon and carbon dioxide equivalents

Fuel	CO^2 equivalent (kg/(kW h))	Carbon equivalent (kg/(kW h))
Coal	0.34	0.093
Coke	0.43	0.12
Other solid fuel	0.41	0.11
Gas	0.20	0.055
Oil	0.29	0.079
Electricity	0.52	0.142

Note: based on 1997 data

Table A2.6 Carbon dioxide performance index for fuels

Fuel source	CO_2 conversion factor (kg/(kW h))
Gas	0.20
Oil	0.29
Coal	0.34
Electricity†	0.52

† based on 1997 figures and may change due to the progressive depletion of fossil fuels or the growth in the use of non-depleting resources, see section 4.3

Index